LIFE SCIENCE

B

Third Edition

Brad R. Batdorf
Thomas E. Porch

bju press®

Greenville, South Carolina

LIFE SCIENCE
Third Edition

Brad R. Batdorf, MAEd
Thomas E. Porch, DMD

Project Editors
Dennis Cone, MA
Michael Pope, MA
Naomi Viola

Designer
Aaron Dickey

Project Manager
Vic Ludlum

Consultant
Jeff S. Foster, MS

Bible Integration
Bryan Smith, PhD
John MacInnis, MMus
Margaret Calhoun

Composition
Caroline McCausland
Carol Larson

Cover Illustrator
Justin Gerard,
    Portland Studios

Cover Design
John Bjerk
Elly Kalagayan

Photo Acquisition
Susan Perry

Illustrators
Amber Cheadle
Paula Cheadle
Caroline George
Justin Gerard,
    Portland Studios
Courtney Godbey
Preston Gravely
Brian D. Johnson,
    Gooseneck Graphics
Sarah Lyons
Kara Moore
Kathy Pflug
John Roberts
Dave Schuppert
Lynda Slattery

Photograph credits appear on pages 261–64 (Book A) and pages 557–59 (Book B).
This book is based on original materials by William S. Pinkston Jr., MEd, revised by David R. Anderson, PhD.

Produced in cooperation with the Bob Jones University Division of Natural Science of the College of Arts and Science and Bob Jones Junior High School.

© 2007 BJU Press
Greenville, South Carolina 29614
First Edition © 1984 BJU Press
Second Edition © 1997, 1999 BJU Press

ISBN 978-1-59166-474-1

15   14   13   12   11   10   9   8   7   6   5   4

CONGRATULATIONS!

Your search for the very best educational materials available has been completely successful! You have a product that is the culmination of decades of research, experience, prayer, and creative energy.

The facts

Nothing overlooked. Revised and updated. Facts are used as a springboard to stimulate thoughtful questions and guide students to broader applications.

The foundation

Nothing to conflict with Truth and everything to support it. Truth is the pathway as well as the destination.

The fun

Nothing boring about this book! Student (and teacher) might even forget it's a schoolbook!

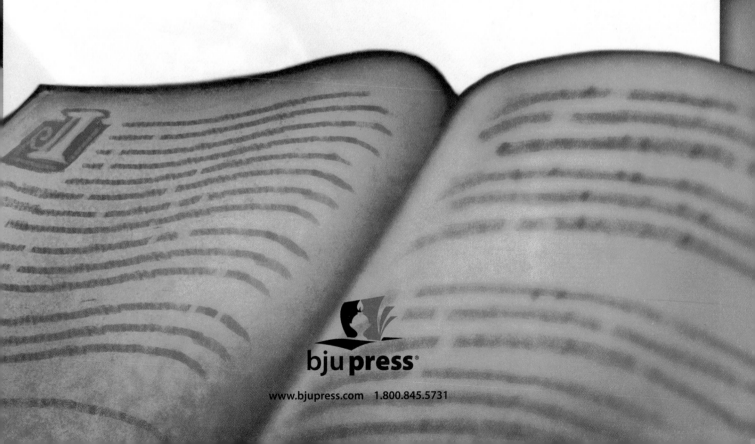

bju press®

www.bjupress.com   1.800.845.5731

Contents

Book A
Unit I Foundations of Life Science

Unit II Heredity and the Origin of Life

Unit III Concepts in Microbiology and Plant Biology

Book B
Unit IV Concepts in the Animal Kingdom

15 Invertebrates I: Sponges, Jellyfish, and Worms 267

16 Invertebrates II: Mollusks, Arthropods, and Echinoderms 283

UNIT V THE NATURE OF THE ENVIRONMENT

UNIT VI STRUCTURE AND FUNCTION OF THE HUMAN BODY

STUDENT ACTIVITIES

IV

CONCEPTS IN THE ANIMAL KINGDOM

INVERTEBRATES I: SPONGES, JELLYFISH, AND WORMS

15

Everyone knows what an animal is, right? You have had plenty of chances to observe them since over one million animal species live on earth today. Even more are being discovered each year. At first, some animals may look like something else. What animals do you see on this page? Suppose you discovered a new animal species. How would you know for sure that it was an animal?

Animals are *living* organisms that are *eukaryotic* and *multicellular*, have organized *tissues*, and *must obtain food* rather than making it by photosynthesis. In addition, most animals can move during at least part of their life cycle, eat their food (rather than just absorbing it), have organs, and reproduce sexually (sometimes asexually too). Earthworms, grasshoppers, and dogs all fit the description of animals given above. However, each belongs to a different animal phylum.

In this chapter and the following three chapters, you will study the major groups of animals. As you read about these animals, try to remember what makes each group special or different from the others. If you have forgotten some of these characteristics, then review the following topics and pages:

- characteristics of life, pp. 34–37
- eukaryotes, p. 62
- multicellular, p. 36
- tissues, pp. 36, 66

15A   What Is an Invertebrate?

Question: What is an invertebrate?

Clue: The prefix *in-* means "not" or "without."

Clue: A *vertebra* is one of the bones along the back of an animal.

Answer: An **invertebrate** is an animal without a backbone.

With just a few technical exceptions and explanations, the answer above is correct. To be called an invertebrate, an animal needs no other characteristic besides the absence of a backbone. Animals as different as starfish, ants, sponges, jellyfish, earthworms, and planarians are all invertebrates. In fact, most animal species are invertebrates.

Mechanical support for muscle attachment and for consistent body shape is provided by a structure called the **skeleton**. Although an invertebrate does not have a backbone, it does have a skeleton. Often, an invertebrate does not have an internal skeleton made of bone. It may have either an internal or external skeleton made of materials similar to limestone, glass, protein, and even ordinary water. While these skeletal materials may seem a bit unusual at first, they make quite effective skeletons.

Invertebrates come in hundreds of shapes and sizes. Some are so small that they easily carry on circulation, respiration, and excretion without special structures. Others are larger and have complicated organs and tissues to maintain their internal balance. In this chapter and the next, you will learn about the systems and special structures God created that make each group of invertebrates unique.

15A-1 A scorpion's skeleton is its outer covering.

Section Review 15A

1. About how many animal species are there? *Over one million*
2. Why is a bee considered an invertebrate? *because it does not have a backbone.*
3. Besides bone, list three substances that could compose an animal's skeleton. *Water, limestone, and protein*

15B   Sponges

Sponges are "pore animals." Their existence depends on the numerous pores in their bodies through which they pump water that brings food and oxygen in and carries wastes out. In fact, this characteristic of having pores is so essential to animals in the sponge phylum that the phylum was named *Porifera* (puh RIF uh ruh).

All sponges live in water, and most species live in the oceans. Only a relatively few species live in fresh water. Adult sponges remain permanently attached to solid objects in the water and thus are unable to move from place to place. However, embryonic sponges can swim around briefly.

Sponges have skeletons made of *spongin*, (a flexible, fibrous protein), of *spicules* (stiff, pointed little spikes made of calcium carbonate or silica), or of both. The skeletons of some sponges are used as bath sponges, cleaning sponges, and even decorative painting sponges.

A typical sponge is diagrammed in Figure 15B-1. The spicules in this species of sponge are made of calcium carbonate. The many small pores (actually pore cells) in the walls of the sponge allow water to enter. The sponge also has a hollow central cavity and a large opening near the top. The cells lining the central cavity, called *collar cells*, possess flagella. The whiplike movement of the flagella causes water to flow inward through the small pores, pass through the central cavity, and exit though the large upper opening. Trace the path of water flowing through the sponge in Figure 15B-1.

Sponges are often called **filter feeders** because they filter water to obtain food. The cells lining the central cavity capture microscopic food particles and absorb oxygen from the water while releasing waste material. Between the outer and inner layers of the sponge body is a jellylike layer. Certain cells whose method of movement is similar to that of amoebas are found in this layer. They transport food and other materials within the sponge.

spicules: (L. SPICA, point)

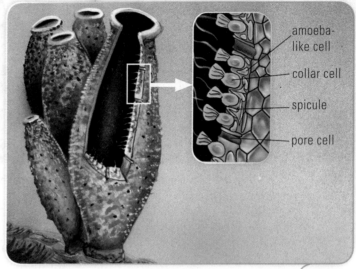

amoeba-like cell
collar cell
spicule
pore cell

Structure of a typical sponge | 15B-1

Section Review 15B

1. To what sponge characteristic does the phylum name Porifera refer? *having pores.*

2. If adult sponges are permanently attached to solid objects, how can they colonize other areas? *by sticking onto the areas.*

3. What and how do sponges eat? *Sponges eat by filtering the water, and eat microscopic food particles.*

This brown tube sponge, *Agelas conifera*, is found in the Caribbean Sea.

15B-2

15C The Jellyfish: A Cnidarian

The jellyfish belongs to the phylum *Cnidaria* (nye DAIR ee uh), as do many other animals that have *tentacles* with stinging cells. Jellyfish and similar animals are usually found living in the oceans. A few species are found in fresh water.

15C.1 *The Body of a Jellyfish*

If you have seen a jellyfish washed up on an ocean beach, you likely understand the descriptive name given to this animal. The primary support for the jellyfish's body is a jellylike mass that fills the space between the two layers of tissue. A jellyfish has the same type of support that a balloon filled with water has, a *hydrostatic skeleton*. They are both supported by the substance that fills them.

Like other cnidarians, jellyfish have a large central cavity surrounded by two tissue layers. They also have tentacles surrounding their mouths. The two layers of tissue found in jellyfish are called the *ectoderm* (EK tuh DURM) and the *endoderm* (EN duh DURM). Both layers are one cell thick. Inside the endoderm is the *gastrovascular*

Objectives 15C

- Describe the body covering, the method of support, and the forms of movement used by jellyfish.

- Define *radial symmetry*.

- Explain how coral animals contribute to the development of a coral reef.

hydrostatic: hydro- (Gk. HUDROS, water) + -static (Gk. STATOS, standing)

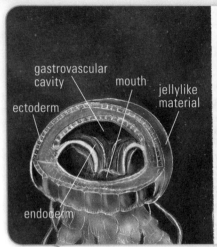

gastrovascular cavity · mouth · jellylike material · ectoderm · endoderm

15C-1 A jellyfish swims by contracting muscles around the rim of its body. This jets water out of the gastrovascular cavity and moves the jellyfish.

gastrovascular: gastro- (Gk. GASTER, belly) + -vascular (L. VASCULUM, vessel)

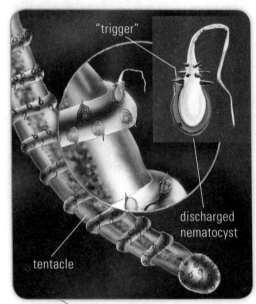

"trigger" · discharged nematocyst · tentacle

15C-2 People are careful to avoid jellyfish tentacles because of the painful stings inflicted by nematocysts. However, some species also have nematocysts in other parts of their bodies.

Love Thy Neighbor

How can knowing more about jellyfish help you love your neighbor better? What about loving God?

(GAS tro VAS kyuh lur) *cavity*, where the jellyfish digests its food. Jellyfish have only one body opening, the *mouth*. Food goes into and waste moves out of the gastrovascular cavity through the mouth.

The jellyfish has a network of nerves throughout its body. It also possesses some muscle fibers that are controlled by the network of nerves. It has no brain to coordinate complex reactions.

15C.2 *Jellyfish Activities*

The jellyfish is not a defenseless bag of jelly. If you have touched a jellyfish's *tentacles*, you probably know about **nematocysts** (nih MAT uh SISTZ). Nematocysts are in special cells found in the ectoderm, or outer layer, of jellyfish and similar organisms. Each nematocyst has a trigger. This trigger can cause a thin tube to be forced out of the nematocyst. The tiny tube easily enters human skin and can also penetrate the scales of fish and the shells of small aquatic organisms. After the tube has penetrated the organism, a poison is forced through the tube. In humans, the poison from nematocysts can cause a painful rash and other discomforts. Small animals are often paralyzed and killed by the poison. The jellyfish uses weak muscle fibers in its tentacles to push the prey into its gastrovascular cavity.

Digestive enzymes are released by cells in the endoderm to break down the food (external digestion) in the gastrovascular cavity. These small pieces of food then enter food vacuoles of other cells of the endoderm. The digestion process is completed inside these cells. Substances that the jellyfish cannot digest are expelled back into the gastrovascular cavity and flow out through the mouth.

Although nematocysts function mainly to provide food for the jellyfish, their defensive usefulness becomes very real to many swimmers. Despite the unpleasantness they sometimes cause humans, we should appreciate the way God has designed these fragile creatures to be able both to defend themselves and to capture their own food.

Jellyfish do not use their tentacles to swim. Most of the time jellyfish just float. When they do swim, a set of muscle fibers around the rim of the jellyfish contracts. This forces water out of the jellyfish's gastrovascular cavity and moves the jellyfish along with a slow, jerky motion.

Facets of *Zoology:* *Corals and Coral Reefs*

Many coral animals resemble plants. Some need sunlight, some branch like trees, and they all stay in a fixed position. However, corals are actually animals, and they share many characteristics with jellyfish and hydras. Unlike these other cnidarians, corals live attached in large colonies.

There are two main groups of coral animals. Both types have a soft body called a *polyp*, which consists of a jellylike mass sandwiched between two layers of tissue (similar to the jellyfish). Both types have tentacles with stinging cells used for defense and capturing food. However, one group secretes a cup-shaped base that is made of calcium carbonate (limestone). The other group does not secrete such a base. These two groups are generally called hard corals (limestone base) and soft corals (no limestone base).

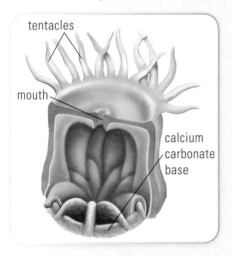

Both soft and hard corals capture small organisms, such as plankton, that pass near the corals' stinging tentacles. Some corals possess stings powerful enough to remind human divers not to touch them. Corals may even sting each other in a competition for space.

Hard corals usually live in relatively shallow depths of 30 m (100 ft) or less. This limitation occurs because most hard corals have algae living inside their tissues. This relationship is beneficial to both the coral and the algae. The algae receive protection inside the coral polyps. What benefits do you think coral receive from the algae? As you answer, consider that hard corals do not survive as well in deeper depths where there is less light. Soft corals can be found attached to solid objects in shallow or deep water.

The limestone bases of hard corals permanently attach these animals to solid objects. When the coral dies, only the limestone base remains. These cup-shaped bases are often intricately designed with symmetrical patterns. After one coral animal dies, another one will settle on top of the old base and secrete its own base on top of the previous one. Eventually, these coral bases will accumulate into great masses of limestone. Reefs and even islands are made from accumulations of coral limestone. But coral reefs are not just masses of accumulated coral. They are also colorful homes to myriads of marine organisms. An area of coral reef is home to more ocean-dwelling organisms than most other areas of equal size in the ocean.

Coral animals can survive only under specific conditions. The 30 m depth limit for hard corals is just one example. Temperature and the saltiness of the water are crucial as well. Most hard corals need water temperatures between 16°C and 28°C (61°F–82°F). Lagoons, which are often warmer and less salty than the open ocean, hinder the growth of coral. Thus, coral reefs are often healthy and growing on the side exposed to the open ocean but dead or barely alive on the lagoon side.

In Job 38:16 God asks Job, "Hast thou entered into the springs of the sea? or hast thou walked in the search of the depth?" In searching out the depths of the sea, we can say with the psalmist, "O Lord, how manifold are thy works! in wisdom hast thou made them all: the earth is full of thy riches. So is this great and wide sea, wherein are things creeping innumerable, both small and great beasts" (Psalm 104:24–25).

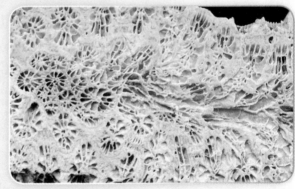

This cut through a mass of hard coral reveals successive coral bases built on top of each other.

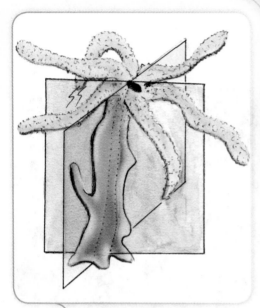

15C-3 The hydra is tubular, is radially symmetric, and has nematocysts. Hydras live in fresh water and capture and eat young insects, worms, and other small creatures.

15C.3 *Other Interesting Cnidarians*

Hydras, corals, and sea anemones are also cnidarians. Each of these animals captures prey with its stinging tentacles and digests it in a central body cavity. The Portuguese man-of-war is a dangerous cnidarian that can grow to be 15 m (50 ft) long. Although it looks like a kind of jellyfish, it is actually a floating colony containing many specialized polyps. Like the jellyfish, its tentacles contain nematocysts. Stings from a Portuguese man-of-war can cause intense pain in humans and in some cases even death.

The bodies of cnidarians have **radial symmetry**. This means that they can be divided into equal halves by any plane along the length of the organism. Consequently, cnidarians have a top and bottom, but no definite left or right sides. These animals have either of two general body shapes: umbrella shaped or tubular (Fig. 15C-1 and 15C-3). The jellyfish, for example, has an umbrella-shaped body. In some species both body forms are found at different points in the life cycle. In addition, cnidarians may be either free-floating or permanently attached to a solid object.

Section Review 15C

1. What is the supporting material in a jellyfish's skeleton?

2. Where do jellyfish digest their prey?

3. What is the soft body of a coral animal called?

15D The Planarian: A Flatworm

Flatworm is an appropriate name for this group of animals, since its members are obviously flat. They also have **bilateral symmetry**. This simply means that there are two equal sides to the animal. One side is like a mirror image of the other side. There is only one possible plane that will divide it into equal halves.

The 2 cm (3/4 in.) long *planarian* (pluh NEHR ee un) belongs in the flatworm group, phylum *Platyhelminthes* (PLAT ee hel MIN theez). The planarian is a *free-living* flatworm that can be found in freshwater streams and in soil. *Free-living* means that it is not a parasite that is dependent on a host. Other flatworms can be found in the oceans, in fresh water, inside other animals as parasites, or in the soil.

15D.1 *The Planarian's Nervous System*

Most animals control their bodies through neurons. **Neurons** (NOOR AHNZ) are long, thin nerve cells found throughout the body of an animal or human. These cells carry impulses from one point to another. A collection of neurons wrapped in protective coverings is called a **nerve**. Neurons, nerves, and impulses can be compared to the electrical system. Neurons are like the thin wires that go to individual outlets in a house. These wires all run from a circuit breaker panel that is supplied by a large cable bringing in the electricity from the power company. The cable is like a nerve. The waves of current traveling through these wires are like impulses traveling along neurons.

Many invertebrates have nervous systems that are fairly complex and require some coordination. An invertebrate's "coordination center" is a **ganglion** (GANG glee un) (*pl.*, ganglia), sometimes called a *simple brain*. Many invertebrates have several ganglia, each one responsible for either a different area of the body or a different set of responses.

The planarian has a simple nervous system. A *longitudinal* (LAHN jih TOOD en uhl) *nerve* runs down each side of its body. A series of *transverse* (trans VURS) *nerves* connects the longitudinal nerves, giving the whole system the appearance of a ladder. Near the front end of each longitudinal nerve is a ganglion.

The planarian's ganglia coordinate its responses to stimuli. A **stimulus** (STIM yuh lus) (*pl.*, stimuli) is something an organism can sense. Planarians have a sense of touch. Therefore, touching a planarian would stimulate it. The neuron that receives the stimulus converts it to an impulse, which travels along the nerves to a ganglion. When a ganglion receives the impulse, it sends other impulses to various structures of the planarian, causing it to respond.

If you touch a planarian on the side of its head, it will turn and move away. The stimulus of being touched causes the response of turning away. In a stream of water, however, a planarian responds by turning and proceeding headfirst into the current. Planarians normally travel upstream. Somehow the planarian is able to tell the difference between the touch of an object and the touch of flowing water. It responds differently to each stimulus.

Planarians also respond to chemicals in the water. Some chemicals cause them to turn away; others attract them. Scientists believe that a planarian locates its food by the chemicals it can detect in the water.

Planarians are sometimes called "cross-eyed worms." If you look at the front end of a planarian, you will see two spots. These areas are sensitive to light. The planarian does not see objects or colors as humans do. The nerves in these areas are sensitive only to the presence or absence of light. Normally light causes a negative response in planarians. If the light comes from a single direction, a planarian usually moves away from it. If a planarian comes from a shadowed area into a brightly lit area, it will turn around and head back to the shadows. Why would a planarian want to avoid bright light? A planarian makes a nice mouthful for fish or other aquatic organisms. During the day the planarian is safest in the shadows. At night, when its dark body is hidden, it can come out and feed in relative safety.

15D.2 *The Planarian's Digestive and Excretory Systems*

The planarian's body covering is a tissue that is one cell-layer thick. Cilia on the underside of the planarian help it glide over underwater surfaces. The mouth of the planarian is on its underside, near the

Since only one possible line (plane) divides a planarian into two identical halves, it is said to have bilateral symmetry.   15D-1

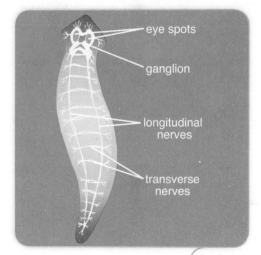

eye spots

ganglion

longitudinal nerves

transverse nerves

The nervous system of a planarian   15D-2

His Mercy Endureth Forever

The abilities of the "lowly" planarian to distinguish between different kinds of touch, detect specific chemicals, and even avoid light demonstrate a level of behavior that is remarkable for such a small organism. Even this testifies of a loving Creator who provides each of His creatures with what it needs to survive.

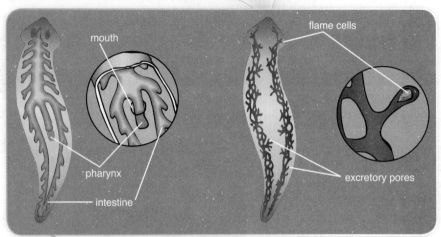

15D-3 Digestive system (left) and excretory system (right) of a planarian

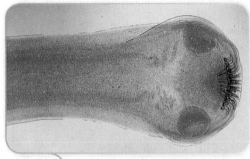

15D-4 The head of a tapeworm is equipped with hooks and/or suckers. These keep the tapeworm attached to its host's digestive system.

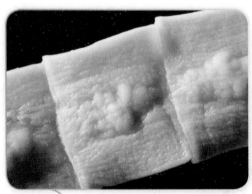

15D-5 The sections that compose a tapeworm's body are connected end to end. One 20 m specimen was found to have three thousand sections.

middle of its body. Just inside the mouth is a long branching cavity called the *intestine*. The intestine is lined with a layer of cells which is called the *gastroderm* (GAS tro durm).

The planarian eats by extending a muscular tube, called the *pharynx*, through the mouth and sucking food into the intestine. In the intestine, enzymes secreted by the gastroderm begin digesting the food. The cells of the gastroderm absorb the small pieces of food and finish breaking down the food by cellular digestion. Nondigestible material is pushed out of the intestine through the mouth.

Branches of the planarian's intestine extend to every area of the worm's body. Food is moved throughout the intestine by the twisting movements of the planarian and by flagella found on some of the cells of the gastroderm. Food is brought near every cell in the planarian's body as it circulates through the extensive intestine.

Between the planarian's body covering and gastroderm is a mass of cells. Some of these cells are specialized for particular functions. For example, some are muscle cells that help the planarian bend and twist. But in spite of this mass of cells, the planarian's body is very thin. It is about as thick as a heavy sheet of paper. This thinness allows the animal's cells to exchange oxygen and carbon dioxide directly with the environment.

The planarian gets rid of its waste products through a system of tiny tubes. At the ends of these tubes are structures called *flame cells*. The cilia that beat at the ends of these structures look like tiny flames flickering in the tubes. These cilia move water and wastes through the tubes to tiny holes called *excretory* (EK skrih TOR ee) *pores*. Here the water and wastes are excreted from the planarian.

15D.3 *Other Interesting Flatworms*

Some other common flatworms include tapeworms, flukes, and brilliantly colored marine flatworms. *Tapeworms* are a common parasite of animals and humans, even in modern America. Have you ever helped give your pet cat or dog a "worm pill"? There are two types of worm pills, one for roundworms (next section) and one for tapeworms.

Tapeworms are parasites found in the digestive tracts of various animals. A tapeworm has a head equipped with hooks and/or suckers to attach it securely to the digestive tract. It is nourished by absorbing dissolved food that is passing through this digestive cavity. Most of the body of the tapeworm consists of reproductive segments. These segments eventually fill with eggs, are released, and later exit in the animal's feces (wastes). They then rupture, releasing eggs that may eventually infect other animals. A tapeworm grows by forming new segments at its head that mature as they move farther from the head.

Parasitic worms in humans are unpleasant and harmful. Their destructiveness is a constant reminder of the consequences of the Fall.

Section Review 15D

1. What type of symmetry does a planarian have?

2. How many longitudinal nerves does a planarian have?

3. Where is the mouth of a planarian?

15E Roundworms

As the name indicates, roundworms, in the phylum *Nematoda* (NEEM uh TOH duh), have round, tubular bodies that are tapered at each end. Some are serious parasites of humans, animals, and plants; others are free living. Many are microscopic, but one common roundworm, *Ascaris*, may grow to be 30 cm (12 in.) long.

> **Objectives 15E**
> - List at least three examples of roundworms.
> - Describe the hydrostatic skeleton of a roundworm.

15E.1 Ascaris—A Common Roundworm

An adult *Ascaris* (AS kuh ris) can be found in the intestines of various animals. Roundworms release eggs into the animal's intestine; these eggs then exit in the feces. When these tiny eggs are swallowed, perhaps by a grazing cow, the eggs hatch. The young larvae burrow into the intestine walls and enter the bloodstream. They eventually reach the lungs and then travel up the throat and are reswallowed. In the intestine again, the larvae grow into adult worms. Humans, cats, dogs, and various farm animals can have roundworms. If an infected animal is not the normal host for the species of roundworm it has, then the larvae continue to wander around in the animal's body, never to be reswallowed and reach maturity.

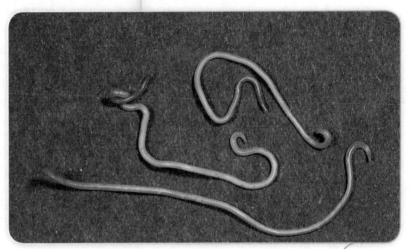

Ascaris is one of the most common parasites in humans. **15E-1**

15E.2 Other Interesting Roundworms

Other serious roundworm parasites include hookworms, pinworms, and trichina worms. Trichina worms often form cysts containing larvae in the muscle tissue of pigs. When infected pork is eaten, the worms quickly infect the one who ate the pork. Can you think of a good way to control the spread of trichina worms?

Another kind of roundworm is the vinegar eel. These worms appear as tiny threads in unpasteurized vinegar and cider products. Fortunately, these worms are not parasitic. Vinegar eels actually contribute to the development of the unique cider taste. Other roundworms cause serious plant diseases.

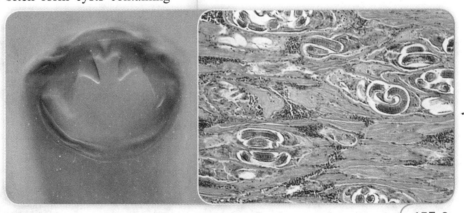

Microscopic view of the mouth of a hookworm (left). Microscopic view of muscle (meat) infected with trichina worm larvae (right). This is one good reason to thoroughly cook meat. **15E-2**

1. Name the phylum that includes roundworms.

2. Where does an adult *Ascaris* normally live?

3. Are roundworms parasites of animals only? Explain.

15F Segmented Worms

The earthworm has a long, slender body made of a series of similar segments. This segmented body plan is what distinguishes earthworms, phylum *Annelida* (uh NEL ih duh), from other groups of worms. While the earthworm is the most familiar segmented worm, it is not the only one. Leeches, tubeworms, scale worms, sandworms, and fireworms also belong to this group.

15F.1 *The Body of an Earthworm*

Covering the earthworm's body is a thin skin called an *epidermis*. The epidermis exchanges gases (carbon dioxide and oxygen) with the earthworm's environment. The epidermis also secretes a thin outer coating called the *cuticle*. This cuticle protects the earthworm from harmful parasites and substances. The earthworm's cuticle must be thin and its epidermis kept moist for gas exchange to occur.

Under its epidermis, the earthworm has two *muscle layers*. These muscle layers provide support for the worm and also help it move. One muscle layer is arranged in circles around the earthworm's body. When the muscles contract, the worm becomes longer and thinner. The other muscle layer is arranged in long strips running from the head to the tail. When these muscles contract, the earthworm becomes shorter and wider.

The earthworm moves by using its muscles and the tiny bristles on each of its segments. The earthworm moves forward by extending the bristles on its rear segments into the soil. Once the worm's rear segments are anchored, it contracts its circular muscles. This causes the worm to become long and thin, pushing its front end forward. Then the worm releases the rear segments' bristles and extends the bristles of its front half into the soil. The worm then pulls itself for-

Objectives 15F

- Describe the body covering, method of support, and forms of movement used by the earthworm.
- Describe the nervous system of the earthworm.
- Identify the structures of an earthworm's digestive system and describe the functions of each structure.
- Explain the processes of circulation, respiration, and excretion in the earthworm.
- Define *closed circulatory system*.
- Evaluate the significance of having earthworms in the soil.

Would You Believe?

An earthworm can move a stone that is fifty times its body weight. For you, that would be like shoving an SUV out of your way!

15F-1 The bearded fireworm (left) lives in the sea and is protected by poisonous bristles. The sandworm (right) is a segmented worm that lives near the low tide level of the shoreline.

ward by contracting its long muscles. The earthworm repeats this process to move itself along.

15F.2 *The Earthworm's Nervous System*

Over the body of an earthworm are many sensory receptors. A **sensory receptor** is a structure that can sense a stimulus and then start an impulse traveling along a neuron. Some of an earthworm's sensory receptors are sensitive to chemicals in the soil, others to light, and some to temperature and various other conditions.

Facets of *Zoology:* "Intestines of the Soil"

Aristotle called earthworms the "intestines of the soil" because they take plant and animal matter and "digest" it so that it becomes usable for plants to gather nutrients from the soil. Earthworms can thrive in soil almost anywhere on earth. They live in Siberia, on islands near Antarctica, and on mountains as high as 3077 m (10,000 ft). Earthworms also come in many different sizes. Some species are less than 2.5 cm (1 in.) long, while others, such as the giant earthworm of Australia, are more than 3 m (9.8 ft) long.

Earthworms remain active both day and night. During the day they dig burrows in the earth. At night an earthworm extends its front end from its burrow in search of leaves and other materials it can drag into its burrow for food. Its back end remains attached by its bristles to the inside of the burrow. After the earthworm reenters its burrow, it blocks the entrance by covering the hole with parts of plants.

The earthworm is very sensitive to vibrations in the soil. It pulls itself quickly back into its burrow at the slightest disturbance. Australian aborigines hunt giant earthworms at night while the worms' bodies are halfway out of their burrows. By carefully approaching the earthworms,

they reach them without their sensing danger. It takes a very quick and strong man to pull a giant earthworm out of its burrow.

An earthworm normally will not leave its burrow unless it is forced out by bad conditions. Once out of the burrow, the earthworm usually cannot find its way back and will probably have to dig a new one. Meanwhile, the earthworm is in great danger. Long before it can dig a new burrow, the worm usually becomes food for birds or is trampled by people, or its skin may become too dry for respiration to occur.

Earthworms dig extensive burrows in the earth. Most burrows lie within a foot of the surface, but some extend as deep as 6 m (20 ft). An earthworm begins a tunnel by placing the tip of its head in a crack in the soil. It forces its head forward into the soil, narrowing as it extends. Then it anchors its head in the soil with its bristles and expands its pharynx region by forcing the fluid of its hydrostatic skeleton into that area. This expansion pushes the soil outward, and the worm moves its body forward. The worm burrows deeper into the soil with repeated headlong advances of this kind. If the soil is particularly firm and unyielding, the worm may actually eat its way through the soil.

Earthworms digest some of the materials in the soil for food. The indigestible materials are returned to the soil as castings, which contain many nitrogen-rich substances. These castings provide valuable nutrients for plants.

Earthworm activity loosens the soil, allowing it to hold more air. With more air in the soil, plant roots and soil organisms grow better. Earthworm burrows also allow water to enter the soil. Water soaks into the soil four to ten times faster when it contains earthworms.

The burrowing of earthworms helps to bring soil from deep in the earth to the surface. The earthworms living in a single acre can turn over as much as 100 tons of soil in one year. Studies have shown that this activity greatly affects the growth of crops. One study produced a crop yield of 1270 kg (2800 lb) per acre on land containing worms, compared to 114 kg (250 lb) per acre on land without worms. Wheat, clover, barley, and oats have all been shown to yield much larger harvests on land tunneled by earthworms.

The addition of organic matter such as decaying plant material to the soil provides ideal growth conditions for earthworms. Many farmers and home gardeners improve their soil's productivity by planting crops that can be tilled into the soil at the end of their life cycle, or by adding compost. Read Psalm 8:4–9. How does a farmer's job accomplish what Psalm 8:6 and Genesis 1:26 say that God wants men to do? What does Psalm 8:6–8 say about our study of sponges and jellyfish earlier in this chapter?

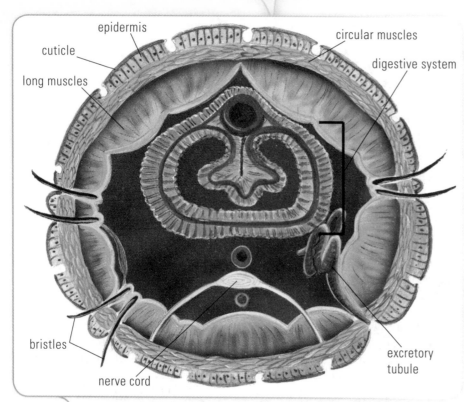

epidermis

cuticle

long muscles

circular muscles

digestive system

bristles

nerve cord

excretory
tubule

15F-2 Cross section of an earthworm

An earthworm has more sensory receptors at its front end than anywhere else on its body. The earthworm normally leads with its front end. The extra sensory receptors in its front end help the worm to sense whether it is approaching food or danger so that it can react accordingly.

An earthworm's neurons carry impulses from the sensory receptors in the front of the worm to two *large ganglia* in the third segment. Sensory receptors in other areas of the worm send their impulses to the nerve cord in the lower half of the worm. The *nerve cord* is a bundle of neurons that begins at the two large ganglia and continues to the tail end of the worm. Along the nerve cord there is one *small ganglion* in each segment of the worm.

The ganglia interpret the impulses from the sensory receptors, and the worm decides what to do about them. *Interprets* and *decides* describe in some respects the worm's response to stimuli. But these words may not provide very good descriptions because they imply intelligence. Earthworms have very little intelligence. Within the ganglia the impulses from the sensory receptors are transferred to the proper neurons. These neurons carry impulses to muscles, bristles, and other structures that will enable the earthworm to respond properly.

For example, if a sharp object touches the earthworm on its front right side, impulses travel from the sensory receptors in that area along neurons to nearby ganglia. From ganglia, impulses are sent along other neurons to muscles and bristles, and the earthworm reacts by pulling away from the stimulus. Thousands of neurons may be involved in the reaction to one stimulus.

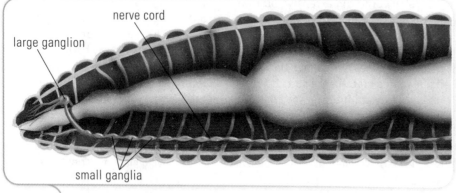

nerve cord

large ganglion

small ganglia

15F-3 The nervous system of an earthworm

15F.3 *The Earthworm's Digestive System*

An earthworm often eats the soil as it forms tunnels. Most of the soil is indigestible, nonfood material. But mixed into the soil are decaying leaves, fungi, and small creatures that the earthworm can digest.

The earthworm has a long, straight digestive tract. At various points along the digestive tract there are enlargements, constrictions, infoldings, and glands. Each of these structures has a separate function in the digestion process of the earthworm.

The mouth of the earthworm secretes fluids that moisten the soil as it enters. By observing closely, you may notice that an earthworm has an upper lip that helps force food into its mouth. From the mouth the moistened soil passes to the *pharynx* (FEHR inks). Glands secrete liquids into the pharynx to lubricate the food as it passes through. Strong muscle fibers in the walls of the pharynx contract to help pull food into the earthworm. The *esophagus* (ih SAHF uh gus) is a tubular passageway that carries the food from the pharynx to the crop. The *crop* looks like a swelling in the digestive tract. It serves as a temporary storage chamber for food taken in by the earthworm.

Food leaving the crop passes into the *gizzard*. The gizzard is another bulge in the earthworm's digestive tract. As muscles in the gizzard's thick walls contract and relax, they push the gizzard's walls in and out. This movement performs mechanical digestion by grinding the usable food substances against the sand and grit particles in the earthworm's food.

The ground-up food passes from the gizzard into the earthworm's intestine. Here digestive enzymes made by cells in the intestinal wall perform digestion outside of cells by breaking the food down into soluble substances. The inner intestinal wall is folded into ridges that provide extra surface area for absorbing food. Food molecules are absorbed through the intestine and into blood vessels. The blood in these vessels carries the food to all the cells of the earthworm.

The indigestible parts of the earthworm's food pass through the intestine and leave the digestive tract through the *anus*. These wastes sometimes accumulate in piles outside the earthworms' tunnels and are called *castings*.

15F.4 *The Earthworm's Circulatory System*

An earthworm's circulatory system is a continuous network of blood vessels. The blood remains in the vessels as it circulates throughout the earthworm's body. Because the blood never leaves the blood vessels, this system is called a **closed circulatory system**.

The large *dorsal blood vessel* (along the back) of the earthworm acts as the heart. It pumps blood forward to the five sets of **aortic** (ay OR tik) **arches**, which help control the earthworm's blood pressure. The blood passes through the aortic arches down to the ventral blood vessel. The ventral blood vessel then carries the blood along the bottom of the earthworm to every segment of the earthworm's body.

Branching from the ventral blood vessel are smaller and smaller arteries. The blood passes through these arteries and enters the tiniest blood vessels, called **capillaries** (KAP uh LEHR eez). Through the capillaries' thin walls, substances can pass between the blood and the earthworm's tissues. Blood flows from arteries through capillaries to **veins**. In a closed circulatory system, veins are blood vessels that carry the blood *toward* the heart. In the earthworm, the tiny veins that collect blood from the capillaries pass the blood along to larger veins that return the blood to the dorsal blood vessel, the structure that functions as the earthworm's heart.

esophagus: eso- (Gk. OIS-, will carry) + -phagus (Gk. PHAGO, eat)

The type of circulatory system in which blood is not always confined by blood vessels is called an open circulatory system. This type of system is discussed in the next chapter (p. 289).

15F.5 *The Earthworm's Respiratory and Excretory Systems*

The earthworm does not have special respiratory structures. Instead, it exchanges oxygen and carbon dioxide through its moist skin. The oxygen that enters through the earthworm's skin is received by the blood in the capillaries that line the skin. Carbon dioxide passes out of the capillaries through the skin in the same way. In emergencies an earthworm can go without a new supply of oxygen for several hours. However, during long heavy rainstorms, the earthworm's burrow fills with rainwater that has little oxygen. At these times the earthworm is forced to come to the surface to get oxygen.

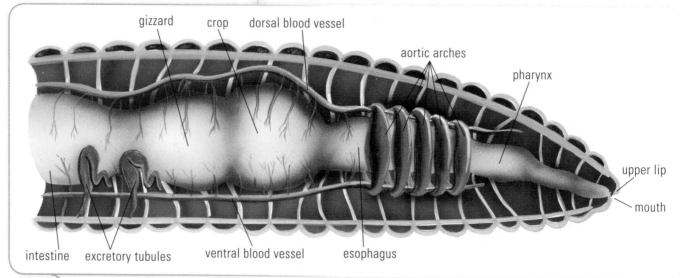

gizzard   crop   dorsal blood vessel

aortic arches

pharynx

upper lip

mouth

intestine   excretory tubules   ventral blood vessel   esophagus

15F-4   The digestive, circulatory, and excretory systems of an earthworm

All but the first and last few segments of the earthworm have tiny looped tubes that collect wastes from the earthworm's blood. The wastes collected in these *excretory tubules* are passed out of the body through tiny pores on the earthworm's surface.

Section Review 15F

1. Name three members of phylum Annelida besides earthworms.

2. In which part of the earthworm's digestive system does mechanical digestion occur?

3. How does an earthworm breathe?

4. How can our study of earthworms help us exercise dominion over the earth?

Chapter Review

1. What does the word *invertebrate* literally mean?

2. What is the key characteristic of sponges?

3. What two materials may compose a sponge skeleton?

4. What material or substance provides support for an animal that has a hydrostatic skeleton?

5. In what phylum do jellyfish and coral belong?

6. Name the structure that jellyfish use for stinging.

7. Why do hard corals live in relatively shallow depths?

8. What kind of symmetry do cnidarians have?

9. What is the name given to the simple brain of an invertebrate such as a planarian?

10. How does a planarian get rid of its waste products?

11. Name three roundworms (genus or common name).

12. When an earthworm moves, what structures allow it to hold on to the soil?

13. What do you call the indigestible soil and food that an earthworm expels as waste?

14. What does the term *closed circulatory system* mean?

15. What organ removes wastes from an earthworm's blood?

What Did You Learn?

1. How do sponges obtain food?

2. If you were to cut through a large mass of hard coral, what would you find?

3. Sketch an invertebrate animal that has radial symmetry and another that has bilateral symmetry.

4. Describe how a planarian eats.

5. Why do we not want pets to have tapeworms?

6. Since they do not have eyes, how do night crawlers (earthworms that come out at night) know to retreat into their burrows when a light is shined on them?

7. How are earthworms beneficial to plant growth?

Scientifically Speaking

invertebrate
skeleton
filter feeder
nematocyst
radial symmetry
bilateral symmetry
neuron
nerve
ganglion
stimulus
sensory receptor
closed circulatory system
aortic arches
capillary
vein

Self Quiz 15

_____ 1. All animals are eukaryotic, multicellular, and have true tissues. (True/False)

_____ 2. An invertebrate is an animal that has no
skeleton. (True/False)

_____ 3. Which of these is a filter feeder?
A. sponge
B. jellyfish
C. planarian
D. both A and B

_____ 4. Nematocysts help a jellyfish
A. protect itself.
B. feed itself.
C. both A and B
D. neither A nor B

_____ 5. Bilateral symmetry is exhibited by a
A. sponge.
B. jellyfish.
C. planarian.
D. starfish.

_____ 6. Neurons and ganglia are associated with

an animal's _____ system.
A. excretory
B. nervous
C. digestive
D. circulatory

_____ 7. _Ascaris_ is a
A. tapeworm.
B. segmented worm.
C. fluke.
D. roundworm.

_____ 8. Which of these is _not_ an organ of the
earthworm's digestive system?
A. excretory tubule
B. esophagus
C. gizzard
D. All are digestive organs.

9. The earthworm's blood pressure is controlled

by five pairs of _____.

10. Match the organism with its phylum.

_____ hookworm   A. Annelida

_____ earthworm   B. Cnidaria

_____ coral   C. Platyhelminthes

_____ sponge   D. Porifera

_____ tapeworm   E. Nematoda

Invertebrates II: Mollusks, Arthropods, and Echinoderms

The three phyla presented in this chapter might best be described as living fortresses. Often having their own portable shields, these invertebrates appear impenetrable. Add to that the possession of stingers, pincers, and spines, and you end up with some of the best-armored animals. Though such creatures may seldom find their way into your diet, these phyla do figure in your survival. As pollinators, pests, and food sources for other organisms, these animals are key links in the web of life. Every creature plays a role in God's design of the earth . . . from ants to zebra mussels.

Objectives 16A

- Describe the body and the forms of movement used by the octopus.
- Describe the body of the clam.
- Explain how the clam obtains food.

What Do You Think?

Of course, all mollusks are invertebrates. Other than being invertebrates, what do you think they have in common?

The purple dye used to color the fabric sold by Lydia in Acts 16:14 was extracted from Murex snails.

16A-1 Major Classes of Mollusks

Class	Characteristics	Examples
Gastropoda	Many with coiled shell; marine, freshwater, or terrestrial	Snails, slugs
Cephalopoda	Most without a shell but have tentacles; marine	Squids, octopuses, nautiluses
Bivalvia	Two-part hinged shell; marine and freshwater	Clams, oysters, mussels

Let Them Have Dominion

In this book we have said a lot about having dominion over the animals of the earth (Gen. 1:26–28). However, it is important to remember that we first of all need to have dominion over ourselves. Read James 3:7-8. What does it teach us about our tongues?

16A Mollusks

Mollusks are animals such as clams, snails, slugs, and octopuses. Since biologists have grouped these animals together, they must have some characteristics in common.

Phylum Mollusca (muh LUS kuh) is quite important. It is the animal phylum with the second highest number of species, and this makes it very significant in the environment. Some of these animals are particularly important to man. We use them for food (clams, oysters, and scallops, and even squid, snails, and octopus). We make things from them (pearls, mother-of-pearl buttons), and they are sometimes serious pests or carriers of parasites. (Some slugs are garden pests, and some snails harbor human liver flukes.) In this section you will learn about mollusks by studying two representatives of the group: the octopus and the clam.

16A.1 The Octopus—Mollusk Without a Shell

The octopus's body lacks structures to give it firm support, but it does have many muscles in its body. Each of its eight arms (tentacles) contains muscles that allow the octopus to move its arms in any direction. On the lower surface of each arm is a series of *suction disks*. These suction disks allow the octopus to grasp items. Food captured in its arms can be moved to its mouth, which is located under the "head" in the center of its arms. The suction disks can also be used to fasten the octopus to things. By moving its arms and then anchoring them, the octopus can move its body. If an arm is destroyed or severed, the octopus has a remarkable ability to *regenerate* (grow) a replacement.

Although the octopus hunts live food (crabs, lobsters, and shelled mollusks are among its favorites), it appears to be a timid animal. Its soft body is easily damaged, and if it senses danger, it quickly hides. Although the octopus normally moves by gliding along on its arms, it is a relatively slow creature. To move rapidly through the water, the octopus forces water though a muscular tube called a *siphon* (SY fun). This jets the octopus through the water. Occasionally, when it is frightened, an octopus releases an inky black fluid into the water to serve as a "smoke screen," allowing it to jet away to safety.

The octopus has a thin, flexible skin that helps its soft body hide easily in cracks between rocks on the ocean floor. It can "pour itself" into gaps, and completely change its body shape. Special cells in the octopus's skin contain different-colored pigments. Some of these cells may contain red pigments; others, yellow pigments; others, brown pigments; and so on. By causing different cells in the skin to spread out their pigments, the octopus can change colors. In this way, many species can become almost invisible against almost any background.

The octopus's colors may also reflect its level of stimulation. If an octopus is startled, it usually turns pale; when it is excited, it often turns red. The octopus has been observed to have waves of several different colors pass rapidly over its body, one after another.

16A.2 The Clam—Mollusk with a Shell

In the same phylum as the octopus are a number of organisms that produce *shells* to protect and cover their bodies. Clams, mussels, and scallops produce two shells that are hinged together. These animals are called *bivalves*. Snails and conchs (kongks) produce a single shell, often coiled, and are called *univalves*.

While most octopuses are relatively harmless to humans, the blue-ringed octopus of Australia produces a venom that is deadly. The blue rings appear only when the animal is threatened and ready to attack.

16A-2

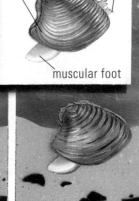

A clam digs through sand by extending, expanding, and pulling its foot. 16A-3

The clam's soft body is covered with a thin skin called the *mantle*. The outside of this skin manufactures the materials that harden to become the shell. As the clam grows, it adds layers to its shell. The oldest part of the shell is the thickest because of all the layers that have been added. The newest part of the shell is the thinnest.

The clam has powerful muscles that can keep its shells tightly closed. When the clam moves, it sends out a muscular *foot*. This hatchet-shaped foot is pushed into the sand and expanded. Then the muscles contract to shorten the foot and pull the animal and shell forward. In this way, the clam digs into the sand. If you have ever tried to dig for clams, you know that a clam can use its muscular foot to move rapidly through sand.

Clams do not hunt for their food or clamp their shells shut on tasty morsels. Clams are *filter feeders*. They dig into the sand and send two tubes called siphons out to the water. One siphon is used to draw water into the shell, where tiny floating food particles are filtered out. The other siphon sends the water away from the clam to remove wastes.

Can you find the siphons on these bivalves? 16A-4

What Do You Think?

What animal that you studied in Chapter 15 is also a filter feeder?

1. Name a mollusk that is edible.

2. What does an octopus use its siphon to do?

3. What part of the clam's body manufactures its hard shell?

16B Arthropods

Phylum Arthropoda (ar THRAHP uh duh) has the most species of any animal phylum, and the insect class is the largest class within this phylum. There are almost a million species of insects identified, and many more unidentified species probably exist. *Arthropods*, and especially the insects, play many significant roles in our world. They serve as pollinators, decomposers, crop eaters, disease carriers, and parasites. They have had profound effects on human civilization throughout history. Figure 16B-2 illustrates some of the wide variety found in insects and other arthropods.

Animals in the phylum Arthropoda have exoskeletons and jointed appendages, such as legs and antennae. An **exoskeleton** is a hard, nonliving outer covering that supports and protects the animal. Muscles are attached to the inside of an arthropod's exoskeleton. They pull on the exoskeleton to move it.

16B.1 *A Typical Insect's Body*

Insects typically have three sections to their bodies: a head, thorax (middle part), and abdomen. Additionally, insects have three pairs of legs (six total). Even caterpillars that appear to have more than three pairs of legs actually have only three pairs at the front end. The others are not real legs. Most insects have two pairs of wings, although some may have one pair or no wings.

Insects also have **compound eyes**. If you examine an insect's eyes with a hand lens, you will notice that they have thousands of small sections. As an insect views the world, it gets a separate view from each section. A grasshopper sees you as a mosaic of smaller images, not one big unified image.

Objectives 16B

- Express that there are more arthropods than any other kind of animal.
- Define *exoskeleton*.
- Contrast advantages and disadvantages of an exoskeleton.
- Describe the processes of circulation, respiration, and excretion in the grasshopper.
- Describe an open circulatory system.
- Distinguish between complete and incomplete metamorphosis, using all appropriate terms and several examples.
- List three examples of noninsect arthropods.

arthropod: arthro- (Gk. ARTHRON, joint) + -pod (Gk. POD, foot)

exoskeleton: exo- (Gk. EXO-, outside of) + -skeleton (Gk. SKELETOS, dried up)

A mosaic is a picture made by fitting together small pieces of colored material.

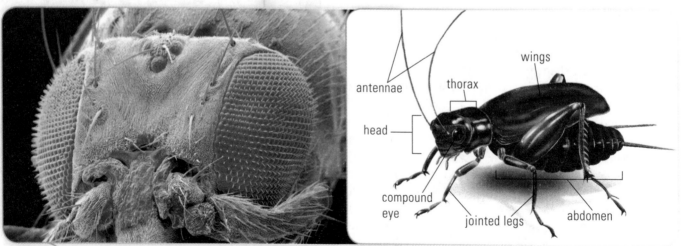

16B-1 Compound eye of a fruit fly; body of a typical insect, the field cricket

antennae · thorax · wings · head · compound eye · jointed legs · abdomen

millipede

Asian land crab

green clear-wing dragonfly

blue crayfish

pill bugs

harlequin bug

yellow crab spider

Examine these photos and identify the jointed appendages of each arthropod. Animals of this phylum can be found on land, in the air, and in water. Using the table on page 293, see if you can assign each example to the correct class.

16B-2

Facets of *Zoology:* *Armor of Knights and Arthropods*

During the Middle Ages, knights wore heavy suits of armor to protect themselves from swords, arrows, spears, and daggers as they fought their enemies. An iron suit of armor usually weighed around 25 kg (55 lb). Wearing such a heavy suit of armor greatly restricted a knight's movements.

Insects, spiders, crayfish, lobsters, centipedes, and other arthropods have exoskeletons that are much like knights' armor. Arthropods also have many of the same problems with their "armor" that knights had with theirs. The weight of an arthropod's

exoskeleton limits how big it can grow. Most arthropods are only a few centimeters long.

The largest living insects are thin, tropical stick insects that grow up to 33 cm (13 in.) long and great owlet moths, which have wing spans up to 36 cm (14 in.). Even larger insects existed in the not-too-distant past. Some fossils have been found of dragonfly-like insects with wingspans up to 70 cm (28 in.). Other kinds of arthropods sometimes grow up to 61 cm (24 in.) long, but arthropods larger than this can live only in water. The largest known arthropod is the giant spider crab, which has a 3 m (11 ft) claw span. The water of deep oceans helps support the weight of these crabs.

Joints in the armor allowed knights to bend and twist. Although good armor allowed plenty of movement, a knight's actions were more limited with armor than without. At the knight's elbows, knees, shoulders, neck, and hips, several thin strips of metal connected the large pieces of armor. When the knight moved, these strips would slide over one another or slide apart to lie side by side. These strips were dangerous, since cracks between the strips were often the targets of skillfully aimed arrows.

Like a knight's armor, the grasshopper's exoskeleton limits its movements. For instance, the grasshopper, with seven joints in each of its legs, can move them in only a very simple walking or jumping motion. By comparison, humans, with their internal skeletons, have fewer joints but can swing their legs quite far backwards, forward, inward, and sideways.

Knights often had two or three different suits of armor during their lifetimes. Young knights whose arms and legs were still growing often found that after a few years they needed to replace their armor with a larger size. If a knight later grew in width, he had to be fitted for a third suit of armor.

Arthropods solve the problem of growing out of their "armor" by molting. After an arthropod breaks out of its old exoskeleton, it swallows air or water to stretch its soft exoskeleton to its new size before it hardens. Young, rapidly growing arthropods often molt once every two weeks, while adult arthropods may molt only once or twice a year.

Armored knights also had problems knowing exactly what was happening around them. Knights could not hear very well, since sounds that came through ear holes in their metal helmets were distorted. It was hard for them to tell where sounds were coming from. Holes were cut in the knight's helmet so that he could see. Even then he could see only what was straight in front of him and hardly anything else. A knight in armor who touched something had to feel it through his gauntlet (metal glove).

This kept him from feeling quickly whether something was hot, cold, moist, dry, rough, or smooth.

In contrast to knights, arthropods have specially designed sensory organs that work perfectly with their exoskeletons. Spiders, for example, have up to eight simple eyes that detect movements. Flies have two large compound eyes, which are made of thousands of microscopic squares. With these compound eyes, the fly can see all around without turning its head or moving its eyes. Other arthropods, such as the lobster, have eyes on stalks and can see in different directions by moving these stalks.

Most arthropods also have antennae that serve as sensitive feelers and can detect smells. Some arthropods, like grasshoppers, have in their exoskeletons small round membranes that receive sound vibrations and transfer them to their inner ears. Bees and some other arthropods have tiny sensory hairs sticking through their exoskeletons. Special sensory organs allow arthropods to have keen senses in spite of their exoskeleton "armor."

It is easy to be amazed at the cleverness in the designs of arthropods' exoskeletons and sensory organs. But don't stop there. Be amazed at the infinite creativity of the God Who not only designed them but also fashioned them from nothing. Human engineers often receive fame and glory for a few good designs, but God has billions and billions of brilliant designs.

16B.2 *Body Systems in the Grasshopper*

Grasshoppers, like all arthropods, have blood and a circulatory system. **Blood** is a fluid tissue made up of cells floating in liquid. The main function of blood is to carry substances to and from all parts of the body. The typical circulatory system is made of blood vessels and a heart. The **heart** is a muscular organ that pumps blood to all body cells.

The grasshopper has a series of small tubular hearts located just under its exoskeleton on its back (upper) side. Blood enters each heart through two slits. When the hearts contract, the slits close and the blood is pumped forward through an **artery** (AR tur ee). Arteries are blood vessels that carry blood away from the heart.

At the end of the grasshopper's artery (its only blood vessel), the blood flows out over the organs. As the blood passes over the digestive organs, it picks up digested food. It absorbs substances from other organs as well. At the same time, the blood deposits these substances in places where they are needed. The blood of the grasshopper passes through small spaces around the organs and finally returns to the hearts. Because the blood does not remain in blood vessels, the grasshopper is said to have an **open circulatory system**.

Grasshoppers' blood, like many insects' blood, is colorless, not red. It carries mainly food and wastes and has little to do with oxygen transport. Usually insects receive oxygen and release carbon dioxide through a system of **tracheae** (TRAY kee EE). The tracheae are tiny elastic tubes that branch throughout the insect. Air is pumped in and out of these tubes through twenty small openings called *spiracles* (SPIHR uh kulz).

Harmful insects can sometimes be destroyed by being sprayed with oils or dusts that cover or clog the spiracles. Other insect poisons can enter the tracheas and then dissolve into the insect's blood. If these chemicals are not harmful to other living things, they can be used as *insecticides* (chemicals which kill insects).

Through Faith We Understand

Often in robotics, scientists will examine how insects and crabs move and function, and then mimic those motions and functions in the robots they design. What does this tell us about how arthropods themselves are made?

spiracles: (L. SPIRARE, to breathe)

insecticides: insecti- (E. insect) + -cide (L. CIDA, kill)

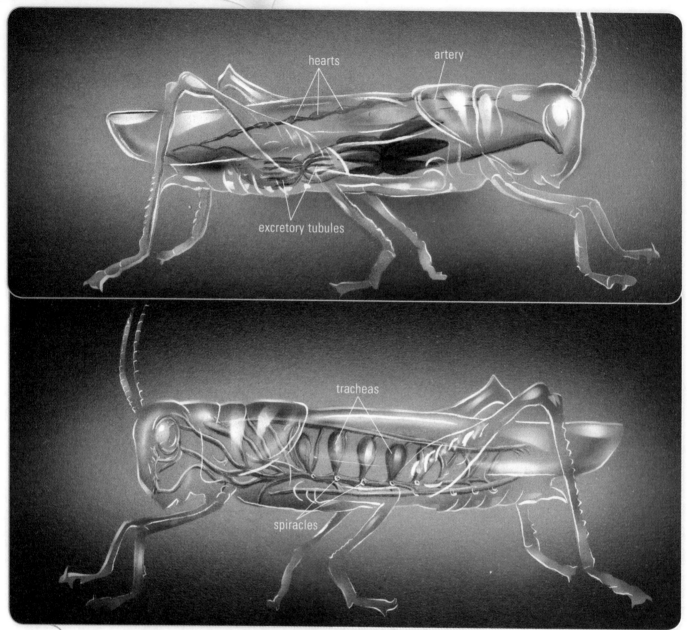

16B-3 Circulatory and excretory systems (top) and respiratory system (bottom) of a grasshopper

16B-4 A molting cicada leaves its exoskeleton. Abandoned exoskeletons are often found on trees.

metamorphosis: meta- (Gk. META, involving change) + -morph- (Gk. MORPHE, form) + -osis (L. OSIS, a condition of)

As blood circulates through the grasshopper, it collects wastes. These wastes are filtered out of the blood and collected by the threadlike **excretory tubules**. The wastes then pass into the intestine and out of the grasshopper's body along with any indigestible materials.

16B.3 *Insect Life Cycles*

Insects go through one of two different life cycles. Some insects, such as grasshoppers, cockroaches, water bugs, and stinkbugs, **molt** repeatedly throughout their life cycles and look about the same each time they molt. Molting occurs when insects shed their old exoskeletons and replace them with new ones. This type of life cycle is called **incomplete metamorphosis** (MET uh MOR fuh sis). **Metamorphosis**, for insects, means "a change in body form." Insects with incomplete metamorphosis start as eggs and go through a series of molts in which they get progressively larger. These developing stages are called **nymphs**. Then they become adults capable of reproduction.

Other insects develop by **complete metamorphosis**. Complete metamorphosis involves four stages: egg, larva, pupa, and adult. The **larva** is usually one of the most active stages. The larvae of moths and butterflies are *caterpillars*. Caterpillars are known for their large and often destructive appetites. Other larvae of insects with complete metamorphosis include *maggots* (which become flies) and *grubs* (which become beetles).

The **pupa** stage is often a resting stage during which the larva uses the food it has eaten to change into the body shape of the adult insect. The *cocoon* of moths, the *chrysalis* (KRIS uh lis) of butterflies, and the *puparium* (pyoo PEHR ee um) of flies are all examples of pupa stages.

Each time an insect with complete metamorphosis (for example, a butterfly) molts, it passes from one stage to another. Unlike insects with incomplete metamorphosis, the butterfly looks completely different each time it molts.

Did you know that little butterflies do not become bigger butterflies? Since butterflies go through complete metamorphosis, they have only a limited number of molts. The caterpillar eats and swells until it fills its exoskeleton. When it molts out of the pupa stage, it is an adult butterfly, which cannot molt again. Most butterflies die soon after they have mated and the female has laid a set of eggs. Some kinds of butterflies have no working mouthparts. They use the food energy they obtained while they were caterpillars. When that stored energy is used up, the butterfly dies.

16B.4 *Other Interesting Arthropods*

Not all arthropods are insects. Some other arthropods are barnacles, crabs, lobsters, shrimp, pill bugs, centipedes, millipedes, scorpions, and tarantulas. These differ from insects in the number of body segments and in the number of appendages (legs and antennae). There are arthropods in almost every imaginable habitat from the tropics to the polar regions—on the land, in the water, and in the air.

Two arthropods people often get confused about are centipedes and millipedes. Both of these look wormlike, but they are not worms. Centipedes are flattened and have one pair of legs per body segment.

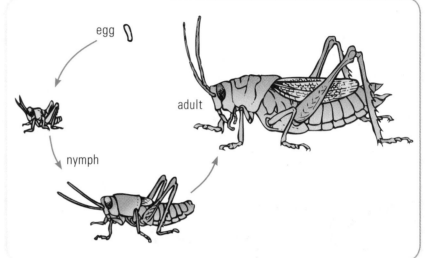

Incomplete metamorphosis of a grasshopper · **16B-5**

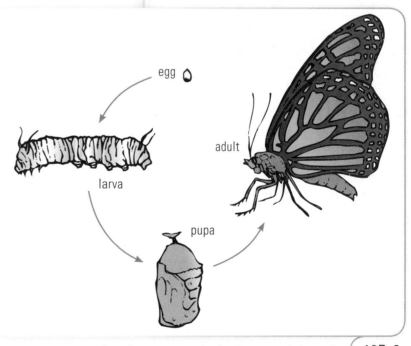

Complete metamorphosis of a monarch butterfly · **16B-6**

Facets of *Zoology:* *The Society of the Bee*

There are over twenty thousand species of bees in the world. Only about 5% of these species are social insects (those that live in colonies).

The honeybee is the only insect humans cultivate in large colonies. Beekeepers carefully build hives for the bees, tend these hives, and then move them to areas near blooming plants. Both wild and cultivated honeybees help humans by pollinating many crops, and managed hives produce

drone
queen
worker

honey and wax. Each year the beekeeping industry in the United States produces about 109 million kg (240 million lb) of honey and 1.8 million kg (4 million lb) of beeswax.

God created the bee society with three distinct levels. The *queen* is larger than the *drones* (the male bees), which are slightly larger than the *workers*. The queen is the only fertile female in the hive. The drones' only function in life is to fertilize the queen. Drones are usually killed by the workers. The workers, like the queen, are females, but they have stingers rather than reproductive organs in their abdomens.

Different worker bees have different occupations. Some bees are *nursemaids*. They attend the queen and take care of the eggs and larvae. Others are *house bees* that work at building and maintaining the comb. Still others go out and look for sources of nectar and pollen and then bring load after load of food back to the hive. These bees are called *foragers*.

The hive always seems to have just enough of each type of worker to maintain the bee population. Only re-

cently did scientists discover how the bee population keeps this balance.

A young worker bee begins life as a nursemaid. Her first jobs include grooming the queen, helping to feed her, and cleaning the comb chambers in which the queen lays the eggs. When a nursemaid is about five days old, nurse glands develop in her head. These nurse glands secrete a substance that the larvae need in their development.

The larvae eat this substance, known as bee milk, or royal jelly, for about three days after they hatch. If the larvae are to become workers, they will receive a diet of pollen and honey. If, however, the hive needs a new queen, the nursemaid bees will continue feeding royal jelly to some of the larvae for a longer period of time. These larvae will develop into queens.

When the worker is about twelve days old, her nurse glands stop making royal jelly. Her time of caring for the nursery and attending the queen ends. At this time wax glands in her abdomen become active. She then becomes a house bee for about one week. After that, she becomes a forager, making many trips from the hive to flowers and back. In about four weeks she leaves the hive and never returns. Most workers die on foraging missions.

Scientists have also discovered that age is not the only factor that determines what a worker bee does. An intricate system of chemical messages that pass from bee to bee also controls bee activity. When scientists removed all the foragers from the hives in experiments, the house bees began foraging long before the age at which they normally would have started.

Bees must communicate to keep their hive working efficiently. God created them with various behav-

iors to accomplish this. For example, when a forager finds a good source of food, she eats some and returns to the hive to tell other foragers the food's location.

First the forager brings up a small amount of the food she ate. This allows other foragers to judge the quality of the food. Then the bees touch the forager with their antennae as she traces a pattern of figure eights on the hive. While she traces the straight part of the eight, she wiggles her abdomen. By the speed and number of abdominal wiggles she puts into her dance, the forager tells the other bees the distance to the food.

Another form of bee communication is through the *pheromones* (p. 274) that the queen bee produces on her body. As the nursemaid bees groom her, they pick up this chemical message on their tongues and pass it around. As long as the queen is alive and well, these pheromones inform the nursemaids not to produce more queens. When the queen dies, the absence of these chemicals stimulates the nursemaid bees to produce new queens. What an amazingly intricate system God has created. Every bee does its own job, and the entire hive functions in such a marvelous way.

They have poisonous claws they use to kill small prey. A few species can inflict painful bites on humans.

Millipedes have a somewhat rounded body and may roll up in a coil when disturbed. They can have up to one hundred body segments. Except for a few segments near the front, most segments have two pairs of legs. Millipedes are not hunters like the centipedes. They eat decaying matter and may occasionally nibble on a live plant.

16B-7 Major Classes of Arthropods

Class	Characteristics	Examples
Insecta	Most with three-part body, three pairs of legs, and two pairs of wings; freshwater or terrestrial	Beetles, flies, bees, butterflies
Crustacea	Most with two-part body and more than three pairs of legs; freshwater, marine, or terrestrial	Crayfish, barnacles, lobsters, shrimp, pill bugs
Chilopoda	Long, segmented body with one pair of legs per segment; terrestrial	Centipedes
Diplopoda	Long, segmented body with two pairs of legs per segment; terrestrial	Millipedes
Arachnida	Two-part body with four pairs of legs, some spin silk; freshwater or terrestrial	Spiders, scorpions, ticks

Section Review 16B

1. What are the three main parts of an insect's body?

2. What type of eyes do insects have?

3. What can we learn from an ant's behavior?

4. List four stages of complete metamorphosis.

5. List three arthropods other than insects.

6. What sex are worker bees?

Let Them Have Dominion

Read Proverbs 6:6 and 30:24–25. What do these verses teach us about the ant? How should we imitate the ant's behavior as we try to live in a way that pleases God?

16C Echinoderms

Starfish, also known as sea stars, are ocean-dwelling animals that, along with sea urchins, sand dollars, sea cucumbers, and similar organisms, are called *echinoderms* (ih KYE neh durmz). The starfish is supported by a system of hard, flat plates just under the skin. These plates are bound together by tough tissues and muscle fibers. In many starfish these plates have sharp spines that stick up through the epidermis. The hard plates and spines provide protection for the starfish.

The overall body pattern of starfish and other echinoderms is that of *radial symmetry*. (See p. 272.) It is possible for starfish to lose rays (arms), perhaps to predators. Fortunately for starfish, they have the ability to grow new rays.

Objective 16C

- Describe the body covering, the method of support, and the forms of movement used by the starfish.
- List three examples of echinoderms.

echinoderm: echino- (Gk. ECHINOS, hedgehog or sea urchin) + -derm (Gk. DERMA, skin)

16C-1   The tube feet of a starfish (left) give it tremendous gripping power, enough to open a clam (right).

How do starfish move? Starfish have a **water-vascular system** that is the key to most of their movements. The most noticeable part of the water-vascular system is the rows of tiny **tube feet** on the bottom of each ray. These tube feet function like tiny suction cups. On hard surfaces the starfish pulls itself forward by stretching the tube feet forward, attaching them to the surface, and then pulling the rest of its body forward.

One of the favorite foods of starfish is clams. How can a starfish, which has no teeth or jaws, eat a hard-shelled clam? The starfish uses the tube feet on its rays to crawl on top of a clam. Then it uses its tube feet to pull on each half of the clam's shell. The clam resists by using its muscles to keep its shell closed. This tug of war may last for several hours, but eventually the clam tires and its shell is opened a tiny amount. The starfish then turns its stomach inside out and pushes it through the opening into the shell of the clam. Digestive juices digest the soft parts of the clam. When it is finished, the starfish withdraws its stomach and begins searching for another meal.

Section Review 16C

1. What is the function of the hard plates and spines in starfish?

2. Where are a starfish's tube feet located?

3. Why does a starfish not need teeth?

Chapter Review

1. In what phylum do clams, snails, slugs, and octopuses belong?

2. Give an example of a univalve.

3. How do clams obtain their food?

4. How many insect species are there?

5. What type of skeleton do insects have?

6. How do insects breathe?

7. What type of circulatory system does an insect have?

8. What are male bees called? What is their only known function in the hive?

9. What starfish characteristic does the term *echinoderm* describe?

10. What animal has tube feet?

What Did You Learn?

1. Did you figure out from the reading what characteristic all mollusks have in common? What is it?

2. Describe two ways an octopus can move.

3. What is an open circulatory system? How does it differ from a closed circulatory system?

4. How do some insecticides affect an insect's spiracles?

5. What would happen to an insect if it lost its ability to molt?

Scientifically Speaking

exoskeleton

compound eye

blood

heart

artery

open circulatory system

trachea

excretory tubule

molt

incomplete metamorphosis

metamorphosis

nymph

complete metamorphosis

larva

pupa

water-vascular system

tube feet

Self Quiz 16

____ 1. Which of these is *not* a mollusk?

    A. slug
    B. octopus
    C. jellyfish
    D. oyster

____ 2. All mollusks live in the water.
    (True/False)

____ 3. Which of these has a foot?

    A. clam
    B. oyster
    C. snail
    D. octopus

____ 4. An exoskeleton with jointed append-
    ages is characteristic of phylum

    A. Echinodermata.
    B. Mollusca.
    C. Arachnida.
    D. Arthropoda.

____ 5. The grasshopper has an open circula-
    tory system. (True/False)

____ 6. Which stage is associated with incom-
    plete metamorphosis?

    A. larva
    B. nymph
    C. pupa
    D. both A and B

____ 7. You would probably find the greatest
    number of legs on a(n)

    A. arachnid.
    B. centipede.
    C. millipede.
    D. insect.

____ 8. Radial symmetry is typical of

    A. arthropods.
    B. mollusks.
    C. crustaceans.
    D. echinoderms.

____ 9. The water-vascular system is impor-
    tant for

    A. movement.
    B. predation.
    C. both A and B
    D. neither A nor B

____ 10. Which of these is *not* an echinoderm?

    A. sea urchin
    B. starfish
    C. sand dollar
    D. squid

VERTEBRATES I: FISH, AMPHIBIANS, AND REPTILES

17

At the beginning of Chapter 15, you learned that a vertebra is one of the bones along the back. All the animals in the **vertebrate** group have vertebrae, skulls, and one other main characteristic in common. What do you think this other characteristic is?

In addition to these two characteristics, all vertebrates have skeletons that are alive! (Invertebrate skeletons, such as the exoskeletons of insects and the shells of clams, are nonliving secretions.) Because vertebrate skeletons are living, they are made of cells, require energy, are capable of growth, and so on.

Vertebrates' **endoskeletons** (EN doh SKEL ih tnz) are made of a combination of bone and cartilage. Animals with endoskeletons have their primary support inside their bodies. **Bone** gives vertebrates a strong support system. **Cartilage** (KAR tl ij) is also strong, but it is more flexible than bone. The tip of your nose and your outer ears are supported by cartilage. Cartilage in the joints between bones serves as a cushion. Jumping rope could damage your bones if there were no cartilage in the joints of your knees and between your backbones. Bone and cartilage are living tissues that grow as the organism grows. Under normal use these tissues keep themselves in good repair because God created our bodies to function in a marvelous way.

endoskeleton: endo- (Gk. ENDON, within) + -skeleton (Gk. SKELETOS, dried up)

In many ways, the skeletons of the various vertebrate animals are quite similar. This is to be expected since they had the same Designer. They all have a vertebral (VUR tuh brul) column and a skull. The **vertebral column** is a series of similar bones that support the body and protect the spinal cord. The **skull** covers and protects the brain. Most vertebrates have *ribs* as well as skeletal structures supporting their *limbs* (which may be fins, flippers, arms, legs, or wings). They also have joints between their various bones and cartilage pieces that permit them to move. Muscles pulling on the bones or cartilage cause the limbs to bend at the joints.

Just like all the animals we have already studied, vertebrates testify to the greatness of God. As we study, we can say with the psalmist, "O Lord, how manifold are thy works! in wisdom hast thou made them all: the earth is full of thy riches. So is this great and wide sea, wherein are things creeping innumerable, both small and great beasts" (Ps. 104:24–25).

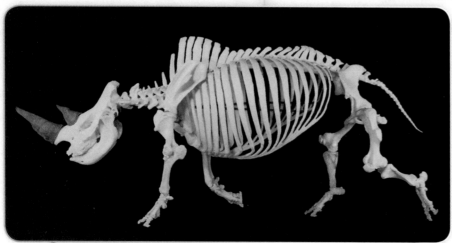

17-1 Can you identify this vertebrate based on its endoskeleton?

Objectives 17A

- Differentiate between bone and cartilage.
- Define *vertebral column* and *skull.*
- Compare oxygenated and deoxygenated blood.
- Describe the circulation in two-chambered, three-chambered, and four-chambered hearts, and name animals that have each type.
- Compare respiration in gills and lungs.
- Describe the two parts of the frog's nervous system.
- Differentiate between a sensory receptor and a sensory organ.
- Differentiate between the central and peripheral nervous systems, and between cranial and spinal nerves.
- List several hormone-controlled processes in animals.
- Identify the structures of a vertebrate's digestive system and describe the functions of each.
- Explain the role of the urethra, urine, urinary bladder, kidneys, and ureters in the excretory system.

17A Body Systems in Vertebrate Animals

Vertebrates have more in common than just their skeletal similarities. God designed them with organ systems that meet their needs for energy, response, movement, and nutrition—in short—everything needed for survival. This section introduces the key systems that make this possible, while specific differences for each vertebrate class are discussed in later sections of the chapter. Sections 17B–17D also contain information on some of the more familiar members of each class.

17A.1 Circulatory System

Blood

All vertebrates have blood, which is sometimes called the "river of life." The blood circulates within the body by the pumping action of the heart. A vertebrate's blood brings food to cells that are far away from the digestive system. It also transports oxygen to and carries carbon dioxide from cells that are distant from the lungs or gills. Wastes, control chemicals, and many other necessary substances travel to and from the body's cells in the blood. Through all of these tasks, the blood maintains the internal balance of a vertebrate's body. Truly, "the life of the flesh is in the blood" (Lev. 17:11) because without the blood the cells of a vertebrate's body would quickly die.

Occasionally you may see diagrams like those on the next few pages that color some blood red and other blood blue. The red in such diagrams represents **oxygenated** (AHK sih juh NAY tud) **blood,**

The Theme of Blood in the Bible

Hebrews 9:22 says there is no forgiveness for sins without the shedding of blood. (*Christ on the Cross*, Peter Paul Rubens, from the Museum & Gallery Collection)

The importance of the shedding of blood appears throughout the Bible. Once God had called the Israelites out of Egypt, He told them that to live before Him they would have to shed the blood of various animals—especially lambs, goats, and bulls. God explained the reason for this requirement in Leviticus 17:11: "For the life of the flesh is in the blood: and I have given it to you upon the altar to make an atonement for your souls." The penalty for sin is death, and if a sinner is to live, someone else must die in that sinner's place.

But the Bible later explains that the blood of those animals was only an object lesson. At the beginning of Jesus's ministry, John the Baptist declared that Christ was "the Lamb of God, which taketh away the sin of the world" (John 1:29). The only One Who could provide the perfect once-for-all blood sacrifice was Jesus Christ. Hebrews 10:4 states, "It is not possible that the blood of bulls and of goats should take away sins." And Hebrews 9:12 says of Christ, "Neither by the blood of goats and calves, but by his own blood he entered in once into the holy place, having obtained eternal redemption for us." Christians remember the shedding of Christ's blood for them each time they partake of the cup in the Lord's Supper (1 Cor. 11:25). Jesus told His followers to drink the cup at the communion table: "For," He said, "this is my blood of the new testament, which is shed for many for the remission of sins" (Matt. 26:28).

which carries abundant oxygen. The blue represents **deoxygenated** (dee AHK sih juh NAY tud) **blood**, which has given most of its oxygen to the body's cells and has taken on carbon dioxide.

The blood of vertebrates is actually all red. Oxygenated blood is just a slightly different shade of red than deoxygenated blood. In humans, oxygenated blood is bright red, while deoxygenated blood is dark red. You do not have blue blood in your body.

Heart Chambers

How does a heart pump blood? Vertebrate hearts contain spaces called *chambers*. The walls of the chambers are made of heart muscle. These muscular walls contract (squeeze), forcing the blood to move out. One-way valves in the chambers prevent the blood from returning to a previous chamber. Thus, as a heart contracts over and over, it pumps blood in one direction. The blood vessels carrying blood away from the heart are called *arteries*. Blood vessels returning the blood to the heart are called *veins*. The blood carried by the veins enters the heart and refills the chambers with blood after contractions have emptied them.

Different vertebrates have different numbers of heart chambers. Fish have two-chambered hearts. One receives blood, and the other pumps blood to the body. The blood that leaves the heart goes first to the gills to become oxygenated. This blood then travels to all the rest of the body, where it becomes deoxygenated. Then the blood returns to the heart.

Most reptiles and adult amphibians (toads, frogs, and salamanders) have three-chambered hearts. One chamber collects oxygenated blood from the lungs, and another collects deoxygenated blood from the rest of the body. Both of these empty into the third chamber, where the two types of blood are mixed. In many of these animals the heart (third chamber) pumps the blood to the lungs and to various parts of the body at the same time.

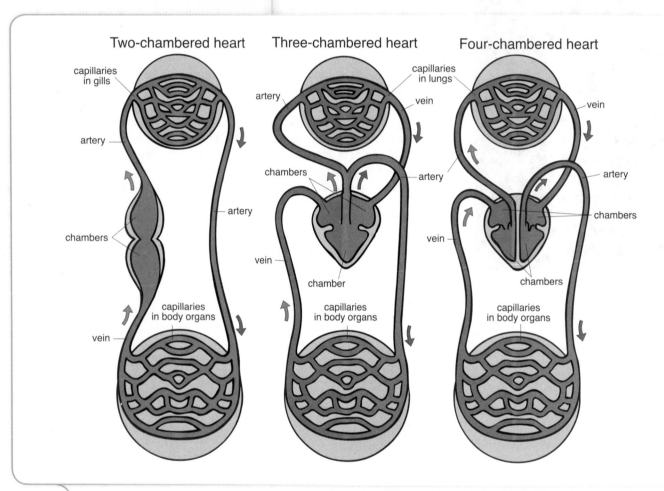

17A-1   Heart chambers and circulations (oxygenated blood in red; deoxygenated in blue)

Birds and mammals have *four-chambered hearts*. The chambers on one side of the heart pump only oxygenated blood, while those on the other side pump only deoxygenated blood. The deoxygenated side pumps the deoxygenated blood to the lungs, where it becomes oxygenated.

The oxygenated blood returns from the lungs to the other side of the heart. This oxygenated side pumps the blood throughout the body. As the oxygenated blood travels through the body, it supplies oxygen to the cells and becomes deoxygenated. In healthy animals with four-chambered hearts, the oxygenated and deoxygenated blood never mix. The advantage of this arrangement is that the blood arriving at the cells carries more oxygen than in systems with three-chambered hearts, where the blood mixes.

Facets of *Zoology:* *Biomimicry: Borrowing Ideas from the Creator*

Animals have intrigued humans throughout recorded history. In fact, the world's first woman was quite taken with a beautiful serpent—but that's another story. Along with this intrigue and interest came inspiration. Animals have inspired sculptors, painters, photographers, poets, and even composers. In more recent times, inventors and engineers have turned to God's creation for winning ideas.

The term *biomimicry*, introduced late in the twentieth century, refers to the study of living things to discover better solutions for human problems. Although both plants and animals of all types have yielded valuable ideas, the following are examples of biomimicry based on vertebrates. Both the bodies and the behaviors of various creatures have provided solutions that have improved our lives and even resulted in new inventions.

Even before the days of da Vinci, inventors studied birds and their wings to perfect their flying machines. The Wright brothers, well-known for achieving the first sustained powered flight, conducted extensive observations of bird flight to perfect their airplane. Even the airfoil shape of the modern aircraft wing is modeled after the bird's wing.

Today's submarines owe much of their success to studies of marine mammals and fish. Fish inspired the tapered ends of some submarines. This form increases the efficiency of

movement by reducing drag (the resistance caused by water moving over the surface). Some submarine designers have even experimented with a rippled surface, near the back end of the ship, that is modeled after the skin near the tail of a dolphin. The ability of a submarine to dive or surface is partly enabled by the emptying or filling of ballast tanks inside the hull of the vessel. Water is taken on to make the craft submerge, and compressed air replaces the denser water to lift the sub onto the water's surface. This works much the same as the swim bladder found in most fish.

Many fascinating biological discoveries have come from underwater

research using submersibles much smaller than submarines. In an ongoing effort to improve the maneuverability and movement of these craft, inventors at the Massachusetts Institute of Technology studied the bluefin tuna, a champion swimmer. The result—RoboTuna! The original RoboTuna was 44 in. long, had nearly 3000 parts, and first swam in a test tank in 1995. A new generation has also been developed. Both versions swim by sideways tail movements, which—like the movements of a live tuna—are constantly evaluated and synchronized to reduce the amount of drag. Resistance sensors and computers make this possible. This project led to the development of other mechanical fish, including the RoboPike.

The invention of the RoboTuna inspired other designers to try to improve the efficiency of boat propulsion. They replaced the standard spinning propeller of a boat with two flaps that move side to side in a carefully timed pattern very much like the swimming motion of some comical but successful marine birds. The result? You guessed it—the penguin boat. In early studies, it has proven to be much more energy efficient than conventionally driven watercraft.

For decades, researchers have recognized the amazing echolocation

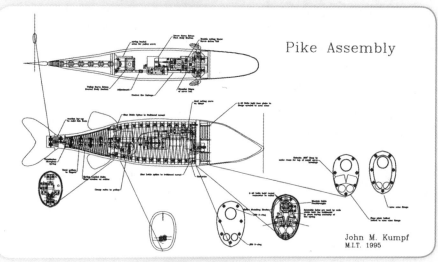

Pike Assembly

John M. Kumpf
M.I.T. 1995

Biomimicry: Borrowing Ideas from the Creator (cont.)

abilities of many species of bats. By emitting short, high-frequency sounds (far above the human level of hearing) and then listening to the sound waves that bounce back, bats can navigate at night through tree branches, wires, and other obstacles while pursuing their insect prey. Using this advanced sonar, some bats can capture and consume more than one thousand mosquitoes in a single evening. While human engineers have crafted some effective sonar devices, they are not even close to the accuracy of the bat.

All of these examples represent the feeble efforts of humans to replicate structures and abilities perfectly devised by the Creator. The very fact that some have been successful points to a God Who equipped mankind to study and make use of his environment. Although we will never create new life forms as God did, we reflect a glimmer of His image as we improve our lives by imitating some of His creations.

The word *sonar* comes from so(und) na(vigation and) r(anging). Sonar technology is applied in situations ranging from naval warfare to ultrasound images of unborn babies.

17A.2 *Respiratory System*

Gills

Many vertebrate animals live their entire lives in water. Vertebrates such as sharks and bony fish have **gills** that take oxygen from the water and give off carbon dioxide. Some invertebrates, such as lobsters, clams, and some worms, also have gills. Amphibians typically have gills during their early development.

A fish's gills are shaped like tiny fingers and are richly supplied with capillaries. Blood circulating through those capillaries near the surface of the gills makes the gills appear red. (*Capillaries* are microscopic blood vessels in which blood often exchanges gases and other materials.) Deoxygenated blood flowing through these capillaries exchanges the carbon dioxide it has collected from the body's cells for the oxygen that is in the water. Thus, in the gills deoxygenated blood becomes oxygenated blood.

The oxygen that gills absorb from the water is not the oxygen in the water molecules (not the O in H_2O). It is oxygen gas that has dissolved in the water, just like sugar dissolved in tea. To us, oxygen dissolved in water gives the water a sweet taste. Water without oxygen tastes flat. When water is boiled, the oxygen in it escapes into the atmosphere, but if the water is exposed to the air again, the oxygen will reenter the water.

Lungs

Vertebrates that have lungs are able to breathe air. **Lungs** are air chambers inside an animal's body where blood can obtain oxygen and give off carbon dioxide. Humans also have lungs. The lungs of reptiles, birds, and mammals are all different. All lungs, however, have many capillaries in which deoxygenated blood becomes oxygenated.

Breathing moves air into and out of the lungs. There are several different methods that animals use to breathe. The frog fills its mouth

Would You Believe?

If a fish is put into water that lacks oxygen, it will die. The fish in aquariums sometimes take so much oxygen out of the water that they begin to suffocate. One sign of this is fish at the surface of the water, gulping air. One of the reasons air is bubbled through aquariums is to keep the water supplied with oxygen.

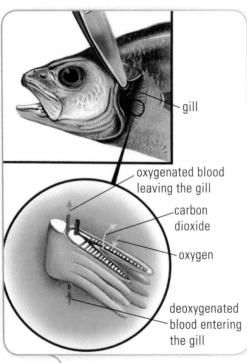

gill

oxygenated blood leaving the gill

carbon dioxide

oxygen

deoxygenated blood entering the gill

17A-2 Fish gill

with air and then forces the air into its lungs, somewhat like swallowing. Birds move air through their lungs by using muscles to control the size of connecting air sacs.

Mammals and humans have **diaphragms** (DY uh FRAMZ) to help them breathe. A diaphragm is a thin layer of muscle that separates the chest chamber from the abdomen. When the diaphragm in a human contracts, it lowers, causing the chest chamber to become larger. This draws air in through the nose and mouth and into the lungs. Other muscles force air back out of the lungs by indirectly pushing the diaphragm back to its original position after it has relaxed.

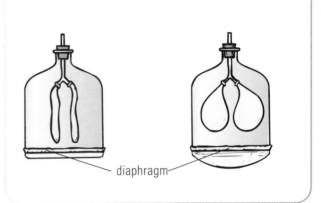

diaphragm

Balloons, a piece of rubber, and a bottle are used to illustrate breathing. The diaphragm is flat (left) after air is forced out and expands downward while drawing air in (right).

17A-3

17A.3 *Nervous System*

The nervous system of a frog is typical of most vertebrate nervous systems. You will study it as an example of vertebrate nervous systems. It consists of two main divisions: the central and peripheral nervous systems.

The **central nervous system** is made up of the **brain**, which is protected by the skull, and the **spinal cord**, which is protected by bones of the vertebral column. The **peripheral** (puh RIF ur ul) **nervous system** is made up of the *nerves*, which branch off the central nervous system, the *sensory receptors* scattered throughout the frog's body, and the **sensory organs**.

A sensory organ is a major collection of sensory receptors and various supporting structures. Normally a sensory organ senses only one environmental factor. The eye, for example, is a sensory organ. Its sensory receptors are sensitive to light. Most of the eyeball, however, is made of supporting structures that collect light and focus it on these sensory receptors.

The nerves that branch from the brain are the *cranial* (KRAY nee ul) *nerves*. These cranial nerves connect the brain with the sensory organs of the head. Cranial nerves carry impulses from the eyes, nasal sac (nose), and tympanic membranes (eardrums) to the brain.

The nerves that branch from the spinal cord are called *spinal nerves*. Some spinal nerves transmit impulses from the sensory receptors of the skin and internal organs to the spinal cord. Others relay impulses from the spinal cord to various muscles and internal organs.

The frog's peripheral nervous system receives stimuli from the environment. The stimuli produce impulses that travel through the peripheral nervous system to the central nervous system. The peripheral nervous system also carries impulses from the central nervous system out to the various muscles and organs that the nervous system controls.

An organism's reactions are controlled in the central nervous system. Although the frog's eye senses a passing fly, it is in the brain that the decision is made either to catch the fly or to let it go. If the decision is to eat the fly, the central nervous system coordinates the frog's efforts to catch it. The nearness of the fly will be judged, and then impulses will be sent to the proper muscles in the limbs, mouth, and tongue. If impulses are sent to the wrong muscles or at the wrong time, the frog will miss the fly. The central nervous system also controls many internal processes, such as the involuntary muscle

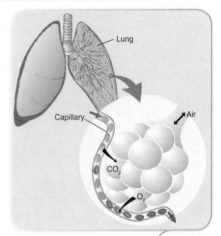

Lung

Capillary

Air

CO_2

O_2

The tiny air sacs of a lung have blood vessels running near them. Gases are exchanged between the blood and the lungs.

17A-4

The circular area just behind the frog's eye is its tympanic membrane, with which it senses sound. What other sensory organs are shown here?

17A-5

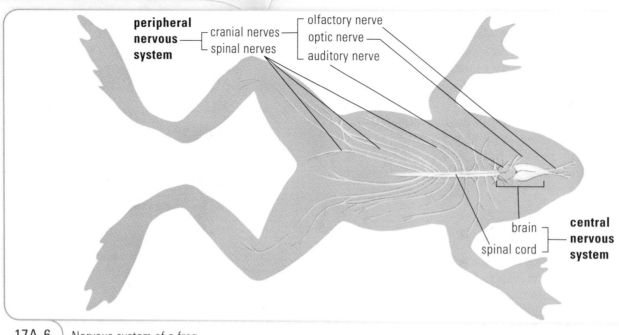

peripheral nervous system — ⌐ cranial nerves └ spinal nerves

olfactory nerve
optic nerve
auditory nerve

brain ⌐
spinal cord └ **central nervous system**

17A-6 Nervous system of a frog

contractions that move the fly along the digestive tract and the circulation of blood that nourishes the digestive organs and absorbs the digested food.

17A.4 *Digestive System*

Food enters a vertebrate's body through the mouth and then passes through the short, tubular *esophagus* into the **stomach**. Muscles in the stomach walls squeeze the stomach in and out to mix the food with digestive enzymes that are already in the stomach. When the food is thoroughly mixed, it is moved into the **small intestine**.

In the small intestine many different digestive enzymes are used to chemically digest the different foods eaten. Cells in the walls of

Hormones in Animals

Animal hormones are chemicals produced by special organs and carried by the blood. Hormones affect tissues and control various processes in animals. Some hormones affect only a few tissues, while others influence almost every tissue in an animal's body. Most hormones are quite specific. A hormone that affects one animal often has no effect on other animals.

The metamorphosis (pp. 290–91) of arthropods is controlled by hormones. Another interesting example of hormones controlling animal growth has been studied in amphibians. A hormone produced by a tiny organ in the tadpole's body is necessary for the metamorphosis from tadpole to frog. Scientists can inject this hormone into tadpoles. If they do so while a tadpole is still small, the tadpole starts to develop into a frog long before it would normally begin metamorphosis. When it becomes an adult, the frog will be much smaller than a normal frog of that species.

Iodine is an important part of the hormone that causes metamorphosis in tadpoles. If a tadpole is raised in an environment without iodine, it cannot make this hormone. Without the hormone, the tadpole will never go through metamorphosis. But if iodine is supplied, the tadpole will eventually start metamorphosis and become a frog.

Hormones are important for many other animal processes besides metamorphosis and growth. Some hormones help the digestive system function properly; others aid in reproduction. There are also hormones that strengthen animals during times of emergency and stress, and some that seem to trigger migration or hibernation.

the small intestine release some of the enzymes for chemical digestion. In this level of digestion, the food molecules are broken down to make them small enough to be absorbed into the bloodstream.

Two organs attached to the small intestine produce additional enzymes and substances for digestion. One of these organs is the **liver**. The liver produces a greenish fluid called bile, which contains substances to help break down fats. Bile released by the liver is stored in a sac called the *gallbladder* until it is needed. The **pancreas** is a smaller organ that makes enzymes and releases them into the small intestine. These enzymes break down sugars, starches, proteins, and fats.

The small intestine is often wound into curves and loops in order to fit inside the animal's body. As a general rule, plant eaters have longer small intestines than meat eaters of similar size because it takes longer to digest plant starches than animal protein. When food has been completely digested, it is absorbed through the wall of the small intestine into blood vessels. Blood in these vessels transports the food to the remainder of the cells of the animal. Food that cannot be digested passes through the tubular **large intestine**, where excess water is absorbed. Undigested food leaves the digestive tract through the *anus*.

17A.5 *Excretory System*

All vertebrates have **kidneys** to filter wastes from their blood. Various waste products, including *urea*, are picked up by the blood as it passes through the body's tissues. In the kidneys are tiny tubes surrounded by capillaries. As the blood flows through the capillaries, wastes leave the blood and enter the tubes. In each kidney, the wastes flow through these tubes into one large tube called the **ureter** (YOOR ih tur).

The ureters of birds connect directly to the digestive tract. The wastes from the kidneys pass out of the body with the indigestible materials. In some amphibians, most reptiles, and all mammals and humans, the wastes form *urine*. This fluid is collected and stored in a **urinary** (YOOR uh NEHR ee) **bladder** before it passes out of the body.

Section Review 17A

1. List two materials that may form a vertebrate skeleton.

2. What is the maximum number of chambers in any vertebrate heart?

3. What happens to blood in gills? In what kind of blood vessel does this happen?

4. What muscle do you use to help you breathe?

5. List the two main parts of a central nervous system.

6. What element is important to the hormone that controls metamorphosis in tadpoles?

7. How does a pancreas aid digestion?

Great Is the Lord

In an average adult grass frog, the spinal cord is about as thick as a pencil lead, and the brain is only about twice that thick. The central nervous system of the frog is only about 76 mm (3 in.) long. The frog's entire nervous system weighs less than a nickel. Yet the millions of cells in this system control the frog's body with amazing dependability and accuracy. This magnificent design is yet another illustration of how great God is: "Stand still, and consider the wondrous works of God" (Job 37:14).

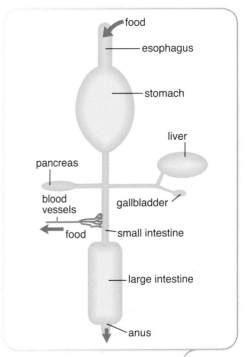

Generalized vertebrate digestive system: The size of the various organs may vary from animal to animal, and sometimes other organs may be present. The digestive systems of most vertebrates follow this general plan.

17A-7

Objectives 17B

- Describe characteristics of a fish that make it especially suited for living in water.
- Identify characteristics associated with each of the three groupings of fish.

ectothermic: ecto- (Gk. EKTOS, outside) + -thermic (Gk. THERME, heat)

17B Fish

Fish are vertebrate animals that have fins, gills, and usually scales and live in fresh or salt water. They are **ectothermic** (EK tuh THUR mik), which means that their body temperatures change with their surroundings. If the water is cold, the fish is cold, and if the water is warm, the fish is warm. A fish's activity changes with the temperature. You will learn more about this in Chapter 18.

Because fish must spend their lives moving, eating, and even "breathing" underwater, their bodies differ from those of land dwelling vertebrates in some interesting ways.

17B.1 Fish Anatomy

A fish propels itself by flexing its entire body, not just its tail. Paired fins are used to control movements, such as stopping and turning, and to maintain balance. Most fish have a streamlined body shape that makes movement through the water easy. Some fish have a *swim bladder* that helps them float at a constant depth. A swim bladder is an air-filled organ that a fish uses to adjust to different water depths.

A fish has a closed circulatory system that includes a two-chambered heart and blood vessels. Blood is pumped from the heart through the gills, through the body, and back to the heart. While passing through capillaries in the gills, oxygen diffuses into the blood and carbon dioxide diffuses out. Using Figure 17B-1, trace the flow of blood through a fish.

Fish *scales* are overlapping plates that give the fish some protection. Scales grow larger as the fish grows. On each side of a fish is a string of sensory structures called a *lateral line*. The lateral line can detect vibrations and pressure. The nostrils of a fish are used not for breathing but for smelling. Fish have an acute sense of smell.

Most fish reproduce by *spawning*. During spawning, some female fish release millions of eggs, which are then fertilized by the male. Of the many eggs released and fertilized, only a few survive to become adult fish. Most fall prey to predators. A few fish, such as guppies, reproduce by giving birth to live fish rather than spawning.

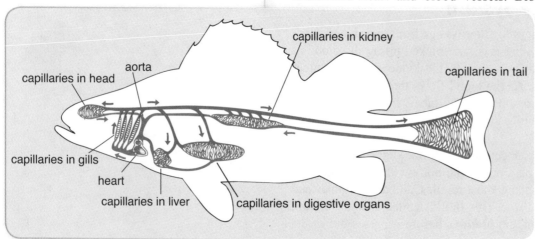

17B-1 | The path of blood in the fish

17B-2 | The body plan of a typical fish

17B.2 *Fish Groups*

Jawless Fish

There are three groups of fish: jawless fish, cartilage fish, and bony fish. Jawless fish have no jaws. They also have no scales or paired fins. They are wormlike creatures with skeletons composed of cartilage.

Two examples of jawless fish are lampreys and hagfish. Some species of lampreys are parasites that attach to other fish and feed on their body fluids. They have round mouths with circular rows of teeth perfectly designed for hanging on to the fish that they parasitize. Hagfish, on the other hand, are scavengers. When disturbed, hagfish secrete slimy mucus from glands located all over their bodies.

Cartilage Fish

Cartilage fish have endoskeletons made of cartilage. They also have jaws, scales, and paired fins. Sharks, skates, and rays are cartilage fish.

Sharks must keep water moving over their gills to ensure a supply of oxygen. They do this by swimming with their mouths open and also by opening and closing their gill slits. Water enters the mouth, flows over the gills, and exits through the gill slits. It was once believed that all sharks must swim constantly to get enough oxygen. Scientists have now learned that many species can survive periods of motionlessness by decreasing their energy needs and by pumping water through their gills.

Lacking a swim bladder, sharks have other means of keeping afloat. A large, oily liver that is less dense than water helps increase their buoyancy. The lift provided by the fins during forward movement also keeps them up.

Skates and rays are found resting or feeding on the ocean floor. They eat small fish and various invertebrates. They propel themselves by flapping their paired fins, which look like wings. They also have a long, narrow tail. The stingray has a poisonous spine on its tail and is capable of seriously injuring unwary humans.

Bony Fish

The bony fish group is the largest group of fish. This group includes the fish you are most familiar with (such as catfish, bass, flounder, goldfish, guppies, and trout). These fish have an endoskeleton made of bone. They also have jaws and paired fins, and most have scales.

While some bony fish grow no longer than the width of a pencil, others can reach 4.3 m (14 ft) in length and weigh over 1800 kg (2 t). Some species live only in salt water, some live only in fresh, and a few are able to make regular migrations from one to the other. There are species of bony fish in the warmest rivers of the tropics and others that thrive in the frigid waters of the polar regions.

The lamprey is a jawless fish that parasitizes other fish. After penetrating its prey's flesh, it sucks out the blood on which it feeds. Note circular rows of teeth in its mouth (top). **17B-3**

The world's fastest shark, the shortfin mako, can swim about 32 km/h (20 mph). That is fast enough to catch tuna. **17B-4**

Math Connection

If there are 45,000 species of vertebrates and 20,000 of these are types of fish, what percentage of vertebrate species are fish?

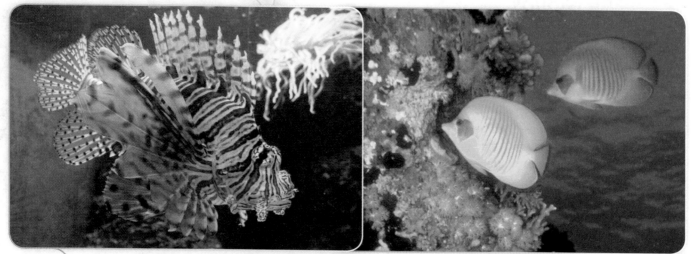

17B-5 The lionfish (left) has venomous spines for protection. Nearly 130 different species of colorful butterfly fish (right) have been discovered.

Section Review 17B

1. What organ helps some fish maintain their position at a constant depth?

2. What does a fish use its lateral line to detect?

3. How many chambers does a fish's heart have?

4. What group of fish is the largest?

17C Amphibians

Amphibians are ectothermic vertebrates that usually live in water when young but that can live on land as adults. The name *amphibian* comes from Greek words that mean "double life." This name reflects these two ways of living, in water and on land.

17C.1 Amphibian Development

The process that changes an amphibian from a gilled, aquatic organism to an air-breathing organism is called *metamorphosis*. Amphibians are the only vertebrates that undergo metamorphosis.

Young amphibians possess gills, but adults usually have lungs. However, gills and lungs are not the only organs they use for respiration. Most amphibians have a thin, moist skin. They can exchange gases (carbon dioxide and oxygen) through the skin because they have tiny blood vessels close to the surface.

Metamorphosis involves more than just the change from gills to lungs. Other changes include the change from a two-chambered heart to the adult three-chambered heart, the growth of two pairs of limbs if the young did not already have them, and sometimes the gradual loss of a tail. Most of these changes would seem to make it easier to live on dry land. However, many adult amphibians live in or near water, and all must return to water or moist places to lay their eggs.

Objectives 17C

- Explain why amphibians are described as having a double life.
- Describe the metamorphosis of the frog.
- Describe the eating habits of a frog.
- List three amphibians other than frogs.

17C-1 Most of South America's brightly colored poison dart frogs go through metamorphosis in the small puddles of water that collect in a tree cavity or at the base of certain leaves.

Facets of **Zoology:** *The Frog's "Tail"*

Tadpoles begin as toad or frog eggs laid during the early spring. Frog eggs are deposited in large jelly-coated masses, and toad eggs are laid in long jelly-coated strings. Some frogs lay as many as thirty thousand eggs. Since a single pond may easily contain hundreds of frogs, millions of frog eggs may be laid in the same pond.

In spite of this, overpopulation is not usually a problem. Eggs, tadpoles, and adult frogs are eaten by many different animals. Large numbers die because of diseases or poor living conditions. For even a few frogs to survive, thousands of eggs must be laid.

Changing from an egg to an adult frog is not a simple growing process. Frogs develop from eggs through a series of changes called metamorphosis. Less than a week after it is laid, a frog egg hatches into a tadpole. The newly hatched tadpole has long feathery gills on each side of its head. The gills soon become covered by a flap of skin. During metamorphosis the tadpole's gills are slowly resorbed as lungs form inside its body.

The heart of a tadpole has two chambers and operates about the same as the heart of a fish. During metamorphosis the number of heart chambers increases to three and the pathway of blood becomes more complicated.

The tadpole's appetite changes as it becomes a frog. Tadpoles have hard lips and jaws to scrape scum (mostly

algae) off rocks and plants. They have neither the proper mouth nor tongue to capture insects as adult frogs do. The tadpole and the frog eat different things and must have different digestive systems. A tadpole's intestine is long and coiled. The vegetable matter it eats takes a long time to digest. The adult frog eats animal protein that is more easily digested and consequently has a relatively short digestive tract.

The most obvious changes during metamorphosis involve the tadpole's tail and the frog's legs. The hind legs are the first to sprout from the tadpole's fish-shaped body. The front legs will remain hidden behind a flap of skin for some time. But even after all four legs are formed, the tadpole's tail will remain.

A tadpole in this condition is an awkward creature. Its mouth is changing from a "scum scraper" to an "insect catcher," and it has a hard time getting food. But during this phase of metamorphosis, the tadpole uses a lot of energy. It gets much of this energy by reabsorbing the material of its tail. The tadpole gradually breaks down the substances that make up its tail and uses them as nourishment while it develops into a frog.

You might think that with all these changes, frog metamorphosis would take years. Metamorphosis takes about three months for the leopard frog. The spadefoot toad may take only thirteen days for the entire egg-to-toad process. Bullfrogs, however, may take as long as three years to develop completely.

A few frogs have special twists in their metamorphoses. Males of a small frog native to Chile watch over the eggs until the tadpoles are almost ready to hatch. Then they "swallow" the eggs into their vocal sacs. The vocal sacs extend nearly to the male's hind legs. The eggs hatch and tadpoles live inside the vocal sacs. When they have developed into small frogs, they emerge through the male's mouth and then hop away and live on their own.

Another South American frog begins life with a "froggy-back ride." The eggs are laid on moist land, but as the tadpoles hatch, they crawl onto their father's back. A sticky substance keeps them there even when the frog jumps through shallow water. The "glue" dissolves only when immersed in water for about ten minutes. The tadpoles are then free to develop. God designed this system so the tadpoles would have enough water to survive. If God cares for these small creatures (Matt. 10:29–31), imagine how much more He cares for you.

hibernation: (L. HIBERNIS, winter)

estivation: (L. AESTAS, summer)

17C-2 Toads, such as this American toad, *Bufo americanus*, are a gardener's allies since they eat large numbers of pests.

maxillary: (L. MAXILLA, upper jaw)

17C.2 Amphibian Groups

Tailless Amphibians

There are two major groups of amphibians—those with tails in adulthood and those without tails. Frogs and toads are tailless amphibians.

Frogs, like most amphibians, have smooth, moist skin and are usually near water. Toads have rough, dry, bumpy skin, and the adults may be found quite far from water. Most frogs and toads lay their jelly-coated eggs in water, where they are fertilized externally. These quickly hatch and become tadpoles. Tadpoles have gills and tails, but during metamorphosis they develop lungs and *resorb* (ree SORB) their tails. This means the tail is gradually dissolved and the materials are reused elsewhere.

Since frogs and toads are ectothermic, the temperature of their surroundings affects their activity. They are less active in the cool autumn and inactive in winter. Frogs usually bury themselves in mud at the bottom of a lake or stream during the winter. Toads burrow in soft, moist soil. This winter state of inactivity is called hibernation. During hibernation, the animal's life processes slow down, and energy supplies stored during the summer months are used up. A similar period of inactivity called estivation sometimes occurs during hot, dry weather.

Frogs eat insects, worms, slugs, snails, and other small animals. A frog will attack anything that moves and is small enough to fit into the frog's mouth. A large North American bullfrog will eat young water birds, ducklings, young turtles, and even small fish. Some frogs will even eat other smaller frogs.

A frog catches its food with its tongue. In the frog's mouth the tongue is short, thick, and attached to the front of the mouth. When the frog sees food, it flicks its tongue out and stretches it. Some frogs can extend their tongues about half the length of their bodies. Usually frogs are extremely accurate with their tongues. They are even able to catch insects that are in flight!

The tip of the frog's tongue is sticky. When the tip of the tongue touches the food, the frog flips its tongue, with the live food stuck on it, back into its mouth. In the frog's mouth are two sets of teeth. Frogs do not use their teeth to chew their food but to keep the live food from escaping. One set of teeth forms a ridge of tiny *maxillary* (MAK suh LEHR ee) teeth around the rim of the upper jaw. The other set, the *vomerine* (VOH muh RINE) teeth, is located in two spots at the front of the roof of the mouth.

You swallow food by pushing it to the back of your mouth with your tongue. The frog swallows by blinking its bulging eyes. When the frog closes its eyes, they push down into the frog's mouth, forcing the food back into the esophagus.

Tailed Amphibians

Salamanders are amphibians that have tails in adulthood. Young salamanders have gills and usually form lungs during metamorphosis. A few species never develop lungs but retain their gills. Gills and lungs are not the only organs used in respiration. Their thin, moist skin also functions in gas exchange.

The Appalachian region of the southeastern United States has more salamander species than any other region on earth. Some of these are brightly colored and can be found in moist areas under logs and rocks. Many species secrete distasteful substances to deter predators. Sometimes if you handle a salamander, these substances can even make your fingers numb. A few species secrete large amounts of sticky mucus that is difficult to remove.

Salamanders are usually rather small creatures. Most North American salamanders are less than 15 cm (6 in.) long. Two notable exceptions are the mudpuppy, which can reach 43 cm (17 in.), and the hellbender, which can reach 74 cm (29 in.). One Japanese salamander species can grow to be 1.5 m (5 ft) long.

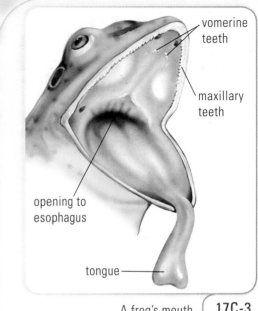

A frog's mouth   **17C-3**

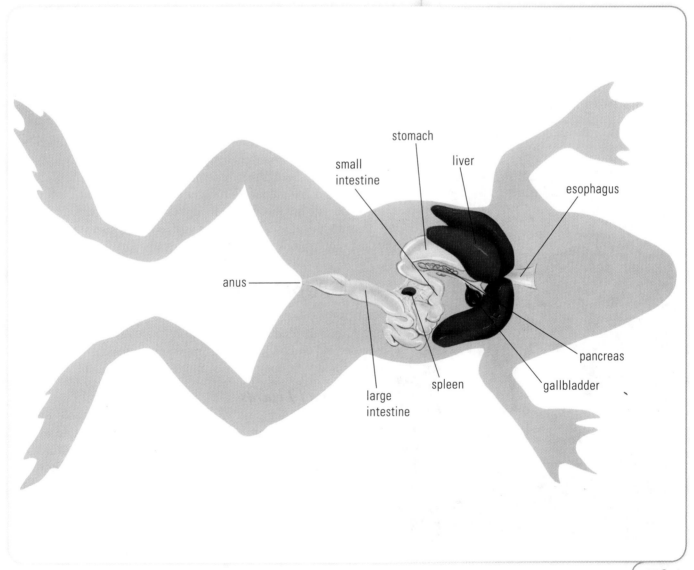

Digestive system of a frog   **17C-4**

17C-5 The red eft is common in the eastern United States. The red eft is the juvenile stage of the red-spotted newt. The adult is dull colored with red spots.

Objectives 17D

- List the four groups of living reptiles.
- Describe the body, special senses, and eating habits of snakes.
- Describe the type of environment in which crocodiles and alligators are usually found.
- Recall that alligators and crocodiles differ from other reptiles by having four-chambered hearts.

17D-1 Diamondback terrapins look like small adult turtles when they hatch. Most reptiles lay eggs with leathery shells.

Section Review 17C

1. How does the meaning of the word *amphibian* describe amphibians?

2. Amphibians are the only vertebrates that undergo

   _____.

3. Besides gills and lungs, what other organ can amphibians use in gas exchange?

17D Reptiles

Reptiles and amphibians are often lumped together in books and may share some of the same secretive habits, but they are really quite different. Although some groups of reptiles move back and forth from land to the water, they all breathe air and do not experience the life-changing metamorphosis of amphibians. Both reptiles and amphibians tend to make many people uncomfortable, but they are fascinating creations worthy of our study.

17D.1 Reptile Characteristics

Reptiles are ectothermic vertebrates that have dry, scaly skin and lay eggs that have leathery shells. Most reptiles have a three-chambered heart. However, one of the three chambers is partially divided. Reptiles are found in both dry and wet environments. They have lungs both as newly hatched youngsters and also as adults. A reptile's scaly skin protects its body from drying out, and the leathery eggshells permit the eggs to be laid on land far from water without drying out.

Reptiles do not fertilize their eggs externally as most amphibians do. Instead, the eggs are fertilized inside the female's body. Newly hatched reptiles look like adult reptiles, only smaller.

17D.2 Reptile Groups

Perhaps the most famous reptiles are the extinct dinosaurs. Living reptiles are divided into four groups: (1) snakes and lizards, (2) alligators and crocodiles, (3) turtles, and (4) tuataras. The tuatara is represented by a single species found in New Zealand.

Snakes and Lizards

Snakes have no legs, no ear openings, and immovable eyelids. Most lizards have four legs, ear openings, and movable eyelids. Both shed their skin periodically in a process called *molting*.

Snakes do not hear, since they do not have ears. They usually have poor vision as well. Their immovable eyelids are actually clear scales that are shed each time the snake molts. What they lack in sight and hearing they compensate for in other sense organs. Snakes have a keen sensitivity to molecules. When a snake flicks its tongue, it is sensing the air. Its tongue transports particles from the air to a pair of organs on the roof of its mouth that detect food or danger.

The rattlesnake (left) is a pit viper. The pits located between the eyes and nostrils are heat-detecting organs. The tuatara (right) is the only species in its order.

17D-2

Some snakes can detect the body heat of their prey. Pit vipers, such as rattlesnakes, have small pits on their heads that contain organs that detect heat. These snakes are capable of launching accurate strikes in total darkness, using these heat-sensing organs.

Snakes are meat eaters. They benefit humans by eating insect pests, rats, and mice. Most snakes are nonpoisonous. Those that are poisonous inject their poison with hollow fangs or grooved teeth. Some nonpoisonous snakes coil their bodies around their prey and squeeze, or constrict, until the prey can no longer breathe and dies by suffocation. Others eat their prey alive.

Snakes are capable of swallowing prey much larger in diameter than themselves. Snakes are unable to tear or chew their food, so they must swallow it whole. The jaws of snakes are doubly hinged to allow them to open their mouths much wider than seems possible. In addition, the two sides of the lower jaw are not firmly attached to each other at the front. This allows the two halves to separate and the snake to open its mouth even farther. The snake's throat may seem too narrow to swallow large prey even if the mouth can open wide enough. However, a snake's throat is elastic and can stretch to accommodate any food that it can get its mouth around. Snakes usually swallow their prey head first. This makes the limbs of the prey fold back and offer the least resistance to swallowing.

Snakes are found in almost every environment—tropical jungles, grassy prairies, hot dry deserts, and even the ocean. Most lizards live in warm or hot, and often dry, places. You may have already seen some of the common lizards in the United States, such as the skink and the fence lizard.

Some lizards can grow to quite large sizes. The Komodo dragon, a large monitor lizard, can grow up to 135 kg (297 lb) and reach 3 m (10 ft) in length. Other especially interesting lizards include the chameleons, which can change their skin color to match their surroundings, marine iguanas, which browse on seaweed in the ocean, and flying lizards, which glide through the air by stretching their skin much like flying squirrels do.

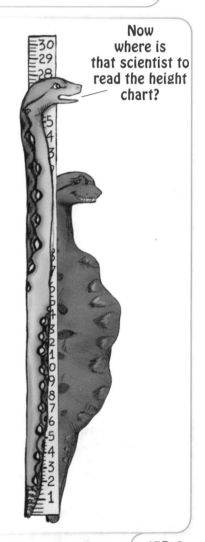

Now where is that scientist to read the height chart?

The reticulated python of Asia and the South American anaconda compete for the record of the world's largest snake. One reticulated python reached a length of 10 m (32.8 ft). Anacondas, while shorter, can become more massive, weighing up to 227 kg (500 lb).

17D-3

17D-4 | The chameleon (left) is a camouflage artist with an amazing ability to change colors. The Gila monster (right) is the United States' only poisonous lizard.

Crocodiles and Alligators

Crocodiles and alligators can be found in and near the relatively shallow waters of warm streams, rivers, swamps, and lakes. Usually these animals are found in tropical and subtropical climates. In some areas they can endure cool or dry periods by becoming dormant. A few species of crocodiles venture into the salty water of the ocean and tidal areas, but most prefer fresh water.

These reptiles use their large tails to propel themselves through the water. The raised nostrils and eyes on their snouts allow them to keep their eyes and nostrils above water while the remainder of their body is submerged. This lets them approach prey while remaining almost completely hidden. Their diet includes fish, turtles, various large and small mammals (usually attacked while drinking), others of their own kind, and occasionally humans.

Alligators and crocodiles can be distinguished by the shape of their snouts. Alligators have broad, rounded snouts, while crocodiles have narrow, pointed snouts. Also, in crocodiles the fourth tooth on the lower jaw fits outside the upper jaw when the mouth is closed. Only two species are found in the United States. The American alligator can

17D-5 | From the description in the text, can you determine which of these is an alligator and which is a crocodile?

Reading Range Maps

Here is a map that shows the range of the American alligator and the American crocodile. Use the legend to identify where each species can be found, and then answer the following questions:

1. Which state is the only one to have both alligators and crocodiles?

2. How many states, according to this map, have alligator populations?

3. In which state would the alligator probably spend the most time hibernating?

4. What factor(s) do you think limit the range of the American crocodile?

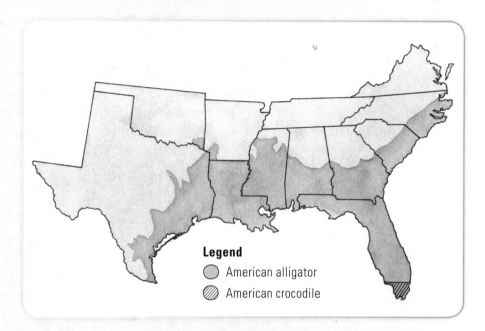

Legend

American alligator

American crocodile

be found in swamps, lakes, and rivers of the Southeast. The American crocodile is restricted to southern Florida.

Turtles

Various names have been given to distinguish various types of turtles. *Sea turtles* live in the ocean, *tortoises* live their entire lives on land, and *terrapins* are freshwater turtles that may venture onto land. Sea turtles have paddle-shaped legs used in swimming. Other turtles have clawed legs.

Turtles have two hard, bony shells that cover their bodies. The shell is composed of bony plates covered with large scales. Some of the turtle's vertebrae and ribs are actually part of the shell. This can be clearly seen on the inner shell surface of a deceased turtle. The turtle's shell serves as a good defense. Some turtles can pull their heads and legs completely inside their shells. Box turtles and a few similar species have a hinged lower shell that closes tightly for added protection.

Try This at Home

To feel the difference that leg shape makes in movement through water, fill your bathtub half full of water and then swish your hand through the water with your fingers spread apart. Repeat the same motion with a plastic bag over your hand. The increased resistance you feel is what gives turtles the push they need for fast swimming.

17D-6   The snapping turtle (upper left) can be found in freshwater habitats east of the Rocky Mountains. The hawksbill sea turtle (right) ranges from the coast of Massachusetts southward to Brazil. The ornate box turtle (lower left) is found over much of the central plains, from South Dakota to Texas.

Section Review 17D

1. Periodic shedding of skin by reptiles is called

   _____.

2. What does a snake do to smell something?

3. Which of the three general kinds of turtles would you most likely find in a desert?

Chapter Review

1. What does a skull protect?

2. How does the number of heart chambers differ in the various major groups of vertebrate animals?

3. What two gases are exchanged in gills and lungs?

4. From which sense organ in a frog does an auditory nerve carry impulses?

5. What is the function of a gallbladder?

6. What organ filters wastes from vertebrate blood?

7. Of what material is a shark's skeleton composed?

8. What organ do sharks not have that most bony fish have?

9. Which group of vertebrates is the only group to undergo metamorphosis?

10. Why are most amphibians found near water?

11. Name three kinds of amphibians.

12. How are hibernation and estivation similar? How are they different?

13. What does a snake detect with its tongue?

14. What do snakes eat?

What Did You Learn?

1. Why would you expect gills to have an exceptionally large number of capillaries?

2. How do you think being ectothermic affects the behavior of a fish?

3. Explain why gill flaps are important to bony fish.

4. Other than loss of the tail, describe one change that occurs as a tadpole changes to a frog.

5. Are snakes slimy? How do you know?

6. Why are the fewer eggs that a reptile produces more likely to survive than the more numerous eggs that an amphibian, such as a frog, produces?

7. Why would a snake always beat you in a "staring contest"?

Scientifically Speaking

vertebrate
endoskeleton
bone
cartilage
vertebral column
skull
oxygenated blood
deoxygenated blood
gill
lung
diaphragm
central nervous system
brain
spinal cord
peripheral nervous system
sensory organ
stomach
small intestine
liver
pancreas
large intestine
kidney
ureter
urinary bladder
ectothermic

Self Quiz 17

1. Match the organ with the system to which it is most closely related.

_____ ureter   A. digestive

_____ spinal cord   B. nervous

_____ diaphragm   C. circulatory

_____ small intestine   D. respiratory

_____ artery   E. excretory

_____ 2. Endoskeletons can contain both bone and cartilage. (True/False)

_____ 3. In a fish, the blood that leaves the heart goes directly to the
   A. rest of the body.
   B. gills.
   C. lungs.
   D. liver.

_____ 4. Gills are found in
   A. fish.
   B. tadpoles.
   C. turtles.
   D. A and B only.
   E. all of these.

_____ 5. Sensory organs of the head are connected to the brain by
   A. cranial nerves.
   B. the spinal cord.
   C. spinal nerves.
   D. peripheral nerves.

_____ 6. Food does *not* pass through the
   A. esophagus.
   B. anus.
   C. pancreas.
   D. stomach.

_____ 7. Because a fish is supported by an internal skeleton, we can say it is endothermic. (True/False)

_____ 8. The lamprey is a
   A. bony fish.
   B. jawless fish.
   C. cartilage fish.
   D. extinct fish.

_____ 9. Amphibians are the only vertebrates that
   A. hatch from eggs.
   B. are ectothermic.
   C. experience metamorphosis.
   D. have gills.

_____ 10. A frog has teeth but does not chew its food. (True/False)

_____ 11. Which of these is so unique that it is in an order of reptiles all by itself?
   A. tuatara
   B. Gila monster
   C. American crocodile
   D. caecilian

_____ 12. There are snake species that live in
   A. deserts.
   B. jungles.
   C. oceans.
   D. all of these.

Vertebrates II: Birds and Mammals

What do the owl and the mouse have in common? Lots of things. Both are vertebrate animals. Both care for their young and share the same environment. Can you think of other similarities?

How do these animals differ? Besides the possibility of one being a meal for the other, comments about size, shape, movement, and color might be included on your list.

This chapter will expand your view of birds and mammals by revealing some of their less obvious, but equally significant, traits.

endothermic: endo- (Gk. ENDON, within) + -thermic (Gk. THERME, heat)

What Do You Think?

If *ectothermic* is a synonym for cold-blooded, what does *endothermic* mean?

You're Myth-Taken

If you thought that endothermic animals were warm-blooded in the most literal sense of the word, you might be surprised to learn that in some hibernating mammals the body temperature falls from 35°C (95°F) to 2°C (36°F). That's barely warm enough to keep their tissues from freezing!

18A-1 A polar bear (top) conserves heat with its thick fur coat. An elephant's large ears (bottom) release heat.

18A Endotherms and Ectotherms

Animals are sometimes classified as being either **endothermic** or ectothermic. These terms refer to whether the animal regulates its body temperature by internal or external means. All of the animals you studied in Chapter 17 were ectothermic.

18A.1 Endotherms

Mammals and birds are the only endothermic animals. God created these animals to maintain a relatively constant body temperature. Most mammals' body temperatures are between 36°C (97°F) and 39°C (102°F). Most birds have body temperatures between 40°C (104°F) and 42°C (108°F).

Some endothermic animals keep their body temperatures within a degree or so of their normal temperature at all times. Others have a wide range of normal body temperatures. For example, the house wren's body temperature may vary as much as 8°C (14°F) within a twenty-four-hour period.

Endothermic animals have various ways of keeping their body temperatures from falling below the proper range. Some have heavy fur or thick layers of feathers that insulate their bodies. Others have small ears that help prevent body heat from escaping. When endo-thermic animals become too hot, blood vessels in their skin expand. This allows warm blood to flow near the surface of the skin, where it is cooled more efficiently.

Some animals, such as horses, secrete sweat all over their bodies. As the sweat evaporates, it cools the skin, which in turn cools the blood. Other animals, such as rabbits, have large ears through which large amounts of blood can be pumped for cooling.

The lining of a dog's mouth and throat contains many blood vessels close to the surface that help cool the blood. The lungs and air sacs of birds are places where blood can give off heat. Dogs, birds, and some other animals pant in order to keep themselves cool.

18A.2 Ectotherms

The ectothermic animals include fish, amphibians, reptiles, worms, arthropods, and several other groups. These animals cannot con-trol their body temperatures internally. In fact, the temperature of their bodies is frequently the same temperature as their surroundings.

Because many enzymes do not work properly if they get too hot or too cold, ectothermic animals must adjust their activ-ities to the changing temperatures of their environments. Many ectotherms become sluggish or completely inactive when their body temperatures get too high or too low.

The advantage of being endothermic is that an animal can be active regardless of the temperature of the environment. However, these animals must eat much more food to supply the energy required to maintain their temperature.

Snakes are often sluggish after a cool night. In the morning these snakes sun themselves to warm their bodies. On hot sum-mer afternoons they hide under rocks to keep their bodies from getting too hot. Snakes are active in the open only when the outside temperature is within their normal body-temperature range.

Learning about how snakes and other ectotherms function allows people to help others in specific ways. Some medicine companies chill poisonous snakes in large refrigerated chambers until they become sluggish. This allows the workers to extract the snakes' venom without being bitten. The venom is then used to make substances for treating snakebites that might otherwise be fatal.

Perhaps you have seen butterflies, early in the morning, holding on to some object and flapping their wings, slowly at first and then more rapidly. On cool mornings many flying insects must do this to warm their bodies enough to be able to fly.

Earthworms come out of their burrows only in the cool of the evening and at night. During the heat of a midsummer day, they stay deep in their burrows, keeping cool. But in the winter they burrow even deeper, below the layer of earth that normally freezes. Sometimes many earthworms come together deep in the ground and share the small amount of warmth that their bodies produce.

How does this desert species maintain a constant body temperature? **18A-2**

If you go to a pond on a cool summer morning or evening, you can easily find a large number of frogs. Yet on a hot afternoon, you will have to look carefully to find any frogs at all. The temperature of the air gets so high that frogs must seek cooler areas. Under rocks or under water, the frogs wait for the cool of the evening before they become active again.

Section Review 18A

1. Which two groups of animals are endothermic?

2. What happens to the body temperature of an endothermic animal as its environment cools?

3. How can large ears help cool an animal?

18B Birds

Birds are endothermic vertebrates that have wings and feathers. Birds are found on every continent. From icy Antarctica to the hot Sahara Desert to your backyard, there are few environments where they cannot be found. Their ability to survive in these extreme environments is due largely to God's giving them the ability to fly.

Birds eat a variety of foods including nectar, seeds, fruit, worms, insects, fish, mice, and even other birds. Birds do not have teeth. God designed birds' beaks and feet to help them catch and eat their food. For example, meat-eating birds have sharp, hooked beaks used to tear meat. Seed-eating birds have short, thick beaks that easily crack hard seeds.

Objectives 18B

- Explain how the structure of a bird's bones is specially designed for flight.

- Realize that flight muscles need large amounts of energy (food) and oxygen.

- Describe the structure of a feather.

- Compare down and contour feathers.

- Identify ways that birds care for their young.

18B-1 | Can you match each beak to the foot that belongs to the same bird?

Look at the three bird beaks and the three feet in Figure 18B-1. Which beak and foot do you think belong to a meat-eating bird? Which belong to a seed-eating bird? Which belong to a bird that strains food from water?

One of the benefits man gets from birds is help in controlling rodent and insect pests. Another benefit is the meat and eggs they provide.

18B.1 *Designed for Flight*

It takes more than wings and feathers for a bird to fly. In fact, God made some birds that cannot fly. Penguins use their wings as fins to help them swim. Ostriches use their wings for balancing when they run, but they cannot fly. Instead, they have powerful legs that make them some of the fastest animals on earth. However, most birds do fly, and having wings is only one of the things necessary for flight.

A low body weight is also essential to flying. One characteristic that gives birds a low weight is the design of their bones. Ground-dwelling creatures have relatively solid, heavy bones. Bird bones are relatively lightweight. Their bones often have air spaces and are reinforced by a crisscross structure inside them. This allows their bones to be lightweight and strong at the same time. Some birds have skeletons that weigh less than their feathers.

18B.2 *Fuel for Flight*

Since birds are endothermic, they need more food than similarly sized ectothermic animals because it takes a continuous supply of energy to maintain the body at a constant temperature. In addition, flight muscles require exceptionally large amounts of energy. During flight much oxygen and many food molecules must quickly be made available to the flight muscles. Birds store energy-rich molecules in their flight muscles. Thus, when a bird needs energy for long or short flights, it is immediately available.

Birds get the energy they need by eating large amounts of food. Many birds eat more than their body weight in food each day. This would be like a typical 45 kg (100 lb) junior high student eating 48 large pepperoni pizzas daily! Birds can rapidly digest their food to quickly supply their energy needs. Sometimes birds eat large amounts of food at one time and store it in an organ called a *crop*.

Birds in flight require additional oxygen to support the cellular respiration of their flight muscles. Air sacs connected to their lungs help supply the necessary oxygen. The lungs and air sacs fill with air when the bird inhales. When it exhales, air from the air sacs flows through the lungs. As a result, a bird's lungs are supplied with oxygen-rich air even while it is exhaling. This provides the extra oxygen that a bird needs. The air sacs are also the chief means a bird has of cooling its body.

"Doctor, I'm worried about my son Mark. He's been eating like a bird lately!"

Facets of *Zoology:* *Feather Facts*

If an animal has feathers, it is a bird. Feathers are the specially designed covering God gave to birds to insulate them from cold, heat, and often water. Most birds also use their feathers for flight. Birds' feathers may serve as camouflage to help them hide in their environment, or they may be brightly colored to attract a mate.

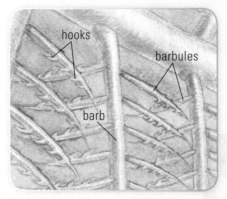

hooks
barbules
barb

A feather is composed of a *central shaft* and a *vane* that extends from either side of the shaft. The *quill* is the part of the shaft that anchors the feather in the bird's skin. Feathers grow from small bumps called *papillae* (puh PIL ee) in the bird's skin. The vane is made up of many parallel strands called *barbs*. The barbs grow out from the shaft and are connected to one another by rows of smaller branches called *barbules*, which fasten to adjacent barbules with tiny hooks.

If a bird's feathers become dry and brittle, their barbs break, just as human hair gets "split ends" when it dries out. If the barbs break, the feathers become useless for insulation and flying. To keep its feathers flexible, a bird *preens* itself. A bird preens by using its bill to take oil from the oil gland near its tail and then running its bill along each feather. By preening, the bird applies oil to the feathers and reattaches any barbs that may have become separated.

Feathers help birds fly. It may seem strange that something as "light as a feather" could lift a bird through the air. It may seem especially strange when you consider that there are birds weighing over 14 kg (30.8 lb) that can fly. However, feathers are strong structures. With more than a million hooks connecting the barbs of a single feather, the vane is a sturdy, flat structure.

Much of the strength of birds' feathers also comes from their arrangement in overlapping rows. In this way, each feather gives support to the feathers on either side of it.

In order to turn, rise, dive, or stop, birds maneuver their feathers into different angles and positions. Birds have muscles attached to their feathers that can turn the feathers in different directions. These papillae muscles slant the feathers so that air flowing past the feathers carries the bird in certain directions.

Once a year (more often for some), birds lose their feathers and grow a new set. This process, called *molting*, happens slowly. Most birds lose a few feathers at a time. The replacements grow before the bird loses more feathers. Thus, most birds can fly even while they are molting.

Feathers also keep birds warm and dry. The short, fluffy **down feathers** next to a bird's skin hold warm air close to its body. The longer **contour feathers** cover the bird and help insulate it, especially from water. The oil that a bird applies to its contour feathers forms a thin, slick coating. Water rolls off this oily coating without penetrating the bird's feathers. The contour feathers also give a bird its streamlined shape. The flight feathers of the wing and tail are the largest of the contour feathers.

contour: con- (L. CON, with) + -tour (L. TORNARE, to turn or to round off)

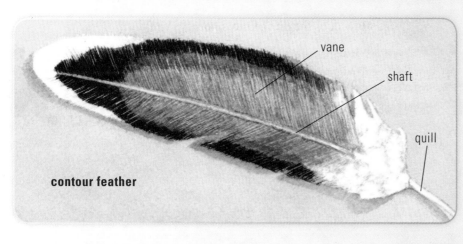

contour feather

vane

shaft

quill

Parrot preening

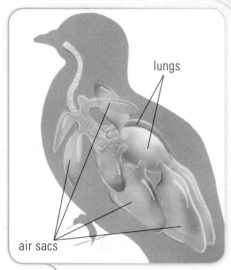

18B-2 Air sacs allow birds to have fresh air in their lungs when inhaling and exhaling.

albumen: (L. ALBA, white)

18B-3 Goslings can swim on their first day of life, but these warbler hatchlings spend weeks in the nest before they can venture out on their own.

They allow more cool air to enter the body and more warm air to leave than the lungs alone would permit. The harder we work (or play), the more oxygen we need. The same is true for birds. They, however, have air sacs to supply the extra oxygen they need for the extremely vigorous activity of flying.

18B.3 *Nests and Eggs*

One characteristic of all birds is that they lay eggs. A fertile bird egg consists of an embryo, a yolk (food supply), albumen or egg white (liquid environment), a shell membrane, and a brittle shell. An egg provides the food and environment necessary for the embryo to develop. Gases involved in cellular respiration (oxygen and carbon dioxide) can pass through the brittle shell and shell membrane.

Usually birds care for their eggs by building a nest and *incubating* the eggs. Nests may be made of twigs, grass, spider webs, stones, or various other materials and are built just about anywhere (in trees, on the ground, on cliffs, in houses). Parent birds warm their eggs while sitting on them, but that is not all there is to incubation.

The contents of the egg, especially the yolk, must remain free of any permanent contact with the eggshell. The yolk floats on top of the albumen (white). If the egg is not moved, the embryo will not develop normally. Parent birds must regularly turn their eggs to ensure normal development.

Some birds, such as turkeys, chickens, geese, and quail, hatch fully-feathered and are able to walk and peck for their own food. Many of these birds nest on the ground. Most birds, though, are blind, nearly naked, and helpless at birth. These hatchlings usually hatch in nests or tree cavities where the parents can protect them.

What Do You Think?

Do the eggs you bring home from the grocery store contain tiny embryos? Could you incubate some and raise your own chickens?

Section Review 18B

1. How does the diet of birds benefit mankind?

2. Why does a bird preen itself?

3. How does a developing chick inside an egg get oxygen?

18C Mammals

The vertebrates that are most familiar to us are the mammals. They provide food, labor, companionship, and even entertainment. While they share many common characteristics, mammals show remarkable diversity in size, form, and behavior. Exploiting nearly every habitat from the ocean depths to the peaks of mountains, they speak to us of a God Whose imagination and powers are limitless.

18C.1 *Characteristics of Mammals*

Mammals are endothermic vertebrates that have hair and produce milk. The hair on some mammals is so sparse that it is hardly noticeable. Whales are mammals that have only a little hair. Other mammals have thick hair that insulates them. We call this type of hair fur. Some hairs, such as a cat's whiskers, are quite sensitive to touch and help the animal to gauge distances.

Milk, as you know, is a liquid substance that mothers feed their newborn offspring. Milk provides the fat, protein, carbohydrates, vitamins, minerals, and water that an infant mammal needs. Milk is produced in the **mammary** (MAM uh ree) **glands** of the mother mammal.

Some mammals drink their mother's milk for only a few weeks; others continue to consume milk for many months. As the offspring grow while continuing to receive nourishment from their mothers, they learn survival skills. A baby elephant receives milk from its mother soon after it is born. When it is six months old, it begins to experiment with feeding itself, but it still receives milk from its mother. During this time it learns from its mother and other elephants in its herd what foods to eat and how to gather them. The baby elephant will not be completely *weaned* (no longer drinking milk) until it is five or six years old. By this time the young elephant has both learned and practiced the skills it must know to take care of itself.

As mammals mature they begin to eat the same foods as their parents. They develop teeth to help them eat their food. Mammals have four kinds of teeth: *incisors* are used for cutting; *canines*, which are long and pointed, are used for tearing; and *premolars* and *molars* are used for grinding. While most mammal species have all four types of teeth, some mammals may be lacking one or more types, depending on their diet.

18C.2 *Groups of Mammals*

Mammals can be divided into three groups based on how they reproduce. The mammals with which you are most familiar are the **placental mammals**. Most mammals, such as dogs, horses, deer, and whales, are placental mammals. These mammals receive oxygen and food and have wastes removed through a structure called the **placenta** (pluh SEN tuh) while they are growing inside their mothers. Developing mammals are connected to the placenta by an **umbilical cord**. This contains blood vessels that transport oxygen, food, and wastes between the placenta and the developing mammal. The place where

Objectives 18C

- List the presence of hair and mammary glands as key characteristics of mammals.

- Describe hair and fur.

- Identify and discuss the three ways that mammals may bear their young.

- Name and describe two egg-laying mammals.

- List and describe several pouched animals.

All mammal species, like this pig, produce milk in mammary glands. **18C-1**

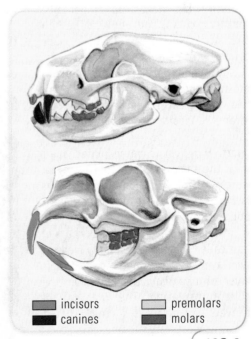

| ■ incisors | □ premolars |
| ■ canines | ■ molars |

Most mammals have four kinds of teeth. **18C-2**

Facets of *Zoology:* *Hair-Raising Reports*

Hair is the characteristic covering of mammals. Some mammals, such as elephants and whales, have very little hair. Lions, beavers, bears, and similar mammals have thick, heavy coats of hair. Some mammals' hair is modified into unusual structures, such as the quills of porcupines and bristles of hogs. The horns of rhinoceroses are actually densely packed tufts of hairs.

The tubular hair-producing organs in the skin of mammals are called *hair follicles*. Live cells added to the base of a hair push the hair out of the follicle and cause it to grow. These cells soon become full of *keratin* (KEHR uh tin) and then die. Keratin is the same protein that makes up fingernails, feathers, claws, and hooves. The hair that sticks out of a follicle is made primarily of dead, keratin-filled cells.

Although tooth enamel is the hardest substance in a mammal's body, hair has the greatest tensile (TEN sul) strength. Tensile strength is the resistance a substance has to being pulled apart. Hair resists being pulled apart with the same strength that an equal weight of rolled aluminum does. This is twice the strength of the strongest bone in your body.

Some mammals have thick coats of hair called fur. Fur is generally made of two layers of hair. One is a short, soft layer of *underhair* that provides excellent insulation. The underhair of beavers and otters is so thick that it prevents most water from reaching their skin. The second layer of fur is made of longer, stiffer hair called *guard hair*.

Guard hair protects the underhair from wear and contains pigment granules that produce the colors of fur. Because certain follicles produce large amounts of pigment and others produce little or none, some mammals can produce coats that are banded, spotted, or mottled. These patterns are usually effective in providing camouflage.

Sheep's wool is an unusual kind of fur. Wool is made of curly underhair that grows longer than the guard hair. About 3.6 kg (8 lb) of wool can be shorn each year from an average sheep. Sheep with excellent diets often produce up to 16 kg (35 lb) of wool. Other mammals, such as foxes and minks, have beautiful fur that is kept on the hide for use in coats.

When a mammal gets cold, its hair can be used to make a thicker layer of insulation. Each hair has its own tiny *erector muscle* that contracts to make the hair stand on end. The upright hairs help hold a layer of warm air next to the mammal's skin.

Mammals use certain hairs for sensing things around them. Animals' whiskers are long hairs that have sensitive nerve endings at the bases of their follicles. These nerve endings send messages to the brain whenever something brushes against these

hairs. A cat uses its whiskers to test whether openings are large enough for its whole body to fit through. Seals use their whiskers to detect vibrations in the water. This response helps them find food and avoid predators or obstacles.

Dogs have sensitive hairs on the backs of their necks that help pro-

tect them. Because the blood vessels that carry blood to the dog's brain are close to the skin in this area, the dog's neck is more vulnerable in a fight. When a dog senses danger, the hair on the back of its neck stands up on end. If something touches these hairs, reflexes cause the dog to react immediately to protect its neck.

The huge variety of different kinds of hair on God's creations is truly amazing. Equally amazing is how effectively each kind of hair does what is needed. This highly technical design shows God's infinite intelligence and His marvelous love. He provides each mammal with hair that not only enables it to survive and be comfortable but that also adorns it.

the umbilical cord attaches to the mammal leaves a mark called an umbilicus, or bellybutton. Placental mammals are born alive. They do not hatch from eggs or develop in pouches.

The mammals that lay eggs are called **monotremes**. The duck-billed platypus and echidna are the only monotremes. They live in Australia, Tasmania, and New Guinea.

Marsupials (mar SOO pee ulz) are the third group of mammals, and they have a pouch in which they rear their young. They are not born in the pouch. Newborn marsupials, which are not well developed, crawl from the birth canal into their mother's pouch immediately after birth. Once in the pouch, they attach to the mother's nipples within the pouch and then complete their development. The marsupials that you are probably most familiar with are kangaroos and opossums. Australia and surrounding regions are the habitat of a wide range of marsupials, including marsupial versions of mice, moles, rabbits, flying squirrels, weasels, and more. This amazing variety of marsupials testifies of the richness of God's creation.

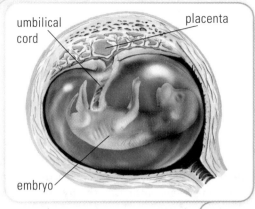

umbilical cord

placenta

embryo

A sheep embryo receives nourishment through the placenta.

18C-3

marsupial: (L. MARSUPIUM, pouch)

Facets of *Zoology:* Mammals That Lay Eggs

Most mammals give birth to live young. But there are two, the duck-billed platypus (PLAT ih pus) and the echidna (ih KID nuh), that lay soft-shelled eggs. These two are considered mammals because their bodies are covered with fur and they have mammary glands that produce milk to nourish their young.

The duck-billed platypus lives only in remote parts of Australia and Tasmania. European scientists were unfamiliar with these animals until 1798, when the British Museum in London received a complete duck-billed platypus skin. Because the animal had a bill like a duck; a broad, flat, leathery tail; and fur like an otter, the museum curators thought the 2 ft long skin was a fake, a trick someone was trying to play on them. Not until they received a complete specimen did the museum curators believe that the platypus was a real animal.

In a nest far back in a hole along a riverbank, the mother platypus usually lays two eggs about the size of a robin's eggs. For seven or eight days she incubates the eggs by curling herself around them or by placing them on her stomach.

When the eggs hatch, the baby platypuses are tiny, blind, and hairless. During this time they feed by lapping the milk that oozes from their mother's mammary glands onto her fur. The young stay in their nest for four months before leaving for their first swim.

Soon the young, like their parents, are searching for snails, small

echidna

fish, and other food in the mud. If danger appears, the young can protect themselves with the poisonous spurs on their hind legs. As the platypuses mature, the female's spurs disappear, but the male's remain. The platypus is one of the few poisonous mammals.

The other egg-laying mammal is the 43 cm (17 in.) long echidna. This porcupine-like creature is amazingly strong for its size. While searching for ants, termites, and worms, it easily overturns large stones twice its weight. When an echidna senses danger, it digs quickly into the ground. But instead of burrowing headfirst, it digs with all four of its legs, sinking its body straight down into the ground. Once most of its body is in the earth, the echidna stops, leaving part of its spiny back exposed.

The female echidna lays one or two eggs, which she immediately places in a pouch on the underside of her body. The pouch is temporary and will later disappear. After seven to ten days of incubation in the pouch, the eggs hatch.

The 12 mm (0.5 in.) long baby echidnas live in the pouch and feed on their mother's milk for six to eight weeks. When they are about 10 cm (4 in.) long, their spines begin to grow. The mother then takes them out of the pouch and carefully hides them in her nest. Here the baby echidnas are protected until they are about ten weeks old. By this time their spines have grown, and they are ready to live independently in their natural environment.

Facets of *Zoology:* *God-Designed Nurseries*

Most of the 289 different species of marsupials live in Australia. The difference between marsupials and most other mammals is the way their young develop. Marsupials do not develop a true placenta in the womb like most mammals do.

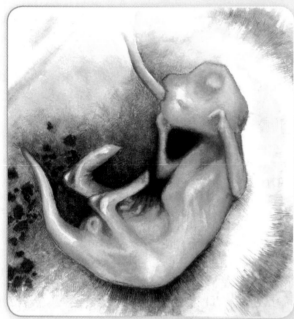

Since the young receive little nourishment from the mother while they are in the womb, they remain there only a short time before they are born.

Kangaroos, for example, stay in the womb for only thirty to thirty-five days. When they leave the womb and are born, they are tiny and fragile. A newborn kangaroo (a joey) is about the size of a bee, has no hair, and weighs about 0.75 g (0.026 oz), a tiny fraction of its mother's weight. Much of the infant kangaroo's body, including its eyes, ears, and hind legs, is not developed.

Soon after a young marsupial is born, it takes one of the most important journeys of its life. Grasping its mother's hair with its front legs, the blind baby wiggles its way up into the pouch. In the pouch the baby will be protected, kept warm, and fed so that

it can continue developing. Mammary glands inside the pouch provide the young marsupial with the nourishment it needs to grow and develop.

The number of mammary glands a mother marsupial has determines the number of young that can survive. Opossums, marsupials native to North America, sometimes give birth to twenty to thirty young. Since the mother has only thirteen mammary glands, only the first young to attach themselves to her glands have a chance to develop. Koalas have only two mammary glands, but these are usually more than enough, since koalas rarely have more than one offspring at a time.

The mammary glands of the kangaroo can produce two different types of milk. Often an older joey must leave the pouch

to make room for a newborn sibling. Once the newborn enters the pouch, it becomes attached to a gland for several months. This type of gland produces milk rich in protein to help the tiny kangaroo grow. When the older joey puts its head into the pouch, it nurses from a different mammary gland. This other gland produces milk rich in fat for the energetic young.

God designed the pouches of some marsupials to be very elastic because the young often stay with the mother, climbing in and out of the pouch until they are one fourth of their adult size.

The womb is also called the uterus. (See pp. 348–49.)

18C-4 Classification of Some Mammals

Order	Description	Examples
Monotremata	egg-laying mammals	duck-billed platypuses, echidnas
Marsupials (7 orders)	pouched mammals	opossums, kangaroos
Insectivora	insect-eating mammals	moles, shrews
Chiroptera	flying mammals	bats
Carnivora	flesh-eating mammals	dogs, cats, bears
Rodentia	gnawing mammals	mice, squirrels
Cetacea	fish-like mammals	whales, porpoises
Pinnipedia	fin-footed mammals	seals, walruses
Proboscidea	trunked mammals	elephants
Sirenia	sea cows	manatees, dugongs
Perissodactyla	odd-toed hoofed mammals	horses, rhinoceroses
Artiodactyla	even-toed hoofed mammals	cattle, deer, pigs
Primates	erect mammals	lemurs, monkeys, apes

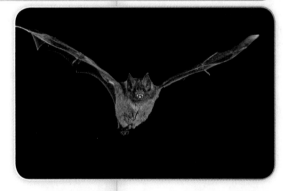

_____   _____

Using Table 18C-4, decide which order each of these placental mammals belongs to and write the order name under the picture.

_____

18C-5

18C-6 Marsupials come in a variety of forms. The Tasmanian devil (left) is a fierce ground-dweller that eats mostly carrion. Koalas (right) spend most of their time in eucalyptus trees, where they eat only leaves.

Through Faith We Understand

According to evolutionists, humans fall into the mammal class and the primate order because of some shared physical characteristics. Like mammals, humans have placental young, body hair, and milk production. However, this similarity does not make humans animals. To say that humans are primates implies that we are not made in the image of God (Gen. 1:26–28). Can you think of other ways that humans and animals are both similar and different?

Section Review 18C

1. What do we call the long, pointed teeth that are used for tearing?

2. What is the special name for the insulating hair?

3. What is a bellybutton?

4. Name a mammal that lays eggs.

5. Which order of mammals includes squirrels?

6. Are humans primates? Why or why not?

Chapter Review

1. How does a dog cool itself?

2. What main advantage is there to being endothermic?

3. Give one example of how a bird's beak is designed especially for the type of food it eats.

4. How are a bird's bones different from those of other animals?

5. Which type of feather helps insulate a bird?

6. List two distinguishing characteristics unique to mammals.

7. List the four kinds of teeth found in mammals.

8. Of what protein is hair composed?

9. What are the functions of a placenta and an umbilical cord?

10. List the three groups of mammals based on their types of reproduction.

What Did You Learn?

1. How would your life be different if you were ectothermic?

2. Why do you think birds usually have higher body temperatures than mammals?

3. What characteristics of birds are helpful for flight?

4. Why is the expression "eat like a bird," meaning to eat very little, inaccurate?

5. Why is it important for a bird's lungs to always be filled with oxygen-rich air when it is flying?

6. Where would you expect to find the mammary glands of a marsupial?

Scientifically Speaking

endothermic
down feather
contour feather
mammary gland
placental mammal
placenta
umbilical cord
monotreme
marsupial

Self Quiz 18

_____ 1. Mammals, birds, and reptiles are all endothermic organisms. (True/False)

_____ 2. Which of these organ systems is/are used by some endothermic animals to cool themselves?
A. circulatory
B. respiratory
C. nervous
D. all of these

_____ 3. A sharp, hooked beak would probably be found on a bird that eats
A. meat.
B. seeds.
C. nectar.
D. worms.

4. In addition to lungs, birds have _____

_____ connected to their respiratory system to increase volume.

_____ 5. Which of these is the food source in a bird's egg?
A. albumen
B. shell membrane
C. yolk
D. none of these

_____ 6. All mammals have some hair. (True/False)

_____ 7. Which of these would be nourished through an umbilical cord during development?
A. monotreme
B. marsupial
C. placental mammal
D. all of these

_____ 8. The mammal teeth used primarily for cutting are the
A. molars.
B. canines.
C. premolars.
D. incisors.

_____ 9. The mammal hair that contains pigments and is responsible for the animal's coat color is the
A. underhair.
B. guard hair.
C. sensory hair.
D. quills.

_____ 10. Which of these is _not_ a marsupial?
A. duck-billed platypus
B. koala
C. kangaroo
D. opossum

Animal Behavior

19

In Job 38–39, God asks Job, who had questioned God's treatment of him, questions about nature and whether Job was in control of it. After describing nine different animals and their behaviors, God asks in 39:26, "Doth the hawk fly by thy wisdom, and stretch her wings toward the south?" Obviously, Job could not tell a bird how to fly or where to migrate any more than he could command a thunderstorm (38:25). Birds' actions do not depend upon man's knowledge, but rather God's wisdom. God created various kinds of animals and gave them amazing abilities to survive.

We humans often evaluate animal behavior by comparing it to our own. As a result, many animals have reputations that may or may not be true. In an old fable the ant is considered a smart insect because it works hard to store food for the winter. Meanwhile the foolish grasshop-per fiddles away the summer and starves in the winter. Is the ant really smart and the grasshopper really foolish because of what they do? We often hear phrases such as "busy as a bee," "sly as a fox," "silly as a goose," and "proud as a peacock." Do these animals really have the human characteristics indicated by such phrases?

Many scientists agree that there are three levels of animal behavior. **Innate behaviors** are those actions and reactions that God has already given an animal when it is born. **Learned behaviors** are those that an animal learns by itself or from other animals (usually its parents). **Intelligent behaviors** are those that are based on special abilities including reasoning, analyzing, problem solving, and understanding. To understand how and why animals behave the way they do, we will study examples of these three levels of animal behavior.

19A Innate Behaviors

Although all animals are born with innate behaviors, different kinds of animals have different innate behaviors. God provides each animal with the specific skills it needs for survival. For instance, a tiger cub is born with a desire and ability to nurse, but a turkey chick knows how to peck at food. These inborn behaviors are sometimes divided into two groups based on their level of complexity: reflexes and instincts.

Reflexes are simple, immediate responses to some change in the environment. A dog pants as a reflex action to heat. Dogs also blink their eyes when there is a bright flash of light, jump when they hear a sudden loud noise, and scratch when fleas bite them. All of these reflexes are useful reactions that are built into the animal.

Instincts, the second type of innate behavior, are complex reactions that often require long periods of time to complete. An instinct is also a type of built-in reaction. Some well-known examples of instincts include building nests (birds), weaving webs (spiders), caring for young (mammals), and hoarding food (squirrels and ants).

The *mating rituals* of many animals are also instincts. For example, during the mating season a male peacock selects a female. (The female is called a peahen.) He then spreads his long, beautiful tail feathers and proceeds with a complex dance in front of the peahen. The peahen initially appears unimpressed, but if she is willing to mate with that particular male, she will eventually join in the dance. This mating ritual is an innate behavior. A peacock that has never seen the mating ritual knows how to do it "step perfect." In fact, if he does not do the dance correctly, he will not win a mate.

Migration is also an instinct. Migration is the long-distance, seasonal movement of animals from one area to another. The best-known migrators are birds. Some birds can migrate great distances. When the temperature gets too low or food becomes scarce for the birds of a particular species in one area, they will migrate to another area. Other migrators include caribou, whales, sea turtles, and salmon.

Objectives 19A

- List the three levels of animal behavior.
- Describe two types of innate behavior in animals. Give examples of each.
- Define *pheromones*.

19A-1 Panting, like many simple actions, is a reflex.

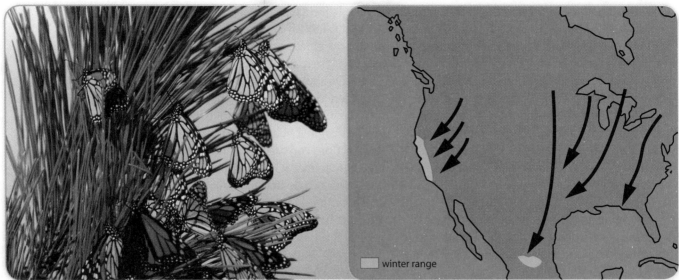

19A-2 Monarch butterflies rest on a branch in Pacific Grove, California, after a long migration. The map shows the major autumn migration paths of monarch butterflies; in the spring they and their offspring will migrate in the opposite direction.

winter range

Even some invertebrates migrate. The monarch butterfly, a common butterfly of North America, migrates to the southern parts of California or to Mexico to spend the winter. Monarch butterflies hang by the thousands on certain trees in these areas, remaining inactive until spring. Then they begin their migration north to almost every area of the United States and Canada.

When the monarch butterflies reach an area with suitable vegetation, they lay eggs and die. The next generation travels farther northward and within weeks will reproduce. The offspring continue the northerly migration, and the pattern is repeated for several generations during the summer. But as the days get shorter in the fall, the monarch butterflies that are alive begin their journey south, in some cases traveling as far as 4800 km (3000 mi). The migrating butterflies have never been to the place they are going. They are born with the ability to get there.

Evolutionists often say that instincts have evolved for millions of years. This, however, is impossible. Many animals die if their instincts do not work properly. A "half-evolved" instinct would be useless and could even be harmful. If a spider could not build a proper web, it would not catch insects. If it did not catch insects, it would starve.

Likewise, if monarch butterflies did not migrate properly, the species would die. If they stayed in the north, the winter cold would kill them. Any eggs they had laid late in the summer would also be killed by the cold. Or if they migrated to the wrong place in the south, they might be killed by unsuitable weather conditions. Any eggs the butterflies laid in the wrong place in the south would not survive, since the proper food would not be available for the larvae. If their migration instincts had not worked properly *the first time*, monarch butterflies would not have survived to this day.

The Bible refers to instincts as God-given behaviors of animals. Jeremiah 8:7 speaks of the stork knowing "her appointed times" and the crane and the swallow observing the "time of their coming." In this verse God reminds us that these migratory birds follow the instincts that He gave them. The Israelites, at the time of Jeremiah's writing, were ignoring what God had told them to do. It is shameful that all of God's creatures except His favored creatures—humans—seem to obey Him.

Let Them Have Dominion

The grape berry moth thrives in vineyards in Texas—much to the frustration of the vineyard owners and grape lovers everywhere. This moth spends the winter as a pupa in piles of leaves around the edges of vineyards. In the spring, it emerges as an adult, mates, and lays eggs on the flower clusters. Each larva chews on several berries, causing discoloration or rot in the grape and loss to the growers. One summer usually sees three generations of grape berry moths ravage a vineyard. How might vineyard owners solve this problem? Evaluate each suggested solution to determine which is best.

Section Review 19A

1. Which type of behavior does an animal have when it is born?

2. Which are considered more complex: reflexes or instincts?

3. _____ is the seasonal traveling of animals over long distances from one region to another.

4. What are ways that animals use pheromones? How can humans use them to exercise wise dominion? (See p. 336.)

Facets of *Zoology:* *Pheromones—Odors with a Message*

Have you ever wondered how army ants know how to get back to the food that they found? Does it seem impossible that a moth can find a mate that is five miles away? These and many other actions of animals are influenced by pheromones (FEHR uh MOANZ).

Pheromones are chemicals that are released by animals and that affect other animals of the same species. Pheromones are similar to hormones. However, they work outside the body, while hormones work internally.

Female gypsy moths secrete tiny amounts of a pheromone that has a particular smell. This odor cannot be smelled by humans, but it attracts male gypsy moths from miles around. If a female gypsy moth secreted all her pheromone at once (which would be only one millionth of a gram), billions of male gypsy moths could be attracted to her.

Japanese beetle

Since the effects of pheromones are very specific, they can be used to control some insects. Pheromones can be used to attract certain harmful insects to traps where they are destroyed. Other insects, which may be helpful, are unaffected by the lure and thus are not trapped.

Japanese beetles are responsible for more than $10 million worth of damage to plants such as grasses and shrubs, fruit trees, and field crops in the United States every year. Traps have been designed to lure these beetles by the scent of pheromones and flowers. Once inside the trap, the beetles cannot fly out, and they fall into a bag and die.

In bee colonies the queen bee produces certain pheromones. These pheromones keep the bodies of the worker bees, which are all females, from developing egg-producing organs. If the queen bee dies or becomes too old to produce eggs, the amount of these pheromones in the hive decreases. Without the pheromones to keep the worker bees immature, they soon become reproductive and lay eggs.

Pheromone trails left by ants help them find their way back to the ant colony. Scavenger ants also use these trails to lead other ants to food. Once the food is gone, the ants stop using the trail and the pheromone disappears. The disappearance of the pheromone eliminates false trails or crossing trails.

The existence of these pheromone trails is easy to demonstrate. The next time you see a line of ants on the sidewalk, floor, or wall, rub your finger several times in a straight line across their path. Because you have now rubbed out their pheromone trail, they will run around in confusion for a short time, within plain sight of each other, until one happens to walk through the invisible break. This reestablishes the chemical trail, and in a short time everything is back to normal.

Ants also use pheromones to signal danger. Warning pheromones secreted in small amounts draw more ants to the area to combat the enemy. Large amounts excite the entire ant colony to action. That's why so many ants come pouring out of an anthill when you disturb it.

Pheromones are also used to mark "property" belonging to deer, bears, foxes, rabbits, and other animals. Prairie dogs use a pheromone to mark their territorial boundaries. Although prairie dogs live in colonies, each colony is divided into smaller sections. Each of these sections has its own territory. The boundaries of these territories are invisible to humans, but to prairie dogs they are as obvious as walls. If a boundary is crossed, a fight can start among the prairie dogs, and sometimes the intruder is killed.

Rabbits also set up boundaries. They secrete their pheromones from special glands located under their chins. After scratching to get the pheromones on their hind feet, they pat out boundaries for the territory they want to claim.

prairie dog

In very crowded conditions, male rabbits will mark not only their territory but also their mates and offspring. This places an invisible "private property" sign for all their rabbit neighbors to heed. People who have a pet rabbit sometimes find their rabbit patting its chin on them. The rabbit is claiming them as "its people."

While you are marveling over the astonishing number of distinct odors God has created and the reaction mechanisms He has built into the creatures that respond to them, also be astonished at the Master Chemist Who conceived of them, and the Engineer Who designed the organs to produce and release them. He is the same God Who had the Old Testament priests burn incense daily, and the same God Who regards the prayers of His saints as sweet-smelling incense (Rev. 5:8).

19B Learned Behaviors

The second major type of animal behavior is learned behavior. A housebroken cat, a dog that "shakes hands," and a parrot that talks all display learned behaviors. Even the fish that rise to the top of the aquarium when you approach to feed them are displaying a learned behavior. Many animals that serve humans, such as horses, bloodhounds, and sheepdogs, are valuable because of the learned behaviors people have taught them. Most of an animal's trained behaviors are accomplished by shaping their natural behaviors into desired responses through a series of rewards.

An animal's ability to learn, however, is not boundless but limited by its physical and mental abilities. A bird could not be trained to follow a faint scent trail because it lacks a keen sense of smell; nor could a bloodhound be taught to fly to a perch like a parrot, for obvious reasons. Although some chimpanzees and gorillas have been taught some sign language and seem to know how to use it, none can communicate on the level of the average first-grader.

Animals also learn behaviors by themselves. Baby birds that live on the ground (such as the chicks of turkeys and pheasants) crouch down and freeze by instinct as soon as they sense movement over their heads. This helps to protect them from hawks and other birds of prey. Of course, the newly hatched chicks also crouch when harmless birds such as ducks or even falling leaves pass over their heads. After a while the baby birds become accustomed to flying ducks and falling leaves and learn not to react when these pass over. Hawks, however, do not pass over often, and the chicks are not accustomed to them; so the chicks respond by crouching and freezing. This behavior pattern is both an instinct and a learned behavior.

Many other animal behaviors are combinations of different levels of behavior. For instance, most songbirds are born with the ability to sing, but if they do not hear their species' song when they are young, they will not be able to sing their species' entire range of songs when they are older.

It is an instinct for squirrels to hold and chew nuts. In one experiment, squirrels were brought up without ever seeing nuts. When nuts were offered to these squirrels, they immediately picked them up and began trying to crack the shells. At first they were not very good at it. They took a long time getting the nutmeat out of their first nut, and by the time they were finished, the shell was in shreds. After about five nuts, however, these squirrels were able to crack nuts quickly and neatly, just like other squirrels. Although squirrels eat nuts by instinct, their ability to efficiently open nuts appears to be a learned behavior they gain by trial and error.

Section Review 19B

1. What kind of behavior is a pet trick?

2. Are all learned animal behaviors taught by humans?

3. Distinguish between the learned and instinctive abilities demonstrated by a squirrel eating a nut.

Objective 19B

• Give an example of a learned behavior in animals.

The herding ability of this border collie is the result of instinctive hunting behaviors that have been shaped by training.   **19B-1**

Squirrels instinctively eat nuts, but some of the tricks of opening them easily must be learned.   **19B-2**

His Mercy Endureth Forever

Read Psalm 104:27–29. According to this passage, God gives food to the animals. How can this be if the animals find food and feed themselves? Does the squirrel receive food from God even though it opens nuts on its own?

19C Intelligent Behaviors

Animals have varying degrees of intelligence. *Intelligence* includes the ability to reason out a solution to a problem. Sometimes this might even involve fashioning or using some natural item as a tool. It also involves the ability to communicate with symbols. At one time people thought that all animals lacked intelligence and that man was God's only earthly creature that could reason and communicate. This opinion greatly underestimated the intelligence of animals, as more recent experiments have shown. Some animals are unable to solve certain problems, but others can solve similar problems easily. Many animals have even been shown to use a "language" of their own.

Dolphins and porpoises are among the most intelligent of animals. Their whistles, which last for about a half second each, change pitch in various high-low patterns (low-high, high-low, high-low-high, etc.). From these whistles a twelve-letter dolphin alphabet has been worked out. But the meaning of these whistles remains a mystery.

A killer whale in a North American marine park discovered that if he spit out partially chewed fish, they would float to the top, attracting scavenging seagulls. The whale would wait just beneath the surface until a bird swooped down for

19C-1   Dolphins are very trainable due to their high intelligence.

Facets of *Zoology:* Are Animals Dumb?

At first glance, some animals seem very intelligent. A bee more than two miles from its hive can find its way back with its eyes covered. Yet if the hive is raised or lowered a few inches, even mature bees coming back to the hive will, with their eyes "wide open," go to the place where the opening to the hive used to be. Sometimes they cannot find the opening for days.

The mason wasp builds its home on a tree and then carefully covers it with pieces of material so that it looks just like the bark it is on. This hiding of one's home seems like an intelligent behavior. But sometimes mason wasps choose unusual pieces of wood on which to build their homes. One wasp chose the mantle of a fireplace. It took over a month for the wasp to complete its home. When it finished, the wasp had built a structure that looked like tree bark, which stood out quite conspicuously from the polished wood.

Birds sometimes migrate thousands of miles without getting lost. But if a bird's newly built nest is moved a few feet, the bird is unable to find it, even though it is in plain view. Usually the bird will begin to build a new nest in the old spot.

When a bird whose nest has been moved six inches returns with food, it

may ignore its screaming chicks as it looks where the nest used to be. Then it flies off and eats the food itself. It is usually some time before the bird will begin feeding the chicks.

If sheep are entering a gate single file and the shepherd puts his foot in front of a sheep, that sheep will jump over it, and so will the next and the next. Even if the foot is removed, the sheep will still jump at the same place. Every sheep in the line will jump over the obstacle that is no longer there just because the sheep in front of it jumped.

One scientist was able to get an ant to make a loop in a bottle. When the other ants came, following the trail, they entered the bottle, which the scientist then closed. The ants marched inside the bottle around and around the loop for two days before they gave up and began running aimlessly. After two hours of high-speed running, they died.

Certain kinds of woodpeckers often store acorns and nuts (and occasionally rocks by mistake) in holes they have pecked in wood. These nuts serve as winter food. But occasionally a woodpecker bores a hole through the boards that serve as the wall of a shed. It then crams acorns through this hole. Some woodpeckers have stuffed bushels of acorns into these "bottomless holes."

Are these animals dumb because of these actions? Not really. In each case these animals were following the behavior patterns God planned for them. In their natural environments these patterns work very well to help these animals survive. A woodpecker must store food for the winter. Ants must be able to find their way back to food. Sheep following closely behind one another on a narrow path must jump in the same place as the leader to avoid falling into deep ravines.

Birds need a strong connection with the location of their nest to properly care for their young. A well-hidden mason wasp's nest helps to protect the larva that is growing inside. In their natural setting, these animals' behaviors appear almost intelligent.

However, animals that follow their God-given behaviors in unusual situations sometimes appear foolish. Moving nests, thin wood, polished wood, and circular paths in bottles are unnatural circumstances for these animals.

They were all caused by man. The fact that these animals' actions appear dumb to us does not really make them dumb.

If you were taken to a foreign country, would you be considered foolish because you could not speak the language? You would not be considered dumb, but your actions and speech might appear unintelligent to the people in that country. In a foreign country you would probably try to communicate by pointing and acting out certain things. These attempts to solve your problem would show your intelligence.

One of the most intelligent invertebrates seems to be the octopus. Crabs are a favorite food of the octopus. A glass jar that contained a live crab and was tightly stoppered with a large cork presented a problem for one octopus. It could see the food but could not get a tentacle on the crab. However, the octopus played with the jar and the cork for a long time. Eventually it worked the cork out of the jar; then it caught and ate the crab. After a little more practice, the octopus could open the crab jar with ease.

Another octopus kept in a tank at a large city aquarium was able to push open the lid on the top of its tank, enter an-

other tank that held crabs, eat its fill, and then return to its own tank. The octopus did this only at night when no one was around. It took the aquarium keepers a long time to figure out what was happening to the crabs. When they sat up to watch the happenings, they were surprised to see the octopus first look into the other tanks, almost as if it wanted to be sure crabs were the best item on the day's menu.

Scientists often test the intelligence of animals by putting them into situations that are slightly different from normal and watching how the animals react. Some animals, such as the ants and the mason wasp described earlier, seem to have very little intelligence. The bird that eventually adjusted to having its nest moved appears to have had a higher level of intelligence. All animals have limited intelligence. These experiments, placing animals in unusual circumstances, are not simply funny or interesting; they are actually useful. They teach us about an animal's intellectual limits. Human intelligence also has limits. But because God created humans in His own image, we are different from animals in fundamental ways. God has even given us the responsibility to care for His creatures (Gen. 1:26–28). And as we learn their limitations, we can act more intelligently in our dealings with them.

19C-2 Some consider the hermit crab to be an intelligent tool user.

a quick bite, then explode out of the water, snatching the bird and the pre-chewed fish in one giant gulp. Before long, several other whales in the pool had learned the same trick. One even modified the new feeding game. He gathered dead fish and fish parts from the drain at the bottom of the pool and used them for bait. Scientists do not know how this new hunting technique spread among the group, but it is quite possible that each one learned by seeing the behavior modeled and recognized the success.

Tool-using animals range from chimpanzees that use two large rocks to crack tasty nuts to the woodpecker finch that holds a stiff cactus spine in its beak to dig juicy grubs out of tree branches. While most tool use among animals seems to be aimed at feeding, some creatures have other goals in mind. Digger wasps sometimes use smooth pebbles to tamp down the disturbed soil around their burrows. Hermit crabs, when they outgrow one borrowed mollusk shell, search carefully for the best replacement to use as their mobile home.

Many observations and studies seem to indicate that certain animals have a level of intelligence higher than might be expected.

Section Review 19C

1. Besides the ability to communicate, what else can be evidence of intelligence?

2. How do dolphins communicate?

3. If an animal has little intelligence, how can it survive?

Chapter Review

1. List the three levels of animal behavior.

2. Which type of behavior takes longer to accomplish: reflex or instinct?

3. Give one example of animals using pheromones.

4. Does a pet dog that rolls over on command exhibit a learned behavior or an intelligent behavior?

5. Give an example of an animal exhibiting an intelligent behavior.

What Did You Learn?

1. Explain how you could prove that a squirrel's instinct for hoarding food is an innate behavior and not a learned or intelligent behavior.

2. How is migrating beneficial to the animal that migrates?

3. Toolmaking is sometimes used as evidence of intelligence. Why do you think toolmaking indicates intelligence?

4. Give an example of an animal's action that could be considered dumb and explain whether you think it is a sign that the animal is unintelligent or that it is merely following an instinct.

Scientifically Speaking

innate behavior

learned behavior

intelligent behavior

reflex

instinct

migration

pheromone

Self Quiz 19

_____ 1. When a lioness cleans and nurses her cubs, she is displaying a reflex behavior. (True/False)

_____ 2. Innate behaviors are those an animal is born with. (True/False)

_____ 3. The mating rituals seen in many animals are examples of
  A. instincts.
  B. reflexes.
  C. learned behaviors.
  D. intelligent behaviors.

_____ 4. Migration has been observed among
  A. mammals.
  B. birds.
  C. reptiles.
  D. all of these

5. The champion invertebrate migrator discussed in our book is the _____

_____.

_____ 6. Which of these *does not* respond to pheromones as far as we know?
  A. gypsy moth
  B. prairie dog
  C. whale
  D. ant

In the following section, match each example with the type of behavior it represents.
  A. instinct
  B. reflex
  C. learned behavior
  D. intelligent behavior

_____ 7. A squirrel *efficiently* opens and eats a nut.

_____ 8. A chimp discovers it can use a wad of leaves as a sponge to get water.

_____ 9. A young wolf tries to attack a skunk, gets sprayed in the face, and avoids skunks for the rest of its life.

_____ 10. A dog snaps at you when you blow in its face.

ANIMAL SEXUAL REPRODUCTION

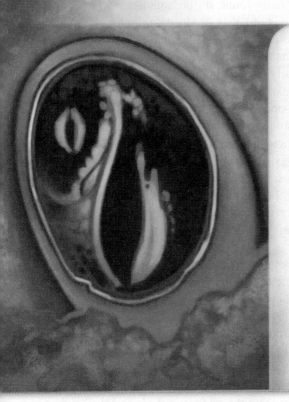

Death and reproduction are the two opposing forces in the survival of living populations. God created life so that it was good, but as a result of man's sin, death entered into the world. Before the Fall, animal reproduction was a means of filling the earth with God's marvelous creatures (Gen. 1:24–25, 28). After the Fall, however, animal reproduction became necessary for species to survive. Without it, entire species would become extinct.

Most animals reproduce sexually and thus are either male or female. A few reproduce asexually as well. Different animals have different ways of reproducing sexually and of providing for their young. This chapter discusses some of the common processes and events involved in sexual reproduction in animals.

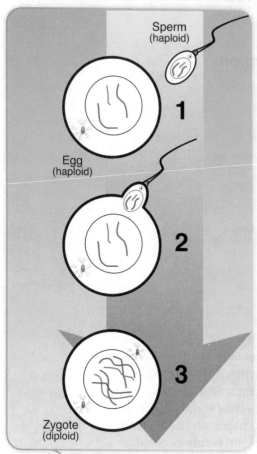

20A-1 | Fertilization: (1) individual egg and sperm are haploid; (2) egg and sperm unite; (3) newly formed zygote is diploid.

20A Meiosis, Gametes, and Fertilization

Gametes are special reproductive cells designed to transfer or receive chromosomes. These special cells have only one, not two, of each kind of chromosome normally found in the organism. *Meiosis* is a process of special cell divisions that produces gametes. The word *haploid* describes gametes and other cells that have only one of each kind of chromosome normally found in the cells of the organism. For example, fruit flies normally have eight chromosomes (four pairs) in every cell. During meiosis, however, gametes are produced that have only four chromosomes—one from every pair. Even though a gamete is haploid, it still contains one set of the organism's genes.

In most organisms, meiosis produces one of two types of gametes: eggs and sperm. **Eggs**, sometimes called *ova* (OH vuh) (sing., *ovum*), are female gametes. The egg is usually larger than the male gamete and does not have the ability to move itself. **Sperm** are male gametes. They are usually much smaller than eggs but have some means of moving. Male animals and certain parts of plants produce sperm.

Animals produce gametes in reproductive organs. The *reproductive organs* that form gametes in female animals are called **ovaries** (OH vuh reez) (sing., *ovary*), and they produce eggs. Although an animal egg cannot move by itself, it is moved by structures in the female's body. In male animals the reproductive organs that form gametes are called **testes** (TES teez) (sing., *testis*), and they produce sperm.

Fertilization (FUR tl ih ZAY shun) occurs when two haploid gametes (one egg and one sperm) unite and form a *diploid* cell. The diploid cell that results from fertilization is called a *zygote* (ZY GOTE). Zygotes contain two of every kind of chromosome typically found in the organism and have the normal number of genes for the organism. In multicellular organisms, the zygote then divides many times by mitosis to grow into an adult.

Section Review 20A

1. How many sets of an organism's chromosomes are contained within a gamete?

2. What animal organ produces eggs?

3. The diploid cell that results from fertilization is called a _____.

20B External Fertilization

With many types of animals, the sperm and egg unite outside the parents' bodies. This is called **external fertilization**. Since sperm must swim in a liquid to reach the egg, external fertilization usually occurs in water. The eggs of animals that reproduce by external fertilization are often covered by a jellylike substance that the sperm can penetrate. If the eggs had hard coverings, the sperm would not be able to fertilize them.

Most fish reproduce by means of external fertilization. Salmon, for example, spend a great deal of time and effort migrating from the ocean to the stream where they hatched. Once there, pairs of salmon line up side by side and begin *spawning*. The female releases a few of her eggs, and the male releases *milt*, the fluid containing sperm. Each pair then swims a few feet away and repeats the process until all the female's eggs have been released. Once the fish are finished spawning, they swim away, leaving the eggs. Soon after spawning, the adult salmon die.

Newly-hatched salmon (left); salmon spawning in an Alaskan stream (right) 20B-1

When a sperm enters an egg, the membrane around the egg immediately changes, preventing other sperm from entering. Sperm do not reach all the eggs. Those that are not fertilized die. Salmon eggs scattered around the stream bottom serve as food for many animals. Many salmon eggs become infected with mold and die. Just-hatched salmon are eaten by many animals in the stream. Out of a possible five thousand eggs laid by the female salmon, only a few will survive to grow up, swim downstream, and return to mate a few years later.

External fertilization may seem a bit haphazard. The meeting of sperm and eggs appears to be left to chance. But most animals that reproduce by external fertilization produce thousands of gametes. This large number of gametes helps to insure that some of them will survive.

Many of the animals that reproduce by external fertilization, however, seem to take more care of their eggs than do salmon. The Siamese fighting fish, a common aquarium fish, is a good example. The male Siamese fighting fish builds a bubble nest by coating mouthfuls of air with saliva. This nest may be 4 or 5 in. in diameter and 1 in. thick. The eggs that are released by the female are quickly fertilized by the male and caught in his mouth. The male then surrounds each fertilized egg with a saliva bubble and adds it to the underside of his bubble nest.

This instinctive action by the male protects the eggs because they are extremely delicate. If they are released in shallow water and fall to the bottom, they will be damaged. If they are released in deep water and sink too far, the water pressure will crush them.

A male Siamese fighting fish with bubble nest 20B-2

After the spawning is complete, the male watches over the eggs. He eats the unfertilized eggs. The others he keeps carefully in the bubble nest. If a bubble breaks, he quickly catches the egg and replaces it in the nest. After several days the eggs begin to hatch, but the tiny fish are not yet ready to survive on their own. The male keeps the squirming fish in their bubbles for several more days. Then at just the right time, he leaves the area, allowing the tiny fish to pop out of their bubbles and swim around in search of food.

Facets of *Zoology:* *Taking Care of the Kids*

Human parents with several small children often seem to be tired. Keeping up with active youngsters is a demanding job.

Some animal parents also seem to overwork themselves taking care of their young. These animals may go for days without sufficient food, water, or rest so they can provide for their young. But for many other animals, being a parent does not require a great amount of effort. Many simply lay their eggs or give birth to their young and then leave them.

How much an animal parent cares for its young is usually related to how many young the animal has. The more eggs or offspring an animal has, the *less* likely it is to care for them. The fewer eggs an animal has, the *more* likely the animal is to care for them. Typically, when an animal has only one or two offspring, it is more likely to protect and care for its young.

In the fall a female grasshopper will lay hundreds of eggs in the soil. The parent grasshopper then abandons the eggs. The eggs will remain in the ground throughout the winter until they hatch the next spring. Though some of the eggs will die during the winter, many will survive. It is during the summer, however, that disease and predators will greatly reduce the number of grasshoppers. By the beginning of fall, only a few adult grasshoppers from the hundreds of eggs will be alive and able to lay eggs.

The female goldfish does not make a nest for her five hundred to one thousand eggs; she simply releases them in the water. The eggs float in the water and stick to nearby plants. Instead of protecting her eggs, the goldfish often eats them.

Unlike the goldfish, cichlids (SIK lidz) are a kind of freshwater fish that take care of their young. The fertilized eggs are carried in either the father's or mother's mouth until they hatch. Even after hatching, the young remain in the parent's mouth until they can swim properly. At this time the young that are cared for by a father usually leave, but those cared for by a mother often stay with their mother longer. Once mature enough to leave the mother's mouth, the young remain close to her side. If danger comes, the young are warned by their mother, and they swim into her mouth for protection. If there is not enough small food for their young, some cichlid mothers prechew the food into smaller pieces. Eventually the mother does not allow the young to enter her mouth, and the young go their own way.

Most reptile young never see their parents. Sea turtles, for instance, bury their eggs in the sand and leave them, never to return. The warmth of the earth incubates the eggs.

The eggs of some other reptiles, however, cannot survive without parental care. The Great Plains skink is

a lizard that spends much time caring for its eggs. Since the mother skink usually lays about nineteen eggs, caring for them is a full-time job.

Inside her nesting hole, the mother spends nearly all of her time guarding the eggs, turning them over, cleaning them, and trying to keep them from drying out. When the baby skinks are ready to hatch, the mother helps them out of their shells and licks them clean. Soon after hatching, the young lizards are able to take care of themselves.

Birds are good examples of parents that care for their young. A European bird similar to the chickadee makes as many as sixty feeding visits per hour to its young. Within one day this bird may make over nine hundred visits to its nest.

As a bird leaves its nest time after time, food in nearby areas becomes more difficult to find. Soon the parent birds have to fly greater distances to find enough food. The common swift travels an average of 1000 km (620 mi) per day to gather food for its young. Good thing it lives up to its name.

The bird that probably works the longest at being a good parent is the bluethroat. This bird

may work twenty out of twenty-four hours in a day to feed its family.

A baby walrus, like most mammals, depends on its mother to provide warmth, protection, food, and training. After the walrus is born, it stays with its mother for the first two years of its life. During this time the baby walrus is taught how to swim. Sitting on its mother's back and holding on with its flippers, the baby walrus learns to swim and dive properly.

The bond between the mother walrus and her baby is strong while the young walrus is dependent on its mother. The mother does not let her young out of her sight. When danger comes, the mother walrus will do whatever is necessary to protect her offspring—that includes sacrificing her own life to save her young.

Although these examples show a wide range of parenting styles and levels of involvement, they remind us that God created a way for each kind of animal to survive from one generation to the next.

Section Review 20B

1. What does *external* in external fertilization indicate?

2. What usually happens to an egg or sperm that is unfertilized?

3. What usually determines how much care an animal parent will provide for its young?

20C Internal Fertilization

If sperm are deposited inside the female's body when the eggs are ready, there is a good chance that fertilization will occur, producing a zygote. **Internal fertilization** occurs when a male's sperm and an egg unite inside a female's body. Animals that carry on internal fertilization usually produce fewer eggs and sperm than those that carry on external fertilization.

There are two main groups of animals that have internal fertilization:

- Animals that lay shelled eggs.
- Animals that give birth to live young.

Egg-laying animals have internal organs for depositing shell material around their zygotes. A zygote that has a shell around it is properly called an egg. Eventually, the egg is released from the mother's body. Inside the shell the zygote develops into a baby animal during

Objectives 20C

- Describe internal fertilization.

- Recognize the two possible definitions for *egg*.

- Give an example of an animal that exhibits internal fertilization and lays eggs.

- Describe the formation of a chicken egg.

- Give an example of an animal that exhibits internal fertilization and gives birth to live young.

- Explain the function of a placenta and an umbilical cord.

There are two different definitions for egg: (1) a female gamete and (2) a zygote surrounded by a shell.

gestation: (L. GESTATIO, to carry or to bear)

Math Connection

The average laying hen starts laying eggs at 18 weeks of age and can lay 270 eggs a year. If this hen lays eggs for a total of 4 years, how many dozens of eggs will she have produced?

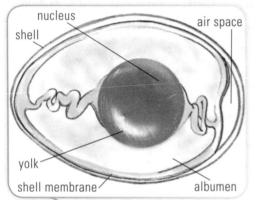

20C-1 | A bird egg

nucleus
shell
air space
yolk
shell membrane
albumen

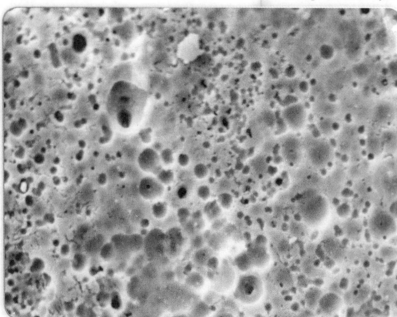

20C-2 | The porous surface of a snake eggshell (1000X)

a period of **incubation** (IN kyuh BAY shun). Incubation provides heat energy to fuel the development of the new life.

Animals that do not lay eggs give birth to live young that have developed inside their bodies. After fertilization, zygotes become temporarily attached to the female parent's **uterus** (YOO tur us). The uterus is a special structure in which the zygote develops into a baby animal. The period of time spent in the uterus is called **gestation** (jeh STAY shun). During gestation the developing animal receives nourishment from the mother's body.

20C.1 Egg-Laying Animals

Birds lay eggs coated with thick, hard shells. Reptiles lay eggs with various kinds of shells. Most snakes and turtles lay eggs with leathery shells. Alligators and crocodiles lay eggs with hard shells. Sharks and rays produce eggs in tough cases sometimes called "mermaids' purses." Although these different coatings help protect the developing animal, they are not strong enough to prevent some animals from destroying the eggs.

Egg Formation

A chicken egg develops within the mother hen for about twenty-four hours before it is laid. It begins its development in the hen's ovary and has a large quantity of yolk. The *yolk* is the stored food that the unhatched chick will use to grow. On top of the yolk is the nucleus. The nucleus contains half of the chromosomes needed to produce a new chick. In order for the egg to develop into a chick, sperm must provide the other chromosomes soon after the egg leaves the ovary. If the egg is not fertilized, the egg continues to form, but no chick will come from the egg. Chicken eggs sold at supermarkets are usually unfertilized.

After the egg is formed, it passes through a long tube that covers the egg with **albumen** (al BYOO min), or egg white. Albumen is composed mostly of water and protein. It also contains vitamins and minerals necessary for the animal's development. Next, the membranes are added to the outside of the albumen. These membranes serve as a lining membrane called the shell. Finally, the egg with the albumen and membranes enters the *shell gland*. Here the shell is added, and the egg is ready to be laid.

An eggshell has tiny pores that allow air to go in and out. This air exchange allows the unhatched animal to obtain oxygen and release carbon dioxide while it is still inside the shell. Odors can also enter the pores of unfertilized eggs. This sometimes causes eggs that have been stored alongside smelly foods to taste like those foods. Because the shells of eggs have pores, the developing young will drown if the eggs are placed in water. For this reason, sea turtles lay their eggs in sand above the high-tide water level.

Egg Incubation

After an animal's eggs have been laid, a period of incubation is necessary. During incubation most eggs must be kept warm. Animals incubate their eggs in many interesting ways. Most snakes and turtles dig holes for their eggs and then rely on the warmth from the earth and the sun for incubation. Birds use their body heat to keep their eggs warm. Crocodiles and alligators make a mound of rotting grass and leaves over their eggs. The heat given off by the rotting plants keeps the eggs warm.

King penguins incubate their eggs in an unusual way. Since nest-building materials are scarce in the Antarctic, king penguins do not make nests like other birds do. And since king penguins stand much better than they sit, they keep their single egg warm by holding it between their feet. Both parents take turns holding the egg for as long as a week at a time. This procedure continues for more than fifty days until the egg hatches. Then, it takes another twelve to fourteen months to raise the chick to maturity. Consequently, most pairs mate only two out of every three years.

Since it is ectothermic, an alligator cannot use body heat to warm its eggs. Instead, the heat produced by rotting vegetation piled up to form a nest keeps the eggs inside warm.

20C-3

Birds and most reptiles lay their eggs as soon as the eggs are ready. However, a few animals, such as some snakes, never lay their eggs. The eggs stay in a special pouch inside the mother snake. The baby snakes develop, nourished by a yolk, in the same way that they would have if the eggs had been laid. When the baby snakes hatch, they and their empty shells leave their mother's body through a special opening.

20C.2 *Placental Animals*

Most mammals produce eggs that contain little stored food. Soon after the eggs have been fertilized, they must enter the uterus and begin their gestation period, or they will die. The **embryo** (unborn animal) usually consists of several cells by the time it reaches the uterus. This undeveloped offspring becomes attached to the wall of the uterus and begins receiving nourishment from the uterus.

In time the *placenta* develops. The placenta is attached to the wall of the uterus and is the structure in which the mother's blood vessels and the embryo's blood vessels come close together. (See Fig. 18C-3, p. 327.) Nutrients and oxygen from the mother's blood enter the embryo's blood, and wastes and carbon dioxide from the embryo's blood pass into the mother's blood.

As the embryo continues to develop, it becomes attached to the placenta by a ropelike structure called the *umbilical cord*. The umbilical cord contains blood vessels that go from the heart of the embryo to the placenta and back. Around the embryo is a fluid-filled sac called the *amnion*. The fluid inside the amnion is called the *amniotic* (AM nee AHT ik) *fluid*. This fluid protects the delicate embryo while it is developing.

Penguins are endothermic and can use their body heat to keep their eggs warm. King penguins do this in the frigid Antarctic winter and without a nest.

20C-4

Great Is the Lord

Read Psalm 104:10–24. Notice how many references the psalmist makes to God's creatures, their habitats, and their young. While studying how these animals reproduce, we can praise God because "the earth is full of [His] riches" (v. 24).

Facets of *Zoology:* *Breaking the Baby Rules*

Babies on Board

After mating, the female giant water bug glues up to 150 eggs on the back of her partner. The male water bug then carries this living cargo for up to three weeks. Eggs laid on land die within a day, and those left underwater are usually killed by a water fungus.

By God's design, the male water bug divides his time between the land and underwater vegetation. This amphibious lifestyle provides just the amount of water and air the eggs need to grow properly. He also periodically strokes his legs across this "backpack" of babies in what looks like an attempt to get rid of them. These leg strokes probably prevent the fungus from developing—while aerating the eggs at the same time. The Creator has given this humble insect the exact instinctive behaviors necessary for the survival of its kind.

male water bug

Shivering Snakes

While all reptiles are considered to be ectothermic and therefore have body temperatures close to that of their environments, some have a special way of incubating their eggs. Several of the larger species of pythons lay their eggs in a mound that they then coil tightly around. By periodically quivering their muscles, some create enough heat to raise their own temperature (as well as that of the eggs) 7°C above that of their environment. The mother's body helps to hold the heat in and also discourages any predators from eating the eggs.

Dirty Birds

Typically, birds lay their eggs in a nest, tree cavity, or occasionally on the ground and then incubate them with their own body heat. Several species found in Australia and the surrounding islands, however, seem to have taken a lesson from crocodiles. The brush turkey builds a nest mound as big as 4 m (13 ft) across and 1 m (3 ft) deep. He then breeds with several females and digs holes into his mound for each to drop her eggs into. Some mounds may contain as many as fifty eggs. The moms are then free to go, but dad's work has just begun.

For the next two to three months, he tends to the nest, constantly checking the temperature by scratching a hole and inserting his heat-sensitive beak. The decomposing vegetation creates heat—enough, in fact, to cook the eggs if the heat is not released. If he finds a hot spot, his powerful, oversized feet scrape away layers of material to release the pent-up heat. When the mound starts to cool, he can reverse the process and rebuild the mound.

With all of this attention, you might think the brush turkey is a protective parent. Ironically, when the chicks finally hatch, the father leaves them to dig their way to the surface—sometimes as much as 0.7 m (2 ft)—all on their own. They then scurry into the forest where they will probably grow up without ever seeing their parents.

Mr. Mom

In sea horse families, the male, not the female, keeps the developing eggs. When the female is ready to lay her eggs, she places them in the male's pouch. As the eggs enter the pouch, the male fertilizes them. Once the eggs are in the pouch, it closes tightly. For forty to fifty days the male sea horse acts as an egg hatchery. The father's pouch begins to swell with his growing young.

male sea horse

As the time gets closer for the birth of the baby sea horses, the pouch begins to open. When the young are ready, the father releases them into the water. The giant sea horse (30 cm, or 12 in., long) releases its two hundred to seven hundred young in one big spurt. For a few seconds the cloud of babies drifts helplessly in the water. Then the tiny sea horses right themselves and swim away on their own.

These four examples display just a bit of the marvelous diversity of behaviors and lifestyles God designed for His creatures. They also remind us how little we really understand the order of nature as we constantly find exceptions to the way we expect things to work.

Serving God as a Marine Biologist

Job Description

A marine biologist may study any type of marine life from algae to whales, although most specialize in a particular kind of organism. Their jobs may include estimating populations of particular organisms, identifying or classifying organisms, assessing the impact of human activities, or studying the relationships between various living things as well as the conditions of the water in which they are found. Some manage the care of captive marine creatures. Many marine biologists also have teaching responsibilities, especially at universities.

Workplaces

research vessel, land area near marine environments, research lab, aquaculture farm, aquarium, marine park, or zoo

Education

A minimum of a bachelor's degree is expected, and most positions require a master's degree. Most marine biologists involved in research have a doctorate degree in their specialty.

Dominion Opportunities

Biologists studying marine ecology act as stewards of God's creation by making recommendations that can maximize the yield from marine resources such as shrimp and fish, while preserving strong populations for the future. By learning more about the nature of marine life and sharing that knowledge, marine biologists help others recognize the fascinating and complex relationships seen in God's underwater world "wherein are things creeping innumerable, both small and great beasts" (Ps. 104:25).

While the embryo is in the uterus, the mother is **pregnant**. The length of pregnancy ranges from about 13 days for the opossum to 645 days for the elephant. Pregnancy ends with the *birth* of the baby animal.

Usually those animals that remain in the uterus for longer periods of time are more developed and better able to take care of themselves when born. Many mammals with long gestation periods are able to move around on their own just a few hours after birth. A foal of a horse spends eleven months in the uterus. Within an hour of birth, the foal can stand on its wobbly legs, and just a few hours later it can follow its mother. Baby rats are born after a twenty-two-day gestation period. Born blind and without fur, they require weeks of additional development before they are ready to leave the nest.

Section Review 20C

1. Where exactly does gestation occur?

2. Why do eggshells have pores?

3. How do alligators and crocodiles keep their eggs warm?

4. What function does the umbilical cord have?

5. Generally, what effect does the length of pregnancy have on a baby animal?

What Do You Think?

Why do you think baby opossums are born after only 13 days in the uterus?

Some animals such as these Grant's gazelles must be ready to run soon after they are born in order to escape predators.

20C-5

Scientifically Speaking

egg

sperm

ovary

testis

fertilization

external fertilization

internal fertilization

incubation

uterus

gestation

albumen

embryo

pregnant

Chapter Review

1. What special cells transfer or receive chromosomes during sexual reproduction?

2. If an organism has 20 chromosomes, how many will each of its gametes have?

3. What name is given to the reproductive cells produced by males?

4. What name is given to the process by which gametes are united?

5. Give an example of an organism that has external fertilization.

6. Would you expect an animal that produces one offspring at a time to provide more care or less care for its offspring than does an animal that produces a thousand offspring at a time?

7. What is the term for the period of development when the zygote is in the uterus?

8. What is the main purpose of an egg's yolk?

9. What part of an egg supplies the water, vitamins, and minerals needed by the developing organism?

10. What is the structure in most mammals that is used to exchange materials between the mother's blood and the embryo's blood?

What Did You Learn?

1. Would you expect a zygote to be diploid or haploid? Why?

2. What purpose is served by the excessive number of gametes that are produced by animals that have external fertilization?

3. How are incubation and gestation similar?

4. Why would it be foolish to keep eggs warm by keeping them submerged in warm water?

Self Quiz 20

_____ 1. A cat has 38 chromosomes; therefore, its sperm cells would contain
A. 19 chromosomes.
B. 38 chromosomes.
C. 76 chromosomes.
D. none of these

_____ 2. The immediate result of fertilization is
A. a zygote.
B. a single cell.
C. a diploid cell.
D. all of these

_____ 3. Gametes are special cells that are most important for
A. growth.
B. reproduction.
C. digestion.
D. movement.

_____ 4. _____ fertilization usually occurs in water.
A. Gestational
B. Internal
C. External
D. Amniotic

5. The process in which a female fish releases eggs and a male fertilizes them is called

_____.

_____ 6. Gestation is a process that occurs inside the
A. egg.
B. uterus.
C. zygote.
D. ovary.

_____ 7. A chicken egg must be fertilized before the shell is formed or it will not hatch. (True/False)

_____ 8. Which of these is *not* found in a bird egg?
A. yolk
B. albumen
C. umbilical cord
D. nucleus

_____ 9. Which of the following is *not* exchanged between the mother and the embryo?
A. blood
B. nutrients
C. oxygen
D. wastes

_____ 10. The embryo is attached to the placenta by the
A. amnion.
B. yolk.
C. uterine cord.
D. umbilical cord.

THE NATURE OF THE
ENVIRONMENT

THE ECOSYSTEM

In flight school, student pilots study how airplanes work. But knowledge of airplanes alone is not enough to pass the written portion of the pilot's test. They must also learn about weather conditions, fuel consumption, visual flight regulations, and how to file a flight plan. Becoming a pilot requires that one understand how a pilot and airplane are affected by, and should respond to, their surroundings.

The same is true when studying a living thing. The organism alone is not the whole picture. How it interacts with its surroundings is as important as its individual traits.

The study of organisms in their habitats is called **ecology**. People who study ecology, *ecologists*, often divide ecology into three relationships:

- How organisms affect each other
- How the nonliving factors of an environment (such as light, temperature, water, soil, and wind) affect an organism
- How organisms affect the nonliving factors of a habitat

For example, an ecologist studying frogs could study these three relationships in the following ways. He might study the types of insects frogs eat and how they respond when their usual food is not available. He also might study how frogs respond to the temperatures during a day or how frogs' wastes affect the purity of the water. The ecologist can use the data he gains from each of these studies to learn how frogs live in their environment.

ecology: eco- (Gk. οικος, house) + -ology (E., the study of)

By studying frogs and their environment, you would begin to realize that the ecology of an area is very complex. Because of this complexity, Christians must study ecology seriously if they are to exercise wise dominion over God's creation (Gen. 1:26–28). As this chapter describes how ecosystems work, think of how this knowledge affects you and your responsibilities. Good stewardship demands a good understanding of our natural resources, and a study of ecology can provide that.

21A Ecosystems

Ecologists normally study ecosystems. An **ecosystem** is a limited area in which living and nonliving things interact. A meadow is an example of an ecosystem. A meadow has living things such as grasshoppers, grass, birds, worms, and flowers. It also has nonliving things such as sunlight, air, water, and rocks. In the meadow all these things interact.

Ecosystems are made up of two major parts: the **abiotic** (A bye AHT ik) **environment** and the **biotic** (bye AHT ik) **community**. The abiotic, or physical, environment is all the nonliving factors in an ecosystem. The biotic community is all the living organisms in an ecosystem. A pond, a forest, a lake, and a beach are other examples of ecosystems. Some manmade ecosystems include a farmer's field, a school yard, and a golf course.

Although some ecosystems are quite large, scientists usually divide them into workable units. A river is a large ecosystem, but an ecologist can divide it into several small ecosystems. This division makes the river easier to study. For instance, an ecologist might use the speed and depth of the water to form smaller ecosystems. He could then study a shallow, fast-flowing water ecosystem; a shallow, slow-flowing water ecosystem; a deep, fast-flowing water ecosystem; and so on. Although these ecosystems are all part of the river, each one has its own unique abiotic environment and biotic community.

The area where an organism lives is often only a part of an ecosystem. This area is called its **habitat** (HAB ih TAT). Normally a habitat provides the right living conditions for an organism. An earthworm's habitat is moist, rich soil, and a grasshopper's habitat is sunny and warm with lots of plants.

A habitat supplies the organism's needs, which include food, water, oxygen, shelter, and more. If even one need is absent or limited, the organism will likely move to another area or adjust to its habitat. Some organisms, however, do neither and eventually die off.

Living things are not separate from their environments and ecosystems; they are part of them. Each living thing has roles to play or

21A-1 A large ecosystem such as a river is better studied by dividing it into several smaller ecosystems. What smaller ecosystems do you think compose this river?

jobs to do. What an organism does is its **niche** (NICH). For example, a woodpecker may consume insects, add wastes to the environment, and be food for both lice and hawks. It also affects trees by pecking holes for feeding and nesting. If the bird did not perform these roles, the ecosystem would not be the same.

To understand how an ecosystem works, you will first study an aquarium. An aquarium is a relatively simple ecosystem. Although it is an *artificial* (manmade) *ecosystem*, it has all the basic parts and functions of a natural one. The water, the air bubbling through the water, the filtering system, the chemicals in the water, and the light it receives are all factors in the aquarium's abiotic environment. The various fish, snails, algae, plants, fungi, protozoans, and bacteria are all organisms in its biotic community.

Section Review 21A

1. Give an example of an artificial or manmade ecosystem.

2. The area of an ecosystem where an organism lives is called

   its _____.

3. What is a niche?

21B The Abiotic Environment of Ecosystems

Anyone who has kept an aquarium is aware that it is difficult to maintain the proper physical conditions inside the tank. One factor of the abiotic environment you must control in an aquarium is temperature. If the water gets too cold or too hot, the fish may die. Most aquariums have a heater with a thermostat to keep the water at the proper temperature.

Light is another important factor in an aquarium's abiotic environment. If the aquarium does not get enough light, the plants will not grow. If it gets too much light, algae may grow too rapidly, coating the glass and almost everything in the tank. One way you can control algae is to periodically scrape the glass, scrub the rocks, and clean the filter.

Another way you can control algae is to put chemicals that reduce algal growth into the water. These chemicals, however, may hamper the growth of the plants. Putting snails or algae-eating fish into the tank is a third method of algal control. But some snails reproduce so rapidly that they upset the ecosystem's balance. They can become a greater problem than the algae. The algae-eating fish also can upset the balance by eating not only the algae in the aquarium but also all the plants.

Whatever method you use to control the algae, you have to *do* something to control it. Because your actions have an effect on the aquarium, *you* are also a factor in the ecosystem even though you remain outside. One of the difficulties that ecologists face in their studies is the effect of outside factors on an ecosystem.

> **Objectives 21B**
> - Define *abiotic environment* and list several environmental factors.
> - Trace the water cycle.
> - Describe succession in an ecosystem.
> - Define *climax community* and *pioneer species*.

What are the abiotic factors in this aquarium ecosystem?

21B-1

21B-2 In many ecosystems, fire is a regular and normal part of the abiotic environment.

21B-3 Describe some of the factors of the abiotic environment that make this area a tropical rainforest.

Great Is the Lord

Look up Psalm 135:5–7, and as you read, notice which specific aspects of the ecosystem God superintends. Truly, "the Lord is great . . . [He] is above all gods" (v. 5).

21B.1 Abiotic Environment Factors

Many different factors influence the abiotic environment. Some ecosystems have more factors than others. For example, fire is not usually a factor in an ocean or a desert. In some forests and grasslands, however, fire is a significant factor. Although it is destructive, fire is beneficial to some forests because it destroys harmful plants and insects. It is also necessary for the germination of certain seeds.

In most ecosystems there are five major abiotic factors: light, temperature, water, soil and substrate, and wind or current.

Light. The amount of light an area receives affects what kind of plants will live in that ecosystem. Intensity (the amount of light at a particular time) and duration (the amount of time the light is available) are both important to many plant and animal species in an ecosystem.

Temperature. The earth's ecosystems have temperatures that range from well below freezing to near boiling. (Certain hot springs have bacteria and algae growing in them.) The more populated ecosystems do not usually have such extreme temperatures, but many of them do have a wide variety of temperatures. For example, some highly populated ecosystems have temperatures between midday and midnight that may differ by more than 14°C (25°F). Many of them also have seasons (summer vs. winter) with even greater temperature differences.

Water. The primary difference among many of the world's ecosystems is the amount of water they contain. Some deserts would be green tropical forests if only they had more rain. The time of year when the rain falls also affects the ecosystem. An area with a wet summer, for instance, will have a different ecosystem than an area with a dry summer and a wet winter will have.

There are also many *aquatic ecosystems.* Aquatic ecosystems have large amounts of water in them. Ponds, streams, rivers, coral reefs, tidal pools, ocean shores, salt marshes, lakes, and swamps are all different aquatic ecosystems.

Soil and substrate. Not all soils are alike. Soils contain varying amounts of sand, clay, silt, and *humus* (HYOO mus). Humus is made of decaying plant and animal materials. Some soils contain chemicals that other soils may lack. Below the soil is the *substrate.* The substrate is usually made up of rock, clay, or both. The bottom of a body of water is also called a substrate. Substrates supply chemicals to the soil or water above them. These chemicals serve as nutrients that may permit certain species (but not others) to live in an ecosystem.

Wind or current. The wind is often an important factor that determines which species can live in an ecosystem. The strong wind in some ecosystems makes it difficult for certain species to survive. Wind also mixes and moves gases such as oxygen and carbon diox-

Thinking Critically About Life Science: *Bar Charts*

Often textbooks, newspapers, encyclopedias, and student reports include detailed information that is difficult to understand in sentence form. (The measurements given in the following lab report are an example of this.) This same information could be presented in other ways that are easier to understand. One such way is a bar chart. You need to learn how to read and make bar charts. Read the bar chart below; then read the student report.

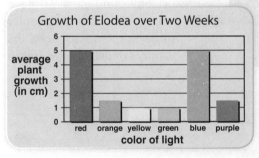

Growth of Elodea over Two Weeks

Student Report:
Elodea Light Experiment

In this experiment, twenty-four pieces of an aquarium plant called elodea were grown in six different colors of light (four pieces per color). The goal of the experiment was to determine whether one color of light would make the plants grow better. The colors of lights used were red, orange, yellow,

green, blue, and purple. The plants were first measured and then placed in an aquarium illuminated with one colored light bulb. After growing for two weeks in the colored light, the plants were again measured.

The four plants in the red light had grown 7, 4, 6, and 3 cm. The four plants in the orange light had grown 1, 2, 2, and 1 cm. The four plants in the yellow light had grown 1, 0, 2, and 1 cm. The four plants in the green light had grown 1, 0, 0, and 3 cm. The four plants in the blue light had grown 5, 6, 5, and 4 cm. The four plants in the purple light had grown 2, 2, 1, and 1 cm.

Both the second paragraph of the student report and the bar chart give the information needed to tell which colors of light promoted growth. Based on the paragraph, what color(s) of light promoted growth? Based on the bar chart, what color(s) of light promoted growth? Which method allowed you to answer the question more easily and quickly, the bar chart or the paragraph? Was the use of the average values in the bar chart helpful? If the paragraph had given the average values, would it have been easier to read than the bar chart?

When making a bar chart, it is important to label the axes. What are the two axes of the bar chart? How are they labeled? How are units of measurement indicated? Charts usually include a caption that gives additional information about the chart. What additional information was given in the caption of the bar chart?

Make a bar chart presenting the information found in the paragraph below. Label the axes correctly, indicate the units used, and include a caption.

"A new crop plant called 'tasty veggie' was planted in twenty fields in Iowa, Oregon, Pennsylvania, and Georgia (five fields in each state) to determine the area of the country in which this crop would grow best. In Iowa the crop produced 30, 23, 50, 43, and 34 bushels per hectare. In Oregon the crop produced 23, 22, 10, 25, and 20 bushels per hectare. In Pennsylvania the crop produced 12, 21, 10, 17, and 20 bushels per hectare. In Georgia the crop produced 54, 49, 60, 55, and 62 bushels per hectare."

A hectare (HEK TARE) is a metric unit of area. It is equal to about 2.5 acres.

ide. In an aquatic ecosystem, most movement comes from the action of water currents rather than from the wind. Currents in the ocean or even in a small stream can affect oxygen levels, temperature, and nutrient levels.

21B.2 *The Water Cycle*

Various abiotic factors of the environment work together in different combinations to determine what an area will be like. The water cycle illustrates how several of these factors work together.

The **water cycle** is the continuous movement of water from the atmosphere to the earth and back to the atmosphere. Changes in water

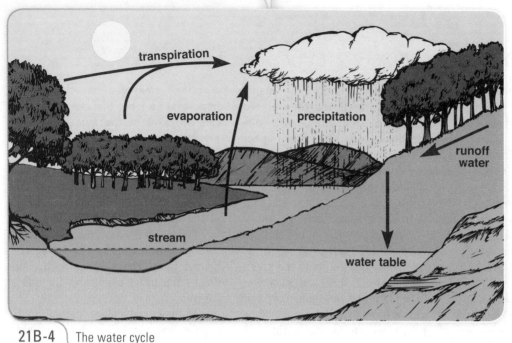

transpiration

evaporation

precipitation

runoff water

stream

water table

21B-4 The water cycle

temperature produce two main stages in the water cycle: evaporation and precipitation.

Evaporation. The movement of water from the earth to the atmosphere is **evaporation** (ih VAP uh RAY shun). It is affected by temperature, wind, and the amount of water already in the air. Most evaporation takes place from the surface of the ocean and other bodies of water. Evaporation also takes place as soil and other wet substances dry.

Precipitation. As water evaporates, it enters the air as *water vapor*. When the wind or convection currents move warm, moist air to a cooler place in the atmosphere, the vapor condenses to liquid

Facets of *Ecology:* Succession in Ecosystems

Beavers build dams on streams. When the water accumulates behind the dam, it forms a pond where the beavers build their homes. As the water floods an area of forest, it kills a part of the forest's biotic community. Yet the flooding also establishes a different habitat for the pond's biotic community.

Shortly after the pond forms, it becomes the home of various aquatic algae, protozoans, and other microscopic organisms. Soon frogs, aquatic plants such as elodea and cattails, and aquatic insects begin to live along the edges of the pond. In time, animals such as fish, turtles, ducks, and herons will also live in or around the edge of the pond.

As the stream flows into the pond, it carries in different materials such as silt, soil, and sand. Tree leaves and other dead materials also fall into the pond. As these materials collect on the bottom, the pond becomes shallower. In time the pond will no longer provide a suitable habitat for the pond organisms, and they will either leave or die out.

As the pond gets smaller, water lilies, which usually grow in shallow water, begin to cover the surface of the pond. Soon young trees sprout along the edge of the pond on land once covered with water. Depending on the size of the pond and how fast it fills in, the forest may replace the pond in a few dozen or a few hundred years.

The stable population of plants and animals found in an area if it is left undisturbed for a long period is called a *climax community*. In the pond example above, a forest is the climax community. Every area has a climax community. These climax communities are relatively stable.

In other words, new species rarely enter a climax community, and the ones present rarely die out.

Occasionally a natural disaster such as a fire, flood, avalanche, volcano, or earthquake will destroy a climax community. Sometimes various organisms (such as the beavers in the earlier example) can destroy climax communities. Human technology

(such as building) also can destroy climax communities.

When a climax community is destroyed, the area usually does not reestablish its climax community immediately. Instead, the area goes through succession (suk SESH un). **Succession** is a series of changes that occur in biotic communities as they progress toward a climax community.

The organisms that live in an area in the early stages of succession are called *pioneer species*. In the case of the beaver pond, the aquatic plants and the microscopic organisms in the water are the pioneer species.

Pioneer species alter the habitat. This change makes the habitat ideal for the next set of species to come and live in the area. As the new species change the area, the pioneer species begin to die off. This succession of biotic communities continues until the climax community gets established.

Krakatoa (JQ@J uh TOH uh) is a volcanic island near Java in Southeast Asia. In 1883 the volcano erupted and destroyed the tropical jungle on the once again. This atmospheric water that falls back to earth is called **precipitation** (prih SIP uh TAY shun). Rain, snow, sleet, and hail are all forms of precipitation.

When precipitation reaches the ground, it either seeps into the soil or moves along the surface of the earth. The water that moves along the surface is called *runoff*. Runoff usually collects in streams and rivers, which eventually reach the ocean.

Precipitation that enters the soil is called *groundwater*. This water helps keep the soil moist and dissolves some of the materials of the substrate. The plants use this water with the dissolved substrate materials to help them grow. Of all the groundwater a plant absorbs from the soil, very little remains in the plant. Most of the water passes from the plant into the atmosphere. (See transpiration, pp. 184–85.)

Gravity pulls the rest of the groundwater down until it cannot go any deeper. Usually a rock layer stops the water. In some areas the water travels only a few meters below the surface of the soil. In other areas the water may continue several hundred meters before it reaches a layer that stops it. As the groundwater collects in the earth, it forms a reservoir called the **water table**. Depending on the amount of precipitation and the type of soil an area has, a water table may hold a few meters to hundreds of meters of water.

island. Hundreds of meters of volcanic debris covered the entire island and destroyed everything, including the soil.

After the eruption stopped on the island, algae and lichens were blown in by the wind and began to grow. When these pioneer species died, they formed a base on which the spores of mosses and ferns could germinate.

As mosses and ferns grew and died, they formed a soil in which the seeds of other plants could germinate. Eventually, coconut palm seeds floated ashore, and the seeds of wild sugar cane and orchids were blown to the island. After these seeds sprouted, they grew to form large populations.

As the pioneer plants grew, the habitat became favorable for various animals. Certain birds and flying insects were among the first animals that returned to the island. Later, other insects and birds, along with snakes and lizards, came to Krakatoa. Some of these animals flew, others swam, and some were blown there during storms. After fifty years of succession, about twelve hundred species were living on the island. Krakatoa was well on its way to reaching its climax community.

It is quite common for humans to alter an area and establish a certain biotic community. This occurs, for example, when a hardwood forest is cleared to make way for a golf course. As long as man prevents succession from taking place, his biotic community will remain.

To prevent succession of the golf course, someone must cut the grass, pull the weeds, trim the shrubs, and otherwise tend the newly established biotic community. If no one tended the golf course, weeds would begin to grow, then shrubs, then pine trees. Finally in about one hundred fifty years, the hardwood trees would reclaim the area.

Beaver pond succession

The water cycle is a good example of the cyclic (SY klik) nature of some materials in a natural ecosystem. *Cyclic* means "occurring in cycles." In nature this means that materials are used and reused, sometimes in the same form, and sometimes in a changed form. A molecule of water may pass through the water cycle many times without changing. Later in this chapter you will study some other examples of natural cycles in which elements form different compounds as they move through ecosystems.

Section Review 21B

1. What two qualities of light should be considered when studying an ecosystem?

2. How can soil affect an ecosystem?

3. How can water enter the atmosphere in the water cycle?

4. _____ is a series of changes in a biotic community that progress toward a climax community.

5. What term describes water in the soil that is available for plants to use?

21C The Biotic Community

The biotic community is made up of all the living things in an ecosystem. In an aquarium, the fish, snails, and plants are the obvious members of the biotic community. However, the biotic community of an aquarium also includes many unseen organisms. For example, in the water and gravel of the aquarium live many algae, bacteria, fungi, and protozoans. There are also smaller organisms, such as tapeworms and protozoans, that live inside the fish and other organisms.

The unseen members of a biotic community often outnumber the more obvious members. For example, a single shovelful of soil taken from a meadow may contain hundreds of different species. Each of those species may be represented by thousands of individuals.

Natural ecosystems are much more complex than artificial ones such as the aquarium. Often scientists must include species that do not live in a particular natural ecosystem as part of that ecosystem. For example, owls may nest in a forest and hunt in a meadow. Because the owl has an effect on the meadow's biotic community, it must be included as part of the meadow's ecosystem even though it does not live there. The mice the owl catches in the meadow then would have an impact on the forest ecosystem since they are a source of incoming energy. In addition, their indigestible remains may be deposited there.

21C.1 *Levels of Organization*

God's creation is highly organized, and recognizing levels of organization within creation is important to the study of biotic communities. At the most basic level is the *individual* organism. All the individuals from the same species in an ecosystem make up a **popu-**

Objectives 21C

- Define *biotic community*.
- Explain the roles of producer organisms and consumer organisms and give examples of each.
- Trace ways in which carbon, oxygen, and nitrogen move through an ecosystem.
- Define *limiting factors* and give examples.

lation. Because no population exists alone, we can study its *community*, which is all the populations in a given area. The term *ecosystem*, introduced in Section 21A, is a biotic community plus the abiotic environment it inhabits. Figure 21C-1 shows the relationship of these terms using our aquarium example.

21C.2 *Population Types*

The populations in a biotic community can be divided into two main types: producer organisms and consumer organisms.

Producer organisms manufacture their own food. Green plants and algae are the most common producer organisms. These organisms carry on *photosynthesis* (see pp. 71–73), a process that converts the energy of sunlight into the stored energy found in sugar. Producers use this sugar as their food source.

Consumer organisms cannot manufacture food; they must obtain their energy from other sources. Consumer organisms usually obtain their energy by eating other organisms. A rabbit eating grass and bacteria breaking down a leaf are good examples of consumers obtaining energy from producers. An eagle eating a rabbit is an example of a consumer obtaining energy from another consumer.

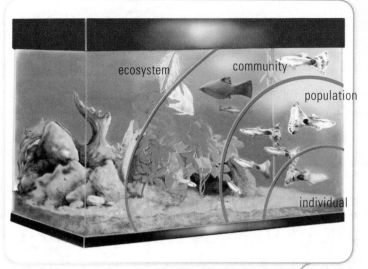

Levels of organization in an aquarium **21C-1**

Let Them Have Dominion

In Genesis 1:29–31 and 2:18–22, what relationship do animals have with one another and the rest of creation? What about man's relationship to animals? How did this relationship change after the Fall (Gen. 3:21; 9:2–4)? How might this influence our study of the ecosystem?

Facets of *Ecology:* Limiting Factors

In 1670 the English Crown gave permission to the Hudson Bay Company to use a large tract of Canada for fur trapping. Each year the company kept careful records of the animal furs they took. From these records scientists believe they can see changes in the size of different animal populations.

Often the changes in animal populations occurred in ten-year cycles. For example, from 1885 to 1895 the number of furs taken from the snowshoe rabbit fluctuated between 135,000 and 20,000. During the same period the number of furs taken from the Canadian lynx changed similarly, fluctuating between 75,000 and 8,000. The lynx population, however, usually rose and fell a year or so after that of the rabbit.

One reason for these changes is that the snowshoe rabbit is the primary food source for the Canadian lynx. When the rabbits are abundant, there is more food for a growing lynx population. When the rabbits are scarce, the lynxes have a more difficult time finding food and fewer can survive.

In time you might expect the rabbit and lynx populations to reach a certain size and stop fluctuating. Yet the cycle seems to be continuous. Because rabbits produce many young, the size of their population tends to increase. If the rabbit population increases so much that they become overcrowded, the stress from this situation causes their livers to stop functioning correctly. This liver disorder kills some rabbits and makes many others easy prey for the lynxes.

With so much available food, the lynx population soon begins to increase. Eventually the lynxes take care of the surplus of weak rabbits. Meanwhile, the rabbit population has taken a sudden drop, and there is not enough food to continue supplying the large lynx population.

Since the lynxes cannot find enough food, some die of starvation.

Limiting Factors (cont.)

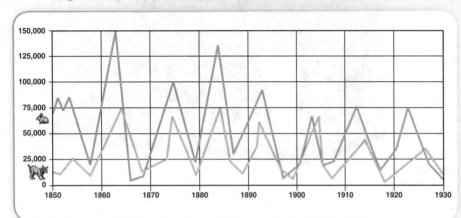

Those that do remain are poorly fed and produce fewer young. This sudden decline in the lynx population, as well as the uncrowded conditions among the rabbits, allows the rabbit population to increase, and the cycle starts over.

In the above example, limiting factors control the size of both the lynx and the rabbit populations. A *limiting factor* is a factor in a habitat that limits the growth or existence of a species. The limiting factor for the lynx population is the size of the snowshoe rabbit population. The limiting factors for the rabbit population are overcrowding and the size of the lynx population.

Often a characteristic of an abiotic environment is also a limiting factor. For instance, the high winds that sweep down some mountainsides are a limiting factor for tree growth. To see how removing this factor would affect the trees, some scientists built high walls on certain mountain slopes. The walls protected some trees but left others unprotected. Those trees that were unprotected grew only a few meters. Those in the protected areas grew as high as the wall.

Traveling west from the Mississippi River to Colorado, you could observe the effect of water as a limiting factor for plant growth. Near the Mississippi River there is enough annual rainfall in the area to supply water for tree growth. As you travel west, the annual amount of rainfall decreases. Instead of forests there are fields of tall grasses. These tall grasses require less water than the trees require.

As you continue west, there is even less rainfall, and short grasses that require less water replace the tall grasses. But in some areas of the West, there is so little rain that even short grasses cannot grow. In these desert areas only cacti and a few other plants that require very little water can survive.

Sometimes a limiting factor for a species is not obvious. Certain kinds of orchids, for instance, grow very well in bright, sunlit greenhouses. However, in their tropical home these orchids normally grow in the shade. Scientists eventually discovered that these orchids grow in the shade because they cannot tolerate the heat of the tropical sun. Heat, not light, is the limiting factor for the orchid.

In the past, American robins traveled to the deep South only in the winter. Scientists thought that robins limited their stay because the southern temperatures were too high for the robins to nest. But today American robins nest in southern Georgia, Alabama, and along the Gulf of Mexico in Mississippi, Louisiana, and Texas. Since the temperature in these areas has not changed, heat was not the limiting factor.

Scientists discovered that as cities and suburbs expanded in the South, the robins were extending their nesting areas. They also found that

Old robin nesting area

Modern robin nesting area

there was more available food for the robins in these areas than in the undeveloped areas. This meant that food had probably been the limiting factor in the natural ecosystem. With the growth of cities and suburbs in the South, food was no longer a limiting factor, and the robins began to fill the available space.

Spiritual growth can also have limiting factors. Are there any in your life? Can you identify what they are? Make a list of possible limiting factors and then ask God to help you overcome them.

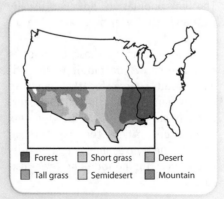

Forest   Short grass   Desert

Tall grass   Semidesert   Mountain

21C.3 *The Carbon and Oxygen Cycles*

The **carbon** and **oxygen cycles** show one way in which the physical environment and different populations of the biotic community work together in an ecosystem. These cycles use two major biological processes: photosynthesis and cellular respiration. (See pp. 69–73.) In these related cycles, the two gases oxygen (O_2) and carbon dioxide (CO_2) pass back and forth between photosynthesis and cellular respiration. The repeated exchange of these gases is a cyclic process.

In an ecosystem the plant and algae populations carry on photosynthesis. During photosynthesis these organisms take in carbon dioxide, give off oxygen, and store light energy as sugar (which contains carbon). Cellular respiration, however, takes place in *all* the organisms. Generally, during cellular respiration an organism combines sugar with oxygen and releases water, carbon dioxide, and energy. The cells of the organism use the energy to perform their functions. The carbon dioxide and water pass into the atmosphere, and the process begins again.

Aquatic ecosystems also use the same cycles. Water has both carbon dioxide and oxygen dissolved in it. The plants and algae use the carbon dioxide in the water and release oxygen as a product. Both the plants and animals complete the cycle by using the oxygen in the water and releasing carbon dioxide.

In some aquatic ecosystems, there may not be enough plants and algae to supply the oxygen needed by the entire biotic community. Additional oxygen from the atmosphere can enter through the surface of the water. But some aquatic ecosystems, like the aquarium, may lack enough surface area to absorb additional oxygen. One method of supplying the biotic community of an aquarium with enough oxygen is bubbling air into the water in the tank.

Which is a producer and which is a consumer? **21C-2**

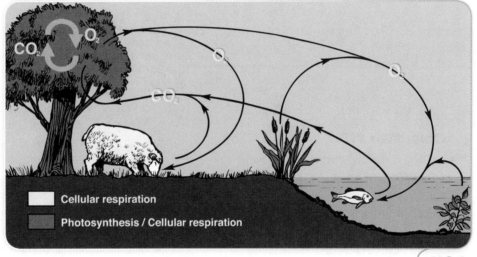

☐	Cellular respiration
■	Photosynthesis / Cellular respiration

The carbon and oxygen cycles **21C-3**

21C.4 *The Nitrogen Cycle*

All living things need nitrogen to survive and reproduce. Seventy-eight percent of the atmosphere is nitrogen, but living things cannot use nitrogen in its gaseous form (N_2). Providentially, God designed processes for converting some of that nitrogen into usable compounds. Considered together, these processes are called the **nitrogen cycle**.

A small amount of nitrogen is combined into a useful compound with oxygen when a lightning bolt passes through the air. This useful nitrogen is then absorbed by raindrops that carry it into the soil. A greater amount of nitrogen is made available by special soil or root bacteria that can turn gaseous nitrogen into a useful form.

Once the nitrogen in the soil is in the form of nitrates (NO_3^-), plants can use it to help them grow. When animals eat these plants

What Do You Think?

If all animals need nitrogen to survive, and plant eaters get nitrogen from plants, where do meat eaters get their nitrogen?

the nitrogen (now in larger compounds called proteins) is taken in by animals that can digest it for use in their own bodies. The waste from these animals is then broken down by soil bacteria to eventually become useful nitrates once again. Other bacteria in the soil are able to convert the nitrogen from these other compounds back into gaseous nitrogen (N_2) so that the cycle can continue.

Section Review 21C

1. From what process do producer organisms ultimately get their energy?

2. Name a producer organism you would expect to find in an ecosystem in your home state. Name a consumer organism in your state.

3. What are the limiting factors for the snowshoe rabbit population in Canada?

4. Which two major biological processes drive the carbon and oxygen cycles?

5. What role do bacteria play in the nitrogen cycle?

21D Rhythms in the Ecosystem

Imagine that you are on a camping trip. Just before dawn you wake up and poke your head out of the tent to see what is going on. The first thing you hear is a high-pitched cricket chorus giving a free concert. As you listen, you notice a mother skunk traveling with her two young. They have been in the meadow all night gathering food. Now the mother is leading them to their den in the woods.

As dawn comes you notice that birds begin to sing, replacing the cricket chorus. All around you animals are beginning to start their daily activities. On a nearby leaf a butterfly flaps its wings a few times and begins flying across a group of poppies that have reopened their petals for the day. Soon bees will begin to visit the poppies' black centers. A squirrel scampers headfirst down a tree. After pausing several times on the way, it scampers into the meadow, looking for food. Suddenly, a red-tailed hawk swoops down, causing the squirrel to scurry back toward the tree and jump to the other side of the trunk. A rabbit, finishing a meal of tender leaves, sees the hawk and races toward its burrow, but it is not fast enough. Effortlessly the hawk picks up the rabbit with its talons and flies toward its nest to feed its hungry young. In a short time you have seen how different populations are active at different times.

21D.1 *God-Designed Rhythms*

In many ecosystems, such as this meadow, not all the populations are active at the same time. The changes that happen on a regular basis in an ecosystem are called **rhythms**. The most obvious rhythms are daily rhythms, lasting twenty-four hours, and seasonal rhythms, which repeat every year. During the fourth day of Creation (Gen.

Objectives 21D

- List several types of rhythms found in an ecosystem and explain their importance.
- Identify several ways in which plants survive seasonal rhythms.
- Identify several ways in which animals survive seasonal rhythms.

21D-1 What rhythms do you think regularly occur in this campground?

1:14–19), God established these two types of rhythms. After the Flood, God smelled the sweet odor of Noah's sacrifice and promised, "While the earth remaineth, seedtime and harvest, and cold and heat, and summer and winter, and day and night shall not cease" (Gen. 8:22). Since God established the rhythms and created the biotic communities they affect, it is not surprising that they all work together with remarkable precision.

To evolutionists, however, the inner workings of an ecosystem are examples of evolution. They believe that organisms "adapt" to the various "problems" and "opportunities" of rhythmic changes by developing new features or characteristics. But an organism does not adapt to its habitat by developing new characteristics. Instead, it can *adjust* its behavior to various differences in its habitat. For example, a bird that finds itself in an area which does not have its usual food may adjust by eating a similar food that is available. However, the organism is not evolving; it is merely adjusting to its environment. This type of adjustment is not evolution. Biological evolution requires a new characteristic that is passed on to future generations. (See p. 137.)

21D.2 *Circadian Rhythms*

The changes in the meadow that were described in the opening paragraphs of this section are part of a **circadian** (sur KAY dee un) **rhythm**. A circadian, or daily, rhythm is a change that takes place during one twenty-four hour period. In the meadow example, the **nocturnal** (nahk TUR nul) species were entering a period of rest while the **diurnal** (dye UR nul) species were entering a period of activity.

In some ecosystems the difference between diurnal and nocturnal activity is even more drastic than in the meadow. In many deserts the high daytime temperatures permit little activity. During the day most desert animals rest under rocks or in other shady places away from the direct rays of the sun. At night, however, when the desert cools, insects, spiders, lizards, snakes, and other populations enter their period of activity. Even the plants operate differently in the desert. Most cactus flowers develop during daylight hours. However, some cactus flowers open only at night and are pollinated by bats, moths, and other nocturnal insects. Nighttime blooming apparently allows those cactuses to avoid the heat and water stress of the day.

The rhythmic activities are reversed in many colder habitats. On high mountains or various near-arctic regions, most animals sleep during the cold night hours. As the temperature climbs during the day, the insects, birds, small mammals, and members of other populations become active.

The daily rhythmic activity of the desert and arctic climates seems to protect organisms from extremes in temperature.

circadian: circa- (L. CIRCA, around) + -dian (L. DIES, day)

nocturnal: (L. NOCTURNUS, night)

diurnal: (L. DIURNUS, day)

The saw-whet owl is a nocturnal predator of mice and other small rodents. Its large eyes help it to see in dim light. **21D-2**

Morning glories exhibit a circadian rhythm. They are open in the early morning (left) but are closed during the rest of the day (right). **21D-3**

The daily rhythms in a meadow, however, serve other functions, such as permitting various populations to live in the same habitat without competing with each other. For example, if hawks and owls were both active at the same time, they would hunt the same organisms. However, since one is diurnal and the other nocturnal, they do not compete for the same food.

21D.3 *Biological Clocks*

It would seem logical to think that the presence or absence of light is what triggers daily biological rhythms. Yet many organisms that have daily rhythms seem to have an internal clock that triggers their changes. This *biological clock* appears to work with or without daily light changes.

Scientists tested the biological clock of a chicken by taking a chicken out of its normal environment and placing it in an area where there was constant light. In spite of its new environment, the chicken maintained its normal periods of activity because of its biological clock. When the scientists put the chicken in constant darkness, it responded in the same way.

Plants also have biological clocks. Tulips normally open their petals in the morning and close them in the evening. A tulip placed in a dark room will open and close its petals at the normal time and will continue to do so for several days. If a tulip is placed in an area where the light and the dark periods are exactly reversed, the plant will begin to adjust to the new schedule. It appears that the biological clocks of some organisms can be "reset."

21D.4 *Seasonal Rhythms*

A **seasonal rhythm** is a change in the ecosystem that occurs with the change of season (usually once per year). For example, in some extreme ecosystems there may be a difference of over 60°C (108°F) between a year's high and low temperatures. An organism that lives the entire year in such an ecosystem must be able to cope with these temperature differences. There are other ecosystems that have a rainy season that lasts for several months. After the rainy season is over, there usually comes a dry season that may have no rain for several months. Organisms living in this type of ecosystem must be able to use the water when it is available and still survive the dry season.

Temperature changes and the amount of water available are two of many factors that change seasonally. These seasonal rhythms have a noticeable effect on the biotic community of an ecosystem.

Considering again the meadow ecosystem, we can see how God has given

21D-4 The seasonal rhythms of abiotic environments cause some ecosystems to appear vastly different from summer to winter.

certain species the ability to survive and grow through seasonal rhythms. The trees on the edge of the meadow and the shrubs within the meadow are alive all year. During the spring, summer, and early fall, they carry on photosynthesis and grow. As the days become shorter and the temperatures begin to drop, these plants stop growing and become *dormant*.

For certain trees and shrubs (such as oak, maple, sassafras, and sumac) dormancy begins as cork cells grow at the base of each leaf. These cells seal off the leaves, which then change colors and drop. During the autumn, the growing tips of these woody plants form **dormant buds**. Dormant buds contain the delicate tissues of new leaves and flowers. Hard scales cover and protect these tissues during the winter. Then when spring comes, the scales drop off, the new leaves and flowers inside the buds appear, and the plant resumes growing.

Evergreen plants, such as pines, junipers, and hollies, are plants that do not lose all their leaves at the same time. When winter approaches, photosynthesis slows in these plants. When spring returns, photosynthesis increases. The leaves of these plants are replaced gradually.

Many plants appear to die in the frosts of autumn. Some of these plants, such as ferns, violets, daylilies, and daisies are *perennials* (puh REN ee ulz). The top parts may die in the winter, but the underground roots or stems remain alive and sprout again the next year. Other plants, such as ragweed, marigolds, lamb's quarters, and cocklebur, are *annuals*. Annuals sprout from seeds in the spring, grow in the summer, produce seeds in the fall, and then die in the winter. The seeds produced in the fall pass the winter as dormant seeds and produce new plants in the spring.

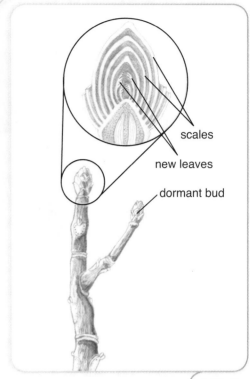

scales

new leaves

dormant bud

A dormant twig **21D-5**

21D.5 *Seasonal Changes in Animal Populations*

When winter comes to the meadow, the animals in that habitat either adjust their activities, move away, or die. For many insects, winter marks the end of their life span. Grasshoppers and praying mantises deposit their eggs in the late summer and die as the temperature drops. Although some of their eggs may die, many of them will survive the freezing temperatures.

Bees and ants, however, build homes that provide protection throughout the year. During the summer these insects stock their homes with food. Bees even have their own heating system within the hive. On cold days bees form clusters. The inner bees eat honey and produce heat for the others. On a winter day a hive may be as much as 24°C (43°F) higher than the outside temperature.

Many beetles and some butterflies and moths spend the winter in a dormant state as *pupas*. A few insects, such as monarch butterflies, migrate to other areas and avoid the freezing temperatures. These butterflies migrate from almost every area of the United States and part of Canada to spend the winter in parts of California, Mexico, and Florida. When spring comes, monarch butterflies migrate a short distance north and lay eggs. Since the life cycle from an egg to an

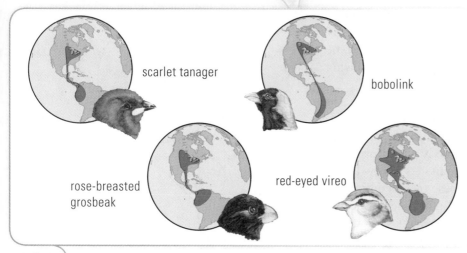

21D-6 Migration routes of various birds

scarlet tanager

bobolink

rose-breasted grosbeak

red-eyed vireo

hibernation: (L. HIBERNUS, winter)

21D-7 Some chipmunks enter a state of deep sleep during hibernation. A long period of shivering is necessary for this warm-blooded animal to raise its body temperature enough for it to wake up.

adult butterfly is rapid, scientists believe that it may be the new adults that continue the migration back north. (See pp. 334–35.)

Many birds also migrate. They often travel from an area with severe winters to a warmer habitat where food is more abundant. During the summer, thrushes, wrens, warblers, sparrows, and swallows are all *summer resident birds* in the meadows of much of North America. In South America, where these same birds spend the winter, they are known as *winter resident birds*. Birds that remain in an area the entire year are called *permanent resident birds*.

Many meadow animals do not migrate. Instead, they make changes in the way they live to survive the winter. The earthworms, turtles, toads, lizards, and snakes which are active during the summer spend their winters inactive. They may be found deep within the earth, on the bottoms of ponds, or hidden under rocks or logs. During the winter the body temperature of these ectothermic animals drops, and their entire metabolism slows down. (See pp. 320–21.) This dormant state, which permits certain animals to survive the winter, is called **hibernation**. An animal in hibernation looks like a "living statue." But when its body warms up, it becomes active again.

Some endothermic animals, such as ground squirrels, chipmunks, and woodchucks, also hibernate during the winter. Yet there are many mammals, such as the skunk, raccoon, squirrel, and bear, that do not hibernate, even though they often spend long periods of time asleep in their dens. Unlike the animals that hibernate, however, these animals can wake up easily, and their body temperature remains near normal throughout their winter naps. These sleeping animals are able to survive through the winter by using the body fat they stored during the summer, when food was plentiful.

Section Review 21D

1. Flowers that open at night exhibit _____ rhythms.

2. What are perennial plants?

3. What happens to an animal's body temperature when it hibernates?

Chapter Review

1. What is ecology?

2. What three relationships do ecologists study?

3. Define *ecosystem*.

4. List five physical (abiotic) factors that are usually important in an ecosystem.

5. What are the two main stages in the water cycle?

6. What is a climax community?

7. What name is given for the species in the early part of succession?

8. What things compose the biotic community in an ecosystem?

9. Which category of organisms in a biotic community carries on photosynthesis?

10. What is a limiting factor? Give an example.

11. Do aquatic ecosystems have carbon and oxygen cycles? Describe the relationship between these two cycles.

12. What type of rhythm do nocturnal and diurnal organisms exhibit?

13. Give an example of an organism exhibiting a seasonal rhythm.

14. How do summer resident birds and permanent resident birds differ?

15. What is hibernation?

What Did You Learn?

1. List three ecosystems near your home.

2. Why is a biotic community alone not an ecosystem?

3. Why is the water cycle appropriately called a cycle?

4. Would you expect to observe succession in a climax community? Explain.

5. How might new organisms enter an area during succession?

Scientifically Speaking

ecology
ecosystem
abiotic environment
biotic community
habitat
niche
water cycle
evaporation
succession
precipitation
water table
population
producer organism
consumer organism
carbon cycle
oxygen cycle
nitrogen cycle
rhythm
circadian rhythm
nocturnal
diurnal
seasonal rhythm
dormant bud
hibernation

Self Quiz 21

_____ 1. Ecology is the study of only the living things in an environment. (True/False)

_____ 2. A description of what an organism does or how it relates to the rest of its environment is called its
   A. niche.
   B. habitat.
   C. rhythm.
   D. none of these

_____ 3. Which of these is *not* a typical abiotic environmental factor?
   A. temperature
   B. seeds
   C. soil
   D. light

_____ 4. Rain, snow, sleet, and hail are all forms of
   A. condensation.
   B. evaporation.
   C. precipitation.
   D. runoff.

_____ 5. Populations in the same area combine to form a(n)
   A. individual.
   B. family.
   C. community.
   D. ecosystem.

6. Organisms such as green plants and algae can make their own food. We can, therefore, call them _____.

_____ 7. In which natural process is carbon dioxide converted to sugar and oxygen?
   A. chemosynthesis
   B. respiration
   C. hibernation
   D. photosynthesis

_____ 8. In which book of the Bible are natural rhythms *first* mentioned?
   A. Genesis
   B. Psalms
   C. Ecclesiastes
   D. Job

_____ 9. Which of these is *not* an example of a circadian rhythm?
   A. A prayer plant folds its leaves every evening.
   B. A rooster crows at dawn.
   C. A sea turtle migrates to a remote island to lay her eggs.
   D. A squirrel awakens and leaves its nest.

_____ 10. Because irises die back to the ground in the winter and sprout again every spring, we call them
   A. evergreens.
   B. perennials.
   C. annuals.
   D. seasonals.

ORGANISM RELATIONSHIPS

22

Most people have seen a dog scratching a flea bite or a mother bird leaving her nest of chicks to squawk at and attack an approaching cat. These are two common examples of the interactions of organisms, but there are many others. A bee visiting a flower, a squirrel burying a nut, and a blue jay catching a grasshopper that is eating grass are all examples of the interactions of organisms.

Each of these examples represents a certain type of relationship. Some relationships help only one member although both interact. For example, the cat under attack would benefit from a meal of young birds. The bird, however, protects its young. The fleas on the dog would benefit by feeding on the dog's blood. The dog, however, scratches to stop the irritation caused by the fleas.

Sometimes relationships between organisms are not so one-sided. Bees obtain their food from flowers. But as they do so, they pollinate the flowers. The squirrel's instinct is to bury nuts. When it buries its food, the squirrel often "plants" the nuts in areas some distance from the tree that produced them. Later, when nuts become scarce, the squirrel digs most of them up and eats them. However, some nuts remain buried. The nuts left by the squirrel then sprout in areas in which they may have a better chance to grow.

Sometimes the relationships of organisms involve more than two species. The blue jay obtains food by eating the grasshopper. The grasshopper obtains food by eating grass. Indirectly, the grass feeds the blue jay, while the blue jay eliminates the grasshoppers that were destroying the grass.

22-1 Is the bear's eating the salmon the only relationship necessary for the bear to live in its environment?

Organisms have many different relationships. An ecologist must understand these relationships before he can decide what is happening in an ecosystem. This knowledge helps the ecologist make good recommendations about what may be done to an ecosystem without harming it.

22A Energy Exchange Between Organisms

If the sun set one evening and never rose again, one of the first noticeable changes on the earth would be a drop in temperature. But even if the earth remained warm, within a few hours another significant problem would begin. Without sunlight, the plants could not carry on photosynthesis. To remain alive, the plants would have to use stored food. Those plants with little stored food would die first, but eventually all plants would die. As the plants died, those animals that eat plants would starve.

Then those animals that eat other animals would die. Within a week many living things would be near death. Within a month almost all organisms would be dead.

This imaginary doomsday will not happen. In the Bible, God promises that day and night will continue as long as the earth exists (Gen. 8:22). Only in the last days will God alter the day-and-night cycle (Rev. 8:12). But this doomsday description does show that energy is important to the many different ecosystems in the world.

Although matter is *cyclic* in an ecosystem (p. 364), energy is not. Living things lose much of the energy they use. Once energy is lost, living things cannot use it again to live. Since energy is not cyclic, an ecosystem must constantly supply its organisms with usable energy. For most ecosystems this supply of energy comes as plants and algae receive sunlight.

22A.1 Food Chains, Food Webs

When the sun shines on a lettuce plant, the plant cells respond by performing photosynthesis. During photosynthesis, sunlight energy changes to stored energy (in sugar). The lettuce uses the sugar to grow. If a rabbit eats the lettuce, the energy in the lettuce passes on to the rabbit. The lettuce also supplies the materials the rabbit needs to live. Later on, when a hawk catches the rabbit and eats it, the rabbit supplies the materials and energy that the hawk needs to live.

Eventually the hawk dies, and certain bacteria break down the hawk's body. Again there is a transfer of energy and materials as the hawk supplies the needs of the bacteria. When each bacterium dies, its cell membrane bursts, and the materials inside become part of the soil. These materials are then available for plants to absorb. However, the energy that passes from the bacteria to the soil is not usable by living organisms. In each of the earlier steps of the process, energy was released when larger molecules were broken apart. After the bacteria finish their work, only simple inorganic molecules remain. These do not contain energy that living things can use.

The passing of materials and energy from one organism to another is called a **food chain**. Every living thing is part of at least one food chain. The first organism in a food chain is a *producer organism*. The rest of the organisms in a food chain are *consumer organisms*. (See p. 365.) Food chains end with a specific type of consumer called a decomposer organism. **Decomposer organisms** are usually bacteria or fungi that break down the remains of dead organisms and return this material to the soil. Decomposers thus complete the food-chain cycle by making the materials available to the producers once again.

The lettuce described in the food-chain example above could be a part of many different food chains. For example, instead of the lettuce, rabbit, and hawk food chain, an insect could have eaten the lettuce; then a toad could have eaten the insect; and finally a snake could have eaten the toad. Rabbits serve as food for owls, foxes, cats, wolves, snakes, and many other animals. Hawks eat squirrels, mice, and occasionally frogs and toads. All of these interrelated food chains and many others that are possible in an ecosystem form a **food web**. In many ways the study of food webs gives a more accurate picture of what happens in an ecosystem than the study of a food chain.

consumer

decomposer consumer   consumer

producer

Food chain · **22A-1**

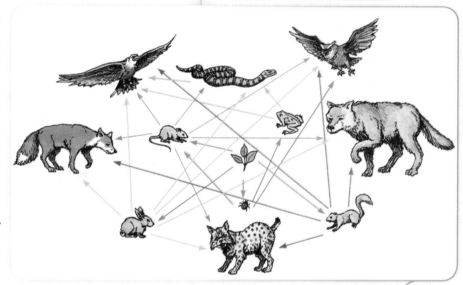

As with food chains, the arrows in food webs represent the possible flow of food energy between various organisms. · **22A-2**

22A.2 *Ecological Pyramids*

Ecologists often use **ecological pyramids** to illustrate energy relationships in a food chain. An ecological pyramid is divided into layers. Each layer represents a different type of organism in the food chain. The bottom layer represents the producer organisms. This layer is the largest since all the other layers depend on the producer organisms for their energy supply. However, not all the energy the plants absorb from the sun is available to the next level of the pyramid. Much of the sun's energy is reflected off the leaves back into space. Some is converted into heat by the growth processes of the plant. The producer organisms must use some of the energy they receive to keep themselves alive.

The next level up in an ecological pyramid contains consumers called herbivores (HUR buh VORZ). **Herbivores** are organisms that eat plants. Because some energy is used by the producer organisms, less energy is available in the herbivore layer than in the producer layer. Herbivores use much of the energy they receive for their own

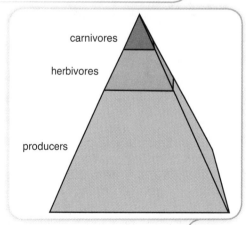

carnivores

herbivores

producers

Three-level ecological pyramid · **22A-3**

herbivore: herbi- (L. HERBA, vegetation) + -vore (L. VORUS, to swallow or devour) carnivore: carni- (L. CARN-, flesh) + -vore

Through Faith We Understand

Some evolutionists claim that Creation science is illogical because it asserts that a loving God has created carnivores, which kill and eat other animals, as well as parasites and bacteria, which cause harm and even death. How would you respond to them?

life processes. Thus, only a small amount of the energy they obtain from the producers is available for the next level.

The next level of an ecological pyramid is made up of consumers called carnivores. **Carnivores** are animals that eat other animals. Because there is less energy available to the carnivores, this level of the ecological pyramid is smaller than the other two.

The loss of energy that takes place in an ecological pyramid can also be explained another way. In each level of the ecological pyramid, the organisms use about 90% of the energy they receive. This leaves only 10% of the energy for the level above. In spite of this great energy loss, some ecological pyramids have an additional fourth and sometimes a fifth level. To supply enough energy for

Facets of *Ecology:* Parasites and Hosts

One of the most obvious methods of transferring energy and materials from one organism to another is the predator–prey relationship. Other relationships, such as the parasite–host relationship, also transfer energy. In a parasite–host relationship, the **parasite**, which is usually the smaller organism, obtains its energy and materials from the larger organism, called the *host*.

"Reading this science textbook makes me itch all over!"

As an example, consider a bird and its parasites. At any one time a single bird may be the host to over twenty-five different species of parasites. For instance, a bird may have a thousand feather lice and, at the same time, may have many bacteria living in its digestive system. Ticks, parasitic worms, protozoans, fungi, and other types of parasites may all be present in large numbers on or in the bird. One scientist has said that birds are really "flying zoos." When a bird flies, it carries thousands of organisms with it.

Almost every known living organism has its parasites. In addition to the protozoans and worms that are found in nearly every human's digestive tract, there are other larger parasites that many of us harbor. Head lice, chiggers, and various mites live in and on the surface of the skin. There are even mites living in the space around your eyelash roots.

Even cells, the smallest living units, can have parasites. Rocky Mountain spotted fever and typhus fever are diseases caused by bacteria that live inside human cells. Because the parasites are inside the host's cell, it is difficult to treat the disease without damaging the host.

Some parasites are very *specific*. This means that they will live with only one species of host and often in only one type of tissue of that host. For instance, one species of parasitic worm lives in the roots of oak trees. These worms will not live in the roots of any other tree, nor will they live in the branches or trunk of an oak tree.

Some parasites kill their hosts relatively rapidly. But if the host dies, the parasite no longer has a home. For many *internal parasites*, death of the host means death of the parasite. Internal parasites that cause death usually reproduce in large numbers and pass some of their offspring on to other organisms before the host dies. Parasitic worms that live in an animal's intestine, for example, usually release thousands of eggs in the

host's feces. Some of these eggs will probably reach another host.

tick

For many parasites (such as fleas and ticks), the death of the host merely means that it is time to move on. Many parasites do not kill their hosts, but they may weaken the hosts so that they die of other causes. A tapeworm living in a human's intestine usually does not kill the person. However, any loss of blood or nutrition caused by the parasitic worm may weaken the individual. Because of his weakened condition, the person is more likely to be infected with other diseases and may die from them.

additional levels, the amount of energy in the producer layer must be very large.

As an example, consider a four-level ecological pyramid made up of grass, grasshoppers, frogs, and snakes. By the time the energy from the grass passes on to the grasshoppers and frogs, very little of it is left for the snakes. In fact, ecologists estimate that it takes one thousand energy units of grass to supply one energy unit for the snakes. Can you see why an ecosystem normally has fewer carnivores than herbivores and fewer herbivores than producers?

Scientists measure the productivity of an ecosystem by calculating its **biomass**, which is the dried mass of the living matter in a given area of the habitat. For instance, to measure the biomass in a meadow, scientists remove all the plant matter from a one square meter of earth, allow it to dry, and then weigh it. Calculating the biomass in a forest would obviously be much harder.

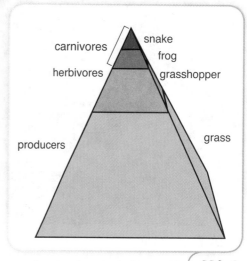

Four-level ecological pyramid 22A-4

22A.3 *Problems with Ecological Pyramids*

Ecological pyramids are models that help show the energy relationships between populations in an ecosystem. But relationships other than a straight food chain make constructing an ecological pyramid difficult. One factor that affects ecological pyramids is the presence of omnivores in an ecosystem. **Omnivores** are organisms that eat both plants and animals. Because they eat a variety of food, omnivores often fit into several levels of an ecological pyramid at the same time. For example, as a spider monkey eats leaves and fruits, it is a herbivore. But as the same primate eats insects and small animals, it is a carnivore. Other omnivores are raccoons, bears, opossums, and humans.

omnivore: omni- (L. OMNIS, all) + -vore

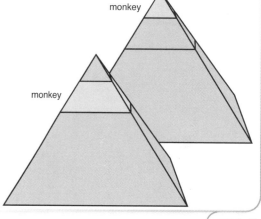

The spider monkey can be on the herbivore level or the carnivore level of an ecological pyramid. At which level is it in this photo? 22A-5

A second factor is the eating habits of some carnivores. Certain carnivores eat not only herbivores but also other carnivores. A hawk may eat a rabbit (herbivore) and then a snake (carnivore). Because the hawk eats both a herbivore and a carnivore, it belongs in two different levels of the ecological pyramid.

A third factor is the movement of many organisms from one ecosystem to another. As these organisms move around, they often become part of the food chains of several ecosystems. For example, if an eagle flew to a meadow and ate a squirrel and then flew to a lake and ate a fish, the eagle would belong to the food chains of both ecosystems. When this happens, ecologists must include the eagle in the meadow pyramid and in the lake pyramid. These three factors are only some of the problems ecologists must deal with while studying the flow of energy in ecosystems.

22A-6 Predators with their prey: a puffin (left) with a fish to feed to its chicks, and a spider (right) with its insect meal

22A.4 *Predator–Prey Relationships*

A **predator** (PRED uh tur) is an animal that feeds on other animals. The **prey** is the animal that the predator eats. Usually a predator kills its prey and then eats it. A spider, for instance, is a predator that kills flies (prey) and then feeds on their body juices. As in the spider-fly relationship, most predators are larger than their prey.

Predator-prey relationships help to keep the populations balanced within an ecosystem. If all the lions (predators) in an area were removed, the zebra population (prey) in that area would increase. Eventually the zebra population would become overcrowded, and the ecosystem would run short of the right kind of food. Without enough food, many of the zebras would become weak, and some would die of starvation. The lions play an important role in this ecosystem by helping keep the zebra population in balance. In another sense, the zebras control the lion population because the prey supply limits how many cubs can survive and mature. These two animals show how the predator-prey relationship helps adjust populations to a size the ecosystem can support.

What Do You Think?

Scripture compares Satan to predators several times. List two of them, along with a Scripture reference for each, and explain how Satan's actions are like a predator's.

Section Review 22A

1. Why do ecosystems not have energy cycles?

2. Name two types of decomposer organisms.

3. What kind of organisms are at the bottom of an ecological pyramid?

4. About what percentage of the energy is transferred from level to level in an ecological pyramid?

5. What is the lowest level (if the bottom is level 1) in which a carnivore can occur in an ecological pyramid?

6. Does the existence of carnivores deny the goodness of God? Why or why not?

22B Relationships Between Organisms of the Same Species

Objectives 22B

- Describe and give examples of the following relationships between organisms of the same species: independent relationships, couple relationships, social relationships, animal societies, and competitive relationships within a population.

- Discuss the social relationships within an ant colony.

The passing of energy and nutrients from one organism to another is one of the primary relationships between organisms. But this relationship is only one of many that exist within the biotic community. To know which relationships are essential to the balance of an ecosystem, an ecologist must study them all.

The nonenergy relationships between organisms are sometimes obvious. Dogs fighting, birds building nests, mosses and ferns growing in the shade of a tree, and ants proceeding across a sidewalk—all of these activities demonstrate nonenergy relationships between organisms. Although the individual organisms use energy, no energy is being transferred from organism to organism. To study these relationships more easily, ecologists divide them into two groups: *relationships between organisms of the same species* and *relationships between organisms of different species*. Section 22B deals with the first of the two groups of relationships—those between organisms of the same species.

22B.1 *Independent Organisms*

Many organisms lead independent lives. An **independent organism** is one that exists without the aid of other members of the same species. However, independent organisms do need other members of the same species for sexual reproduction. Most plants are independent organisms. An oak tree, for example, is not dependent upon other oak trees except during the spring, when they exchange pollen in sexual reproduction.

Spiders are independent organisms. Once mature, the garden spider builds a web and remains there until it dies. Occasionally, several garden spiders build their webs on the same plant. Although they are neighbors, each may be completely unaware of the others' presence. If one happens to come upon its neighbor's web, the owner of the web will quickly attack and kill the intruder. Trespassing rarely occurs among spiders.

Normally the only time two garden spiders occupy the same web is during the mating process. Garden spiders mate on the female's web. When they complete the mating process, the female may kill her smaller male partner by biting him. This is the same way she kills those insects that become entangled in her web. The male may then become the "bridal dinner."

Bears are independent vertebrate organisms. Normally a bear hunts, eats, and lives alone. However, for a few days during the mating season, male and female bears may travel together. After mating, the couple separates and may never see each other again. When the cubs are born, they remain with their mother for many months while they grow and learn to hunt for themselves. When the cubs become young adults, they leave their mother.

A bear usually remains in its own territory. If another bear comes into this territory, the first bear will challenge the intruder to a fight. Usually the intruder leaves, but if it does not, a fight may begin that could end with two injured bears. Bears, however, can be somewhat sociable to one another. For example, when salmon are migrating in Alaskan streams, there may be dozens of bears congregating on the shore for a feast. However, the bears will fight for the best fishing spots. Usually the larger bears get the prime locations, and the others take the remaining fishing spots.

This spider is an independent organism since it does not depend on other spiders for survival.

22B-1

22B.2 *Couple Relationships*

Some animals choose a mating partner and rarely separate from that partner for the rest of their lives. This relationship is called *mating for life*. For most animals this relationship is truly "till death do us part."

Some birds mate for life. For example, when bald eagles reach maturity, they choose a lifelong mate. If the eagles live to an old age, they may remain together for thirty or more years. Each spring they will produce eggs and share in the responsibility of caring for the eggs and the young. The partners, however, remain together even when they are not raising young. Other birds that mate for life include some species of penguins, owls, parrots, sea birds, and swans. Most of these will choose a new partner if their mate dies prematurely.

While about 90% of all bird species have only one partner each season, some may form new bonds each year or after several years. There is also variety in the amount of involvement from the male, ranging from merely protecting the territory to incubating the eggs and feeding the young.

There are also a few fish, such as the aquarium angelfish, that mate for life. To get a mating pair of angelfish, aquarists (uh KWAIR ists) raise twenty to thirty young angelfish in a large tank. As these fish approach maturity, certain ones pair off and begin spending all their time together. Soon each angelfish pair establishes its own territory in the aquarium. These fish are very protective of their territory and will not allow any other fish into the area. When an angelfish pair reaches this stage, an aquarist often puts the pair into another aquarium.

Once two angelfish mate, they will not mate with any other angelfish. Often, when transferring a mating pair to another tank, an aquarist will catch both members in the same net. If he separates the pair for even a short time, they may never mate again.

22B-2 The albatross is a sea bird that mates for life.

An aquarist is a person who maintains aquariums.

Try This at Home

Using dictionaries and other word resources, see if you can find what kind of animals make up each of these groups. The first is done for you as an example.

a gaggle of _____geese_____

a gang of _____

a mob of _____

a pod of _____

a sounder of _____

22B.3 *Animal Societies*

An **animal society** forms when a number of animals from the same species live together. Some animal societies provide a means of defense. When a predator finds a *school* of fish, it must choose which fish it will pursue. This gives the rest of the school a chance to escape.

Birds form animal societies called *flocks*. Like a school of fish, a flock of birds forces a predator to pursue a few birds and to let the others escape. Nesting colonies also provide safety in numbers. For example, in California thousands of seagulls may nest in one small area. This often makes nesting sites very visible to predators. However, the collective attack of hundreds of birds is enough to turn most predators away. Although a few birds may become prey to attack, most survive because of the actions of the social group.

A *herd* of musk oxen under attack will position themselves side by side to form a circle around the calves. As the mature musk oxen face the outside, they form a ring of sharp horns. This defensive arrangement can withstand a pack of wolves.

Besides producing a good means of defense, many animal societies provide other types of help to their members. A group of lions is called a *pride*. A pride usually consists of a couple of adult males, a few females, and a collection of cubs. Each pride has its own territory, ranging from 15 to 150 square miles. The male lions defend the pride's territory when other lions present a threat. To inform other lions that the land is occupied, the male lions leave a special scent on bushes and grass. His daily roars are also loud territorial claims.

The lionesses of the pride do about 85% of the hunting. Lions often live on open grasslands, where a single lion would find hunting difficult. Lionesses, however, usually hunt in groups. These hunting groups can outmaneuver their prey in ways a single lion could not. When the lionesses make their kill, the males of the pride feed first. A large male can eat 35 kg (77 lb) of meat at a time. After they have eaten, the females eat their fill, and then the cubs may eat. Occasionally, when there is only a little meat remaining, a male lion will approach the females while they are eating, chase them off, and permit the cubs to eat. If the lionesses are still hungry, they will go for another kill.

Hunting, eating, and catnapping are all social events for these lions. 22B-3

Elephants live in *herds*. An adult elephant may eat for sixteen hours a day and consume up to 200 kg (440 lb) of leaves, fruits, grass, and bark. Thus a herd of elephants can quickly reduce the size of the producer populations. The difficulty of finding enough food is a drawback of living in a herd, but there are also benefits to herd life. For instance, large predators may attack a solitary elephant, especially if the elephant is young or elderly. But a herd of elephants has no animal predators.

Young elephants also benefit from instruction by the herd. They learn what to eat, how to eat, when to migrate, how to care for their skin, and many other things. Since it takes about fifteen years for an elephant to reach maturity, young elephants have many opportunities to learn.

22B.4 *Social Insects*

Animals of the same species often form groups. Some of these groups have well-defined roles for their members. Other groups appear to be quite informal. Some of the most rigid animal societies are found among the **social insects** such as ants, termites, wasps, and bees.

Ants, like most social insects, normally have one queen per colony. The queen's function in the colony is to lay eggs. Within a few days, an ant queen may produce thousands of eggs. Most of these eggs develop into workers. At certain times of the year, however, some eggs develop into winged males and females. These winged ants fly away from the colony and mate in the air, and then the females begin new colonies.

In an ant colony there are workers that build, repair, and defend the nest. There are also workers that care for

Would You Believe?

The few male ants in a colony usually live only two or three weeks. The large majority are female workers who can live for two or three years. Some species of queens have lived nearly thirty years in captive colonies. In the ant world, "girls rule!"

Ants are social insects that live in large colonies. 22B-4

His Mercy Endureth Forever

The ant queen, better named the ant mother, does not actually rule the colony; she merely lays the eggs. Who rules the colony? No one. Although ants have very complex social relationships, no single ant is in control. God graciously gave each ant the ability to communicate using the presence or absence of chemicals, moisture, food, and heat. The organized, diligent behavior of the ants becomes a humbling object lesson for humans. We are far more important to God than ants. But ants often live better than we do: "Go to the ant, thou sluggard; consider her ways, and be wise: which having no guide, overseer, or ruler, provideth her meat in the summer, and gathereth her food in the harvest" (Prov. 6:6-8).

the eggs, nurse the young, and gather food. Gathering food is one task that differs among certain types of ants. Some ants search for plant food to carry back to their nests, while others attack and kill their food. Some ants grow fungi for food; others eat the honeydew (a sugary liquid) they receive from aphids. A few ants store nectar in their swollen abdomens to become a kind of "living honeycomb."

22B.5 *Competition Within Populations*

Competition is the struggle between organisms for some essential factor that is in short supply in the environment. Many animals, for example, compete for mates. Certain male birds attract mates by using bright feathers, fancy songs, wing flapping, and various other displays. The females get to choose their mates.

Many organisms that live in groups establish relationships based on the competition among the members. A *pecking order*, for instance, is a system of rank that occurs among a group of chickens. When two chickens meet, they may start fighting with each other. The chicken that wins the fight is dominant over the loser. To show its dominance, the winner will peck the loser every time they meet. Sometimes one chicken will submit to another chicken without a fight and take the pecking. When this happens, the yielding chicken is admitting that the other chicken is dominant.

In time a pecking order is set up. The first chicken in a pecking order dominates all the others. The second dominates all the others except the first. The third dominates all the others except the first two, and so on. This ranking continues throughout the group down to the last chicken in the pecking order. The last chicken will submit to every chicken in the group. Occasionally a low-ranking chicken may challenge a higher-ranking chicken to a fight, but once the chickens establish their pecking order, it rarely changes.

Members of other populations often compete among themselves for dominance. In a wolf pack, for example, there is one male leader. He is called the alpha male. This wolf has first choice of meals and mates. He decides when and where the group hunts. He also chooses the places where the pack rests and determines where the boundaries of the pack's territory will be. Sometimes a younger male will challenge the alpha male, and a fight follows. If the leader is old, he may recognize that he is too weak to win and will surrender to the young wolf. To surrender, the wolf first bows his head and then lies down, showing his neck to the challenger. If the younger wolf has overestimated his power, he may surrender to the alpha male. If, however, they are evenly matched, the fight continues until one of the wolves wins. Sometimes a well-matched fight results in the death of one of the wolves.

22B-5 | What signs of submission are the outer wolves showing to the wolf in the center?

The term *competition* also refers to the relationship between certain plants. However, competition between plants does not mean that they are consciously struggling for survival. It simply means that when an essential factor is in short supply, some plants will live, while others will die. If, for example, a large number of seeds sprout in a small area, the lack of sunlight, water, soil nutrients, or space will prevent some of them from reaching maturity.

Section Review 22B

1. When do independent organisms interact with other members of their species?

2. Which lions defend a pride's territory? Which do most of the hunting?

3. What benefits do elephants receive from living in herds?

4. Why might a social insect permanently leave its original social group?

5. _____ may occur when an essential factor is in short supply.

22C Relationships Between Different Species

The predator-prey and parasite-host relationships are only two of many different types of relationships between populations in an ecosystem. Scientists are just beginning to understand some of the other relationships.

22C.1 Competition Between Populations

Competition between populations occurs when two or more different populations have the same requirements. For example, all the robins, blue jays, and mockingbirds in a single area may compete for the same food. If the food supply is small, the competition will be strong, and the bird populations that get the least amount of food usually leave the area. If they stay, the limited food resources may reduce the number of chicks the birds can produce, decreasing their population over time. However, if the area has plenty of food, there will be less competition and all the birds may stay.

Sometimes the factors in an ecosystem limit the size of two competing populations so that they can exist together. For example, the rabbits and grasshoppers in an area may compete for the same food. However, if the grasshopper population becomes too large, the toad population or the insect-eating bird population may increase. The presence of more toads and birds in the area would limit the number of grasshoppers. If the rabbit population becomes too large, the hawk or eagle population may increase, limiting the rabbit population and keeping the ecosystem balanced.

Objectives 22C

- Describe and give examples of the following relationships between different populations within an ecosystem: competition, commensalism, and mutualism.

- Identify and give examples of the following survival strategies: camouflage, warning coloration, and mimicry.

commensalism: com- (L. COM-, together) + -mensalism (L. MENSA, table)

epiphyte: epi- (Gk. EPI, upon) + -phyte (Gk. PHUTON, plant)

22C-1 The epiphytic fern growing on this tree benefits from its location by having better access to water, minerals, and sunlight. The tree gets nothing in return.

22C-2 Salamander living in a bromeliad

mutualism: (L. MUTUUS, exchanged)

22C-3 Lichen growing on granite

22C.2 *Commensalism*

A relationship between two populations that benefits one and does not hurt or help the other is called **commensalism** (kuh MEN suh LIZ um). If a leopard kills an antelope and eats its fill, soon vultures, hyenas, and jackals will come to "clean up" the leftovers. The animals that eat dead or decaying bodies are called **scavengers** (SKAV un jurz). The relationship between a scavenger and a predator is an example of commensalism.

The relationship between certain orchids and the jungle trees they live on is another example of commensalism. In most tropical forests the canopy of tree branches is so dense that the forest floor is almost dark. Many plants are unable to grow in this deep shade. However, certain orchids, ferns, and various other plants live in the treetops where they can get the light they need to grow. These plants are called epiphytes (EP uh FYTS). **Epiphytes** are plants that usually grow on the branches of trees but do not take nourishment from the trees. These orchids obtain the minerals they require from the dust that collects in the ridges of the tree bark.

A bromeliad (bro MEE lee AD) is another epiphyte. The leaves of this plant form a cup that catches and holds water for future use. This water also serves as the home of many different organisms, including some tiny salamanders. These salamanders may live, breed, and lay their eggs in this water. The bromeliad and the salamander have a commensal relationship, just as the bromeliad is commensal with the tree.

22C.3 *Mutualism*

Mutualism is a relationship between two populations that is beneficial to both. For instance, as a bumblebee gathers nectar and pollen from a red clover flower, the flower is pollinated by the bee. Both the insect and the plant benefit from this encounter.

Another example of mutualism is the relationship between certain ants and aphids. Some ants keep herds of aphids just as ranchers keep herds of cows. The ants move the aphids along plant stems. As the aphids push their mouthparts into the plant, the ants stroke the aphids' backs. This stroking causes the aphids to secrete a sweet substance called honeydew, which the ants eat. As the aphids provide food for the ants, the ants provide protection for the aphids. If another insect tries to harm the aphids, the ants attack the predator and protect their herd.

Many mutualisms are *obligatory*. In an obligatory mutualism both organisms must be together or they will die. Termites, for example, have a type of protozoan inside their digestive tracts that helps them digest cellulose. Without these protozoans the termites would die of starvation, no matter how much wood they ate. Without the termites the protozoans would die.

Lichens (LY kunz) also demonstrate obligatory mutualism. A lichen is a combination of an alga and a fungus and often lives on bare rocks or on tree bark. Although neither the alga nor the fungus could live alone in the lichen's harsh habitat, together they produce the necessary conditions for survival.

Facets of *Ecology:* *Animals That Are Dressed for Success*

thorny devil

In the struggle to eat—or to keep from being eaten—animals demonstrate a wide range of behaviors and characteristics. Some of the most interesting strategies for survival involve the many ways animals are "dressed for success."

Camouflage is one way organisms are dressed for success. Many organisms have protective colors or patterns that hide them from predators. A white-tailed deer fawn has a brown, spotted coat. The fawn blends so well with the dead leaves and dappled sunlight of the forest that it is almost invisible. Many predators have overlooked a quiet fawn lying on the forest floor.

In the winter, certain ptarmigans (TAR mih gunz) are pure white. Sitting on the snow-covered ground, they look like little snowdrifts. As the snow melts, these birds grow new feathers that are drab, mottled, and brownish. This color pattern camouflages them in the warmer seasons.

In addition to their coloring, many organisms have shapes that help protect them from predators. Many insects look like twigs, leaves, or thorns. For example, the dead-leaf butterfly with its wings closed looks like a brown leaf. The wings even have veinlike markings and darker splotches that resemble holes. When the butterfly sits on a branch, its ap-

pearance fools many predators. When the butterfly spreads its wings, however, it reveals its brightly colored upper surfaces.

Camouflage also can help animals obtain food. A tiger's stripes help it disappear in the grass as it stalks its prey. An alligator drifting slowly and half submerged in dark water looks like a log as it floats along looking for a meal.

Many animals use camouflage to hide from both their predators and their prey. For example, African chameleons can change their skin color in a way that helps them blend in with the surrounding foliage. Their appearance hides them not only from lizard-eating birds and reptiles but also from the insects they feed on.

Some animals use tactics exactly opposite to camouflage. They advertise their presence. This type of dressing for success is called *warning coloration*. A skunk's contrasting black-and-white fur is a clear signal to any animal that has ever been blasted by the skunk's scent glands.

Most frogs are nocturnal and blend well with their surroundings. In the tropics, however, poisonous tree frogs hunt during the day. These brightly colored frogs do not try to hide from their predators. Instead their showy colors warn predators that these frogs are deadly, not tasty.

leafhopper

chameleon

Animals That Are Dressed for Success (cont.)

orchid mantis

Many insects have false eyes that ward off predators. Some caterpillars, for example, have brightly colored facelike patterns on their back ends. These patterns frighten away birds, which may think they are encountering some larger animal. Some moths have eye spots on their wings. These eye spots, which look somewhat like an owl's eyes, are not used for sight. Instead, they probably help startle predators.

One of the most interesting ways animals can be dressed for success is by *mimicry* (MIM ih kree). When one organism looks like another, their relationship is called mimicry. In some cases one organism is harmful or distasteful, but another similar-looking one is not. Mimicry helps protect the harmless and tasty organisms. For example, there are a number of harmless insects, such as the robber fly and the bee fly, which look very much like bees. Toads and birds that have been stung by bees ignore these bee look-alikes. The yellow jacket is obviously an insect to avoid. Usually if an insect predator attempts to eat one, it will not try another. The hover fly does not have a stinger, but it looks like the yellow jacket. Because of this mimicry, predators that avoid yellow jackets also leave the hover fly alone.

Sometimes mimicry not only aids protection but also aids predation. Some mantises in tropical regions are brightly colored and look like orchids. This mimicry helps the mantis both hide from predators and catch its prey.

Animals do not possess camouflage, warning coloration, and mimicry because they realized that having a certain appearance could help them. Animals cannot change themselves because they "desire" or "need" to change. The Designer-Creator God dressed these animals for success. The Bible states that even man, who is an intelligent being, cannot change his physical features "by taking thought" (Matt. 6:27).

The fungus, for example, forms a protective coat that prevents the alga from completely drying out or blowing away. At the same time, the alga carries on photosynthesis and makes food for both organisms.

Section Review 22C

1. In _____ relationships, one population receives benefits and the other is unaffected.

2. What do the predator-scavenger relationship and tree-epiphyte relationship have in common?

3. How is warning coloration beneficial to a species?

Chapter Review

1. How does the original energy enter most ecosystems?

2. What is the smallest number of species that can be present in a food chain that includes a carnivore?

3. What do decomposer organisms do?

4. What is an ecological pyramid?

5. What type of organism eats only plants?

6. Why is it a disadvantage for a parasite to kill its host?

7. What type of organism eats both plants and animals?

8. Give an example of an independent organism.

9. Give an example of an animal that mates for life.

10. Give an example of a social insect other than bees.

11. What do schools, flocks, herds, and prides have in common?

12. Define *competition* as it relates to the survival of organisms.

13. What type of relationship between species is beneficial to both?

14. What kind of relationship does a lichen illustrate?

15. Does camouflage always consist of drab colors? Explain.

What Did You Learn?

1. Beginning with entering the ecosystem, describe the pathway (through various organisms) that energy might take until it reaches a predator such as a snake.

2. Why is a food web probably a more accurate description of certain interactions in an ecosystem than a food chain?

3. In each level of an ecological pyramid, why is there less energy available than there is in the level below?

4. Why are predators important in an ecosystem?

5. Would examples of obligatory mutualism support the theory of evolution or point to a Creator? Why?

Scientifically Speaking

food chain
decomposer organism
food web
ecological pyramid
herbivore
carnivore
parasite
biomass
omnivore
predator
prey
independent organism
animal society
social insect
competition
commensalism
scavenger
epiphyte
mutualism

Self Quiz 22

_____ 1. Which of these are most often decomposer organisms?
   A. protozoans and algae
   B. insects and crustaceans
   C. birds and mammals
   D. fungi and bacteria

_____ 2. Which one of these would be highest on an ecological pyramid?
   A. carnivore
   B. producer
   C. herbivore
   D. prey

_____ 3. Some predators may also become prey for other predators. (True/False)

_____ 4. Which of these is *not* a social insect?
   A. ant
   B. fruit fly
   C. termite
   D. wasp

_____ 5. Competition occurs between populations of different species, but not within a population of the same species. (True/False)

_____ 6. The relationship between a wolf and a magpie, which picks the meat off the bones of a deer after a wolf has eaten its fill, is best described as
   A. mutualism.
   B. competition.
   C. commensalism.
   D. parasitism.

_____ 7. In the above example, the magpie would be considered a
   A. scavenger.
   B. parasite.
   C. host.
   D. partner.

_____ 8. Epiphytes are
   A. plants that depend on animals.
   B. plants that depend on other plants.
   C. animals that depend on plants.
   D. animals that depend on other animals.

_____ 9. Which of these is an example of *obligatory* mutualism?
   A. lions and vultures
   B. ants and aphids
   C. bromeliads and salamanders
   D. termites and digestive protozoans

_____ 10. A colorful poison dart frog is a good example of
   A. camouflage.
   B. mimicry.
   C. warning coloration.
   D. commensalism.

NATURAL RESOURCES

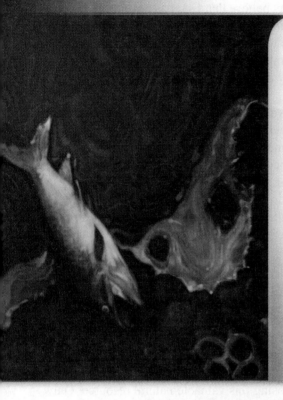

God has repeatedly promised to supply the physical needs of His children (Ps. 23:1; Phil. 4:19). Occasionally He supplies those needs miraculously. But God usually does not do for us what He has given us the resources and power to do for ourselves. Although we should ask God to meet our needs and should trust Him to keep His promises, we are responsible to obey His commands.

God has placed man on a planet with abundant natural resources. **Natural resources** are usable materials that man can obtain from the physical world. Natural resources that man has used include plants, animals, land, water, substances from the ground (such as coal, oil, gems, and metals), and even features of the ground (such as hills, prairies, and coastlines).

Forests (left) and coal (right) are both natural resources, but what is a key difference between them?   **23-1**

Some natural resources are *renewable*. For example, trees are a renewable resource. When trees are cut down, seedling trees may be planted to replace them. In a number of years, there will be more trees to cut down and use. Many other natural resources are *nonrenewable*. Oil is a nonrenewable resource. Once it is removed from the ground, it cannot be replenished.

Many Christian scholars believe that God has put enough natural resources in the world to meet the needs of all mankind. Yet some people in the world will go to bed hungry tonight. Others have inadequate clothing or poor living conditions. If there are enough natural resources on the earth, why do some people still have great physical and material needs?

Many times the reasons are political. Problems between countries that are rich in resources and those that lack resources often hamper people from having their needs met. Other times those who have an abundance have no concern for those who do not have enough. Often, those who lack what they need are not willing or able to use the natural resources they do have.

We must consider another factor when we talk about God's supply of natural resources for human use. Humans often waste natural resources. Like a person who purchases luxury items and then cannot afford to buy groceries, man often wastes natural resources and then finds himself in need.

Once vast forests covered large portions of North America. Wood seemed to be an endless natural resource. However, by the mid-1800s people had cut down most of the original trees in North America. They used some wood to build buildings, heat homes, and run industry; but at least half of it was wasted. As the forests dwindled, people became concerned about losing this valuable natural resource. Only then did they begin to stop the waste and renew the resources they had used.

If a resource is nonrenewable, mankind may exhaust the supply. Then we must find another resource to take its place. For example, coal is a nonrenewable resource. When it is used up, we will have to use other sources of energy.

In this chapter you will study several important natural resources and the problems related to their use. Every day you make decisions about the use of these natural resources. As you grow older, these decisions will become increasingly important. The more you understand about natural resources and their use, the more likely it is that you will exercise wise dominion over God's earth.

23A Living Things as Natural Resources

The living things that share our planet are a type of natural resource that we often overlook. Today many people think of plants as only decorations and animals as only pets. But humans are quite dependent upon the other living things on the earth. We rely on three types of organisms: producer organisms, consumer organisms, and decomposer organisms.

Producer organisms trap energy from the sun and convert the energy into food that is critical to the survival of animals and humans.

Plants also produce fibers for clothing, materials for building, and even medicines.

Consumer organisms provide food, transportation, and labor, as well as fibers and skins for clothing and other products.

Decomposer organisms are important for removing and recycling wastes. Without organisms such as bacteria, fungi, and worms and other invertebrates, all ecosystems would soon stop functioning.

In times past, the small population of humans could take from nature all the plants and animals they needed. Their actions did not greatly affect the ecosystem. As the human population grew, many people continued this practice. They did not consider its effects on the populations of animals and plants. But living things do not exist in unlimited supply. Man's abuse of these natural resources has had long-lasting effects.

23A.1 *Man's Use of Wildlife*

The fur-trading industry provides an example of man's unwise use of wildlife. In Europe during the 1600s and 1700s, wearing fur was very fashionable. Because Europe had few fur-bearing animals, many trappers went to North America where the supply was plentiful. Trappers in America caught minks, martens, otters, foxes, muskrats, raccoons, and beavers. The pelts were sold in Europe and brought the equivalent of over $100 million each year to the trappers of North America.

Beavers were among the most sought-after fur-bearing animals. Their fur could be processed into felt, making it a popular material for hats and other articles of clothing. These animals were almost wiped out in Europe due to excessive trapping, but were plentiful in many areas of North America. Soon, however, the trapping was so extensive in the woods near the Atlantic coast that it greatly reduced the beaver population. Trapping in this area became unprofitable. Many trappers moved westward to work where the beaver population was still plentiful. By the 1800s all the beavers had been killed in many areas of America. If heavy trapping had continued, American beavers might have become **extinct**. A species is extinct when no members of that species are left alive on the earth.

Beavers have been reintroduced to some of the areas where they once lived, and today they are gradually growing in number. What saved the American beavers from extinction? People in some areas saw that fur trapping threatened the beaver population. They passed laws against killing beavers. Another circumstance helped to save the beaver population. Beaver hats and beaver furs simply went out of fashion. The price of beaver pelts dropped, and trapping beavers became less profitable.

Man still uses animal fur for clothing and other purposes. Today, however, he is a wiser steward of living natural resources than he was in early America. Now many fur-bearing animals, such as mink, rabbits, and foxes, are raised on special farms instead of being trapped in the wild. Raising the animals allows man to supply his needs without harming the natural population of the animals.

Beaver hats were popular in the 1700s. **23A-1**

Beavers have been reintroduced into many areas. **23A-2**

Facets of *Ecology:* The Game of Game Animals

In the past, hunting was the main source for supplying meat for food and skins for clothing. Now most meat comes from the supermarket, and most clothes come from the department store. This change makes hunting for food and clothing less of a necessity. Today hunting is primarily a sport, and most hunters do it for enjoyment.

When Europeans first came to America, they found abundant game. As America's human population grew, people began using more land for cities and crops. This left less land for the game animals. Soon the decrease in suitable habitats and an increase in hunters reduced the populations of many animals. Some game animals even became extinct.

More animals might have become extinct if the government had not established game laws. Game laws either restrict the number of animals a hunter can kill or prohibit the hunting of certain types of animals altogether. The buffalo (bison), wood duck, pronghorn, whooping crane, and northern fur seal have probably escaped extinction because of game laws.

Another way the government has helped wildlife is by setting aside certain natural habitats as refuges. These refuges protect both land and water areas across the continent.

Game management areas support populations of many animals including the white-tailed deer. These deer are so well managed that in several areas there are more deer now than when American Indians hunted the area. In some ways hunters have domesticated the white-tailed deer by furnishing the money (payment of taxes and hunting license fees) to provide the deer with good living conditions. This has been so successful that in many areas, deer have even become a pest, causing agricultural damage and increased motor vehicle accidents.

Sometimes when there is a decrease in the number of game animals, hunters try to solve the problem themselves. The case of the ring-necked pheasant is an example. Although the ring-necked pheasant is a popular game bird in the United States, it is not an American bird. It was brought to America from Asia to help replace some of the disappearing native game birds. Once in America the pheasant thrived, finding a suitable habitat in South Dakota and many nearby states.

pronghorn

During the 1960s the pheasant population began declining in South Dakota. When this happened, a group of people began a private organization that encouraged the killing of red foxes. These people were convinced that the red fox was responsible for the pheasant's decline. To help restore the pheasant population, they began special bounties, contests, and fox hunts to eliminate red foxes.

However, scientists working for the state of South Dakota found that red foxes rarely kill pheasants. In fact,

ring-necked pheasant

in a five-year study, fox control made very little difference on the pheasant population. However, when the skunks, raccoons, badgers, and foxes were controlled, the pheasant population grew 132% per year.

This information made some people want to begin a large-scale predator control program for all these animals. But such a program would require using poisons. Poisons can kill livestock and nontarget species, as well as the target predator. This and other deadly controls are not a permanent solution to the problem since survivors can repopulate.

Such controls also would be bad for the environment. As these predators died, various pests such as rats and rabbits would increase. People need to ask themselves if maintaining a large pheasant population for hunting is worthwhile. We must consider the expense, the increase of pests, and the loss of natural wildlife as we seek to exercise wise dominion over God's earth.

23A.2 *Farming*

Caring for a concentrated group of plants or animals so that they can be used to supply human needs is known as *farming*. Farming gives man the products he needs without reducing the natural population of organisms. Man typically raises plants such as corn, wheat, apples, and bananas and various animals such as cows, pigs, and chickens. Man also "farms" organisms that are not usually thought of as typical crops or farm animals. Some of these organisms and their products are trees for lumber, ostriches for feathers, roses for fragrances, bees

Replanting a field immediately following a harvest (left); belted Galloway steer on a farm in Maine (right) **23A-3**

for honey and wax, and caterpillars for silk. Although we usually think of a farm as an area of land, some farms are in or under water. Today man farms oysters in the ocean, fish in ponds, and algae in large tanks.

Domesticated (duh MES tih KATE ud) *organisms* are those living things that man raises primarily for his own use. After plants and animals are domesticated, man usually breeds them (pp. 114–115) for the characteristics he wants them to have. This often produces domesticated forms that are quite different from their wild ancestors. However, since man cares for these organisms, he is not concerned about characteristics that permit them to survive in the wild. A barnyard chicken, for example, looks somewhat like its wild ancestor, the red jungle fowl. The jungle fowl and the chicken are very different, though, in characteristics such as egg production and flying ability.

23A.3 *Agriculture and the Soil*

For thousands of years, farmers have known that they must have good soil to produce good crops. Farmers have also known that some soils are better than others for growing certain crops. But only in the last one hundred years has agriculture become a science. *Agriculture* is the science of growing crops and livestock.

Agricultural scientists have studied what different crops require to produce large harvests. They have experimented with the genetic makeup of various crops. Together these scientists have increased the *harvest* a farmer can expect from his land. Today many crops produce ten to fifty times more per acre than they did fifty years ago.

To encourage people to settle in the New World, the countries that colonized America gave sections of land to groups of people. As recently as one hundred years ago, the United States government

Facets of *Ecology:* *When Species Expire*

Since Creation, many plants and animals have become extinct. The fossil record reveals thousands of organisms such as most dinosaurs, saber-toothed tigers, woolly mammoths, seed ferns, and many others that are not alive today. Many scientists believe that the organisms in the fossil record became extinct through natural causes. They use the term natural extinction to describe their view that man was not responsible for their deaths.

However, if the Creationist explanation of how the earth was changed by the Flood is true (p. 132), man was, at least indirectly, responsible

California condor

for the extinction of these organisms. Because of man's wickedness, God passed judgment on the world and destroyed it with water (Gen. 6:5–7). If man had not sinned, God would not have sent the Flood and many extinct organisms might be alive today.

Within the past few centuries, man has been directly responsible for the extinction of many living things. One way man has forced different species into extinction is by excessive hunting. The great auk (AWK) was a large flightless bird that nested on islands in the North Atlantic. This black-and-white bird was an excellent swimmer and migrated as far south as Florida and as far east as Great Britain.

Sailors discovered that the great auk was a good source of cheap, fresh meat. Using oars, sailors would herd the waddling birds into pens for slaughter. Their oil and feathers were also valuable resources. Later when great auks became rare, collectors caught and preserved these birds for museums. No one has reported seeing a living great auk since 1844.

The Steller's sea cow, a large mammal about 8 m (26 ft) long and weighing 7 to 8 tons, lived off the coast of Alaska. In 1742, while shipwrecked near Alaskan waters, Russians on an exploration vessel discovered these animals. To keep from starving, the crew hunted the sea cows and found the meat delicious. As news about these animals traveled to other areas, hunters and traders came to Alaska and began killing the sea cows. In less than thirty years from the discovery of Steller's sea cows, man had hunted these animals into extinction.

The passenger pigeon suffered a similar fate. In the early 1800s there were probably over two billion of these bluish gray birds in America, making them the most abundant bird on the planet. Because of the pigeon's tasty meat, people began slaughtering them.

Besides supplying food for humans, passenger pigeons were also used to feed pigs. Although all this killing greatly reduced the size of the pigeon population, there were still many left.

Passenger pigeons, however, are social birds that require huge colonies to breed. One breeding colony in Michigan covered an area of about 190 square miles. When their numbers

began to decrease, the birds stopped breeding. By 1900 passenger pigeons were extinct in the wild, but a few remained in captivity. The last known passenger pigeon died in the Cincinnati Zoo in 1914.

Normally the Carolina parakeet, a small colorful parrot native to the southern United States, ate cockleburs, thistles, and pine nuts. But when farmers planted orchards in its habitat, it began eating unripe fruit. To prevent damage to their orchards, the farmers began killing entire flocks of parakeets. When a farmer shot one or two of the birds in a flock, the others would scream and hover over the dead and wounded. This made the rest of the birds easy targets.

Although Carolina parakeets were a nuisance to farmers, they did have commercial uses. During the 1880s and 1890s this colorful bird was a popular decoration for ladies' hats. Entire stuffed birds often sat on the hats of fashion-minded women.

The parakeets were also popular as pets and were easy to tame and train. In spite of their quick adjustment to living in cages, these birds did not reproduce in captivity. In 1918 the last captive Carolina parakeet died in the Cincinnati Zoo.

Today man usually does not force organisms into extinction by excessive hunting. Yet by destroying their natural habitats, he has forced some organisms to the point of being endangered. An **endangered species** is a species that may soon become extinct if man does not take care of it. If a species' habitat has been destroyed, the only way to avoid extinction is to find another habitat for the species or to raise it in captivity.

Some scientists believe that certain American animals are endangered species and should be protected. As a result, the Endangered Species Act was first passed in 1973. A few of the animals included on the list are the Wyoming toad, the leatherback sea turtle, the manatee, the Key deer, and the black-footed ferret. Also included on the endangered species list are American birds such as the Eskimo curlew, the California condor, the whooping crane, and the wood stork. Plants such as the Florida golden aster, Santa Cruz cypress, and snakeroot are also endangered species.

A great barrier to rescuing endangered species is the cost involved.

In some cases large areas of valuable land must be left undisturbed, with logging, farming, mining, etc. prohibited. Private landowners may even be prevented from using their own land if endangered species are found there. In other situations expensive devices must be used. One such device used today keeps sea turtles from being trapped in fish nets.

Easy solutions are rare. We should not force endangered species into extinction by needlessly killing them or

by destroying their natural habitats. Such actions would make us unwise stewards of the living natural resources that God has provided. But we must remember that man is more important than other living things and that God does want us to use land for things such as logging, farming, and mining.

gave land to people who settled an area of land. These *land grants*, as they were called, helped to make the wilderness land productive.

Often when people first moved into an area, they prepared the land for farming. In some areas they chopped down trees. In the prairies the settlers plowed under the natural grasses. After they planted their crops, they gathered abundant harvests. After several years, however, the harvests began to grow smaller. In time, the harvests became so small that many farmers had to move to new areas to feed their families.

In these cases, the soil had lost its *productivity* because of poor farming techniques. Some of the loss in productivity is related to decreased soil fertility. When soil loses its fertility, crop plants will not grow as well as they previously did. However, noncrop plants may continue to grow on this depleted soil. In time, as noncrop plants die and decompose, they restore the soil fertility. Many

Pioneers in America often initially reaped abundant harvests. But poor farming practices led to poorer yields and eventually to abandonment.

23A-4

early farmers did not understand this concept. Long ago God had told the children of Israel to let their land rest every seventh year (Ex. 23:10-11). Such resting would prevent the loss of soil fertility. But this biblical concept was ignored.

Land can lose its productivity in several ways. One is the *depletion* (dih PLEE shun) of soil nutrients. Every plant takes certain nutrients from the soil. Normally a plant dies and decomposes where it grew. Its nutrients return to the soil. However, when a farmer harvests his crop, he takes some of the nutrients away. In time the soil may no longer have the nutrients the plants need.

History Connection

Research the causes and impact of the dust storms that hit the Great Plains in the 1930s, earning the region a nickname—the Dust Bowl. Could this happen again today? Why or why not?

23A-5 Fertilizers supply essential plant nutrients

Nitrogen Cycle

Farmers apply their knowledge of the nitrogen cycle when they plant legumes to add nitrogen to the soil. This natural process started a long time before tractors were invented. God designed ecosystems to reuse materials so that life can continue. When we work in harmony with these natural rhythms, we are being good stewards of the earth.

In addition, when farmers remove crops from a field, they also remove the material that would normally become humus. (See p. 360.) Humus, or decaying plant matter, is important to soil fertility. Without humus, the organisms that live in the soil begin to die off, and many of the processes that enrich the soil stop.

Today farmers understand what will happen if they deplete the soil of nutrients and humus. Many prevent nutrient depletion by adding *fertilizer* to their soil. A fertilizer is a substance that contains the nutrients needed by plants. For instance, a farmer may know that the crop he wants to plant needs large amounts of potassium and that his soil is low in potassium. He can add to his field a fertilizer that is high in potassium. Some farmers use fertilizers produced by chemical factories. Others use manure and other natural substances as fertilizers.

Some plants actually add certain nutrients to the soil. Clover, alfalfa, soybeans, and other *legumes* (LEG YOOMZ) have bacteria living in their roots. These bacteria can take nitrogen from the air that permeates the soil and change it into nitrogen compounds that the plant can use. Legumes grow well in nitrogen-poor soil, and when they die they can increase the nitrogen content of the soil by releasing the nitrogen stored in their roots. In fact, sometimes these crops are planted just to be tilled under and become humus. This natural flow of nitrogen, in its different compounds, through an ecosystem is known as the *nitrogen cycle*.

Most farmers practice crop rotation to keep their soil in good condition. *Crop rotation* is a method of farming in which a farmer changes the kinds of crops he grows in a particular field every year or two. A crop raised one year may use more of one nutrient from the soil than other nutrients. The following year a different crop, which uses more of a different nutrient, would be raised. This practice helps prevent nutrient depletion of the soil. The farmer may even plant some crops, such as the legumes already mentioned, to supply nutrients to the soil, making it better for the next crop.

Many plants are killed or have limited yields because of viruses, bacteria, roundworms, insects, or weeds. Because many of these harmful organisms affect only certain plants and have life cycles that last more than a year or that become worse over time, crop rotation can break the cycles and make the land more productive.

A fairly recent practice to prevent soil depletion is to cultivate the soil as little as possible and to harvest only the seeds or fruits. The seeds for the new crop are planted among the remains (dead stalks and leaves) of the previous year's crop. This practice improves the soil in two ways. First, the soil is not opened to erosion. Second, as the old plant material decomposes, it enriches the soil with nutrients and humus. This type of farming is called *no-till agriculture*, or conservation tillage.

You might wonder how weeds in these fields are controlled without cultivation or tilling. Only certain herbicide-resistant varieties of crop plants are planted in this type of agriculture. When the weeds begin to grow, the farmer sprays herbicide on the field. The herbicide kills all the plants except the resistant crop plant. The crop plants continue to grow, saving the farmer the expense and soil loss of repeated plowing.

Section Review 23A

1. What is the main disadvantage in using nonrenewable natural resources?

2. Why do most hunters in modern America hunt?

3. List three endangered species.

4. _____ organisms are raised by humans rather than living in the wild.

5. Why should a farmer practice crop rotation?

23B Man's Role in the Ecosystem

In the Middle East an old story is told about a craftsman who gave the king of Persia a beautiful chessboard. The king was so delighted with his gift that he asked how he could repay the craftsman. The man replied by asking the king to give him one grain of rice for the first square of the chessboard, two for the second, four for the third, eight for the fourth, and so on. The number doubled for each of the sixty-four squares.

The king agreed, but he was soon sorry when he realized the amount of rice he owed the craftsman. For the tenth square the man received 512 (2^9) grains of rice; for the twentieth square he received 524,288 (2^{19}) grains of rice; for the twenty-eighth square he received over 1 billion grains; and for the thirty-sixth square he received over 1 trillion grains of rice. To pay the amount he owed for all sixty-four squares, the king had to give the craftsman every grain of rice in Persia.

Such a type of increase is called *exponential* (EK spuh NEN shul) *growth*. Exponential growth describes a constant rate of dramatic increase. In the rice example, the amount doubled for every square.

The *human population*, which is the number of people living on the earth at one time, has experienced exponential growth. Historians estimate that at the time of Christ, the population was about 0.25 billion, but by 1650 the population had doubled, making a total of 0.5 billion. Two hundred years later, in 1850, the population had doubled again, reaching 1 billion people. Then by 1930, eighty years later, the population had reached 2 billion. Forty-four years later, by 1974, the human population had doubled again to a total of 4 billion people. If this growth had continued at about the same rate, the population would have doubled by the mid-1990s. However, most projections now predict that the global popluation won't exceed 8 billion until 2025 or beyond.

23B.1 How a Population Grows

The *birthrate* and the *death rate* of a population affect its growth rate. The **birthrate** is the rate at which members enter a population. The

Objectives 23B

- Describe the growth of the human population since the time of Christ.

- Suggest methods that man can use to conserve fossil fuels.

- Explain what factors may affect the growth of a population.

- Discuss doomsday ecology in light of human population growth and the Word of God.

- Define *conservation*.

- List some resources that may need to be conserved.

- Recognize that fossil fuels are nonrenewable resources.

- List and describe several energy sources that man is just beginning to develop for modern use.

death rate is the rate at which members leave a population. If the birthrate and the death rate are the same, there will be *zero population growth*. If the death rate increases or if the birthrate decreases, there will be a *population decrease*. If the birthrate increases or if the death rate decreases, there will be a *population increase*.

Facets of *Ecology:* *Stretching Fossil Fuels*

As the cost of finding and extracting fossil fuels increases, scientists are looking for better ways to use these fuels. One method is to dilute fossil fuels with a renewable energy source. Gasohol is a mixture of alcohol (a renewable energy source made from plant material such as corn) and

gasoline (a nonrenewable energy resource made from a fossil fuel). By combining alcohol and gasoline, scientists hope to stretch the limited supply of fossil fuels.

Gasohol is readily available at many gas stations as a mixture of 10 percent alcohol and 90 percent gasoline. Many manufacturers are selling cars that can use a gasohol mixture containing 85 percent alcohol. Alcohol-containing fuels have advantages and disadvantages. One advantage is that alcohol burns with less exhaust. This results in less air pollution. A disadvantage is that a car running on gasohol experiences a 5%–15% drop in mileage. This might be balanced out by lower prices for gasohol, especially during times of high fuel prices.

Another method is to develop fossil fuels other than oil and natural gas. For example, coal is more abundant in the earth than either oil or natural gas, but it is the fossil fuel that we use the least. Only about 20% of the energy used in the United States today comes from coal.

People use coal less than other fuels because it produces large amounts of dust and smoke when it burns. It is also difficult and dangerous to mine. Coal mining has a very high accident rate compared to most other occupations. Although surface mining of coal is less dangerous than underground mining, it damages the land. Any area that has been surface mined is practically worthless unless expensive measures are taken to restore it.

Coal is also very hard to reach. In the United States much of the coal is located as deep as 1800 m (6000 ft) under the ground. Yet most mines in the United States are less than 150 m (500 ft) deep. Practical and inexpensive ways to reach deep coal reserves are currently unavailable.

Because coal is such a plentiful resource, scientists are trying to develop good methods of converting coal into gasoline and other products. Unfortunately, many of these methods of coal conversion are still experimental.

Every year consumers use more fossil fuels. It is easy to waste energy from fossil fuels in our homes, cars, and businesses. Because this is not an unlimited resource, we must be wise in our use of it. When we waste energy from these fuels, we are displaying an unloving attitude toward future generations.

Imagine a car with an engine that was virtually silent and that produced only water vapor as exhaust. That is the promise of fuel-cell technology. The fuel, hydrogen, could be obtained from water or renewable resources such as plants. Oxygen from the air is mixed with hydrogen within a fuel cell. This causes a flow of protons from one electrode to another that creates current like a battery. In tests, these fuel-cell cars have nearly three times the efficiency of a conventional car engine. One current drawback is the need for a network of hydrogen "filling stations" that would make longer trips practical.

In the past few decades, a primary factor affecting human population growth has been a decrease in the death rate. The discovery of cures and treatments for many diseases is one reason that a smaller percentage of the population dies in a given year. Good medical care and improved standards of living have also enabled people in many areas of the world to live longer. The decrease in the death rate has been so dramatic that, in spite of a decrease in the birthrate, the population is still growing.

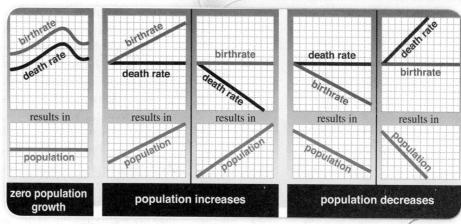

How the relationship of birthrate to death rate affects population 23B-1

23B.2 *Doomsday Ecology*

Some ecologists predict a horrible doomsday when humans will ultimately destroy the earth by their abuse of the physical world. These people believe that the earth will become so overpopulated that there will be an overwhelming demand for natural resources. As the supply decreases, people will have to struggle to meet their basic needs.

According to the doomsday ecologists, the enormous number of people will pollute almost all the earth with wastes and poisons. As the supply of natural resources decreases and the pollution increases, humans will eventually become extinct.

Global warming is another issue that often makes the news. Some drastic predictions have the ice caps melting, sea levels rising, and major coastal cities around the globe being flooded. Many scientists connect this with the increased use of fossil fuels and the carbon dioxide they add to the atmosphere. While some data seems to indicate temperatures may be increasing, the consequences of any increase and the cause are far from certain.

Some people have used doomsday stories to promote special interests. For example, they use the threat of overpopulation to wrongly justify abortion (the killing of unborn babies). They may also support *euthanasia* (YOO thuh NAY zhuh) (the killing of people who are old or very sick). They also use the problems of pollution and the projected shortage of natural resources to promote the idea of "turning back to nature." Some even carry this idea to the extreme by saying that humans should not use the earth's natural resources at all.

You're Myth-taken

Many newspapers, magazines, and books predict that overpopulation will soon lead to mass starvation. Much of this hype is based on inaccurate projections of population growth and an underestimation of what the earth can support. More reliable data indicates that the total population will probably peak around 11 billion by the year 2200 and then begin to fall.

Mothers and children wait for food at a relief station in Africa. 23B-2

23B.3 *Planning for the Future*

In spite of what doomsday ecologists say about a future population explosion, it is difficult to predict how large the human population will be. In the past, natural disasters, wars, and epidemics have all had drastic effects on the population growth. For example, during the 1300s about one-fourth of the population of Europe died from the epidemic of the "black death," or bubonic (boo BAHN ik) plague. It

Let Them Have Dominion

According to Scripture, is population growth a good or a bad thing? Can you think of passages that apply?

is quite possible that an epidemic, a natural disaster, a nuclear war, or another factor could greatly reduce the human population again.

Even if the human population does continue to increase, the earth may still be able to provide enough food for the human race. Using the best techniques and the most productive crops, we could produce an abundance of food. Some people estimate that farms can produce enough food to feed up to 100 billion people. Yet, today people are dying of starvation. Political problems, poor farming techniques, and wasteful food practices are just some of the factors that contribute to the food shortage in some areas.

Starvation is a horrible way to die. At first the body lives off its fat reserves. But then it begins to digest muscle tissue. The reason that poor children in Africa are often seen with bloated abdomens is that their abdominal muscles have been consumed and their vital organs have tipped forward. Death by starvation is slow, humiliating, and painful. When the Christian considers that such suffering is avoidable, he should think of Christ's story of the Good Samaritan (Luke 10:25–37). The story teaches us to love our neighbor as much as we love ourselves. Who is that neighbor? Christ indicates that he is anyone whose needs we have the power to meet. Some Christians contend that working to feed the hungry will keep us from effectively spreading the gospel. But Christians should remember that the same Lord Who gave the command, "Go . . . and teach all nations" (Matt. 28:19) also gave the command, "Go, and do thou likewise" (Luke 10:37) when referring to the mercy shown by the Good Samaritan.

23B-3 The national park and forest system (green areas) includes lands that have been set aside for limited use.

23B.4 *Conservation*

Conservation is the preservation and wise use of natural resources. Sometimes it is difficult to decide what wise use is. For example, cutting down some of the trees may destroy the ecological balance of an area. But, in another area, cutting the same number of trees may be beneficial to the environment. Ecologists and others who decide how to use natural resources must be informed about ecological matters to make wise decisions.

One way some countries are trying to conserve their natural resources is by reserving certain areas of land for protection and controlled use. For instance, the United States has established over fifty national parks and more than one hundred fifty national forests for conservation. These parks and forests include over 200 million acres of land. The government allows people to have limited use of some of the land. Other areas are completely closed to the public.

Although you may not think of it at first, energy is a natural resource that must be conserved. Coal, oil, and natural gas are fossil fuels. **Fossil fuels** are the remains of plants and animals that once lived on the earth. These materials are not renewable resources. Therefore, careful management of these resources is necessary until other energy sources can be found.

Conservation is a concept some people have taken to an extreme. Christians should not abuse natural resources; they must use them carefully so that they are available for others. They should not, however, completely refrain from using the earth's natural resources. God commands Christians in Luke 12:42–44 to be good stewards of all that He has given. This includes wise use of the physical planet on which He has placed them.

Section Review 23B

1. The human population has experienced _____ growth.

2. What two substances are in gasohol?

3. What disease limited the growth of the human population in Europe during the 1300s?

23C Pollution

Pollution is the addition of impurities to an ecosystem. It is one way humans have abused the physical world. But not all pollution is harmful. To understand what impurities do to the environment, you should first know the two major types of *pollutants* (puh LOOT nts): substance pollutants and energy pollutants.

A *substance pollutant* is a solid, liquid, or gas that pollutes an ecosystem. There are two different types of substance pollutants: biodegradable (BYE oh dih GRAY duh bul) and nonbiodegradable. Those substances that living organisms can break down are **biodegradable pollutants**. Sewage, paper, and wood products are all examples of biodegradable pollutants. Those substances that the environment cannot break down are **nonbiodegradable pollutants**. Plastic, glass,

What Do You Think?
Can you list some alternative energy sources that are not based on fossil fuels?

Objectives 23C
- Define *pollution*.
- Differentiate between a substance pollutant and an energy pollutant.
- Differentiate between a biodegradable pollutant and a nonbiodegradable pollutant.
- Recognize problems associated with the disposal of hazardous substances.
- Describe water pollution and sewage treatment.
- List several common components of air pollution.
- Define *smog*.
- Discuss the problems associated with trash disposal and recycling.

biodegradable: bio- (Gk. BIOS, life) + -de- (L. DE-, down) + -gradable (L. GRADUS, rank or step)

Facets of *Ecology:* *Disposing of Hazardous Wastes*

Hazardous substances are chemicals that can harm living things. Many of these chemicals are products called *hazardous wastes*. Some hazardous wastes have vapors so strong that a single breath of them would kill a human. A single drop of certain wastes would poison all the water in a swimming pool. If a person drank one glass of that poisoned water, he would suffer kidney disorders, nerve damage, and other serious effects.

Some hazardous wastes come from nuclear reactors. While the production of nuclear energy is safe and efficient, its waste products are a long-term challenge. These wastes give off radiation, causing mutations in living cells. These mutations may produce many disorders, including birth defects and cancer.

Where can we dispose of hazardous substances without harming the environment? In the past, many factories packed their hazardous wastes in special metal drums and then carefully sealed the drums. These drums were disposed of in various remote places, including the ocean, caves, and old mines. Some drums were simply stacked on land in remote areas of the country.

In time, however, the drums rusted or the chemicals in the drums ate away the protective lining, and the drums began to leak. These highly poisonous substances were then released into the environment.

Scientists have discovered recently that hazardous wastes that seep into the environment many miles away from civilization can still affect humans. Often these pollutants are carried by the movement of water. For example, when a nonbiodegradable waste leaks into the ocean, it may become so spread out that its presence cannot be detected. Still, the waste is present.

As the waste comes into contact with different organisms, it enters their bodies. If these organisms become part of the food chain, the chemical waste and its effects pass on to other organisms. Later a contaminated organism may be used as food on your dinner table. The chemical waste that was released thousands of miles away would find its way to you.

When drums of hazardous waste are dumped on land, the wastes can leak into the soil. As rainwater passes through the soil, it carries these chemicals farther below ground. In the past, scientists thought the soil acted as a filter, cleaning the pollutants passing through it. Biodegradable substances that have been put into the soil will eventually break down. But most hazardous wastes are nonbiodegradable; that is, the microscopic organisms in the soil are not able to break them down.

Eventually the hazardous wastes in the soil water reach the water table and contaminate it. In time the wastes will show up in springs and wells. Once these materials are in the soil and moving through the groundwater, removal is almost impossible. It can take years or decades before contamination levels drop to safe levels.

Sometimes very useful substances escape and become hazardous wastes, affecting water supplies. Many service stations, for example, have leaky gasoline storage tanks in the ground. As the gasoline leaks out, it can pollute the water supply in that area. In this case, however, the United States government has passed a law to eliminate leaky tanks. All underground gasoline tanks must be leak proof and spill proof.

Chemicals used in a city's sewage treatment plant or put into a septic tank can also cause problems. The water that drains from these facilities sinks into the soil and eventually becomes part of the water table. If a dry-cleaning shop put 5 gal. of trichloroethylene (trye KLOR oh ETH uh LEEN), a cleaning fluid, into its septic tank, that chemical could pollute the water used by 50,000 households for a year.

Some chemicals entering America's water supply are nonbiodegradable insecticides. Farmers use *insecticides* on their fields to control insects. Rain often washes these chemicals away into streams and lakes. To keep the insects under control, the farmer must apply more insecticides after the rain. If the farmer keeps replacing these chemicals, a high concentration of insecticides may build up in the streams and lakes.

Nonbiodegradable insecticides also reach the water table. In California's San Joaquin (wah KEEN) Valley, farmers sprayed their crops with a pesticide called DBCP. Scientists later found that DBCP causes cancer and other serious disorders, and people stopped using the chemical. Today, however, over one million people in that area drink from wells that contain dangerously high levels of DBCP.

For many years few people recognized hazardous substances as a significant problem. Now hazardous substances in the water affect about five million Americans and have caused the closing of over two thousand wells. This could be only the beginning of the problems caused by hazardous substances. If man stopped producing hazardous substances now, the world would continue to suffer from the pollution that has already been produced. Scientists are looking for ways to safely use and dispose of hazardous substances.

and many different chemicals are examples of nonbiodegradable pollutants.

An *energy pollutant* is any form of energy that pollutes an ecosystem. Heat, light, sound, and radiation are all examples of energy pollutants.

Pollutants can affect living organisms in a variety of ways. One way is to kill the organisms that normally inhabit an area and at the same time to produce an ideal habitat for other organisms. For example, when a factory dumps hot water into a cool stream, it may kill some of the cool water species. In time, however, warm-water species will begin to live in the warmer parts of the stream.

Another way that pollutants affect living organisms is to kill them indirectly. For instance, excess fertilizer that runs off a lawn or field and collects in a pond may cause an abundant growth of pond algae. Later when the algae die, a large population of microscopic organisms will begin to decompose the algae. If the microscopic organisms use all the available oxygen in the water, there will not be enough for the fish, and many of them may die. Although the fertilizer did not harm the fish directly, it produced a chain reaction that caused their death.

Pollution often occurs little by little. Although any amount of impurity in an ecosystem is still a pollutant, small amounts may not be harmful. Most ecosystems are usually able to deal with small amounts of biodegradable pollutants. However, if the pollutants are nonbiodegradable, these small amounts build up and may cause serious problems.

Substance pollutants, such as the ones that have been thrown into this stream, are either biodegradable or nonbiodegradable. **23C-1**

23C.1 *Water Pollution*

In America almost all streams, rivers, and lakes have some pollutants in them. In some areas the *water pollution* is minor, and it causes few, if any, problems. In other areas, however, the water pollution has destroyed all the natural

The floating booms shown here form a barrier to contain a petroleum spill on a river during clean-up efforts. **23C-2**

23C-3 Fertilizer runoff can cause excessive algal growth in ponds.

plants and animals of the area. Water pollution also can have a drastic effect on humans. The bacteria or viruses that cause hepatitis (HEP uh TY tis), cholera (KAHL ur uh), typhoid (TY FOYD), dysentery (DIS un TEHR ee), and other diseases often travel in polluted water. Water pollution looks bad, smells bad, and is a waste of a God-given natural resource.

Many water pollution problems in America result from sewage. *Sewage* is primarily made up of biodegradable wastes and water from homes, restaurants, hospitals, factories, and other similar sources. To help control the problems caused by sewage, many cities have built *sewage treatment facilities*. Although there are three levels of sewage treatment—primary, secondary, and tertiary—most facilities do not use all three levels.

Primary treatment, the first level of sewage treatment, filters out solid pieces of wastes; later this material may be buried or burned.

Secondary treatment, the next level of sewage treatment, reduces the amount of biodegradable material in the sewage. In many facilities this is done by passing the sewage along a series of canals or tanks while air is pumped through the sewage. With plenty of available oxygen, microscopic organisms thrive in these canals. These organisms break down the biodegradable material.

Tertiary (TUR shee EHR ee) *treatment*, the third level, removes the various chemicals that remain in the water after secondary treatment. This treatment stage is often omitted because it is especially expensive. Without it, however, some pollutants remain in the water system.

If the water leaving a sewage treatment facility has undergone all three processes, it may be cleaner than most drinking water. In fact, some cities recycle the water from the sewage treatment facility directly into their water systems. For those cities with polluted water supplies or those in drier areas, recycling the water from treated sewage may be less expensive than getting water from another source.

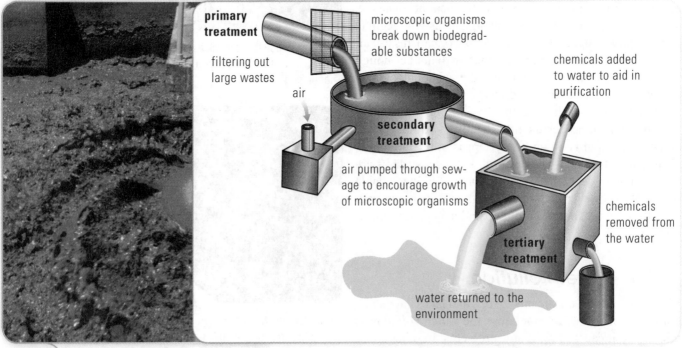

primary treatment
filtering out large wastes
air
microscopic organisms break down biodegradable substances
chemicals added to water to aid in purification
secondary treatment
air pumped through sewage to encourage growth of microscopic organisms
chemicals removed from the water
tertiary treatment
water returned to the environment

23C-4 At a sewage treatment facility air is bubbled through the sewage (left) to increase the activity of microscopic organisms as they break down biodegradable materials.

Why do some cities fail to treat their sewage completely? The major reason is the expense. It is very costly to build and operate a sewage treatment facility. The more treatment the sewage undergoes, the more expensive it is to operate the facility.

A more serious type of water pollution than sewage is the dumping of nonbiodegradable chemicals such as salts, mercury compounds, iodine, and solvents into lakes and streams. Many of these chemicals are poisonous. Those that are not may become dangerous to living things if they build up in the environment.

Although nonbiodegradable chemicals have a greater effect on the organisms that live in or drink from polluted waters, they also can affect humans. If a person eats an organism contaminated with these chemicals or eats the organism's products (such as milk), the chemicals will pass on to that person. As the chemicals collect, they may slowly poison the person. Recognizing these problems, various governments have passed laws that restrict the dumping of nonbiodegradable chemicals into water.

23C.2 *Air Pollution*

Every year the United States alone puts nearly 150 million tons of pollution into the air. *Air pollution* is a combination of liquids, gases, and small particles that collect in the atmosphere. Some of the major components of air pollution include carbon monoxide, sulfur compounds, and nitric oxide.

Carbon monoxide (CO) is one of the most abundant components of air pollution. When various fuels (coal, wood, oil, gasoline) do not burn completely, they produce carbon monoxide. Carbon monoxide is a poisonous gas that is colorless, odorless, and tasteless. (See p. 439.)

Sulfur compounds are the second most abundant type of air pollutant. *Sulfur dioxide* (SO_2), which is a product of burning coal and oil, is a heavy gas with a choking odor. This gas can combine with water in the air to form *sulfuric acid* (H_2SO_4). Sulfuric acid and sulfur dioxide are both harmful to living things.

Nitric oxide (NO) is a gas found in automobile exhaust. In the air, nitric oxide may combine with oxygen to form a deadly gas called *nitrogen dioxide* (NO_2). When this gas combines with water, it becomes *nitric acid* (HNO_3), which is harmful to plants, animals, and humans.

A common air pollution problem in many industrial areas is smog. *Smog* is a combination of smoke, automobile exhaust, and fog. When these components react together, they can destroy plants and damage the exposed metal in buildings, fences, and statues. Smog also harms humans and animals, causing irritated eyes, damaged lungs, and sometimes death.

Because people are concerned about clean air, many states have passed laws to force factories to release less air pollution. These laws have been unpopular among the industries because antipollution equipment is expensive to install and operate. Although many factories now use the required equip-

Love Thy Neighbor

Knowing that pollutants affect people's health, what should our attitude towards pollution be?

Air polution has many sources **23C-5**

Smog is a problem in many metropolitan areas. **23C-6**

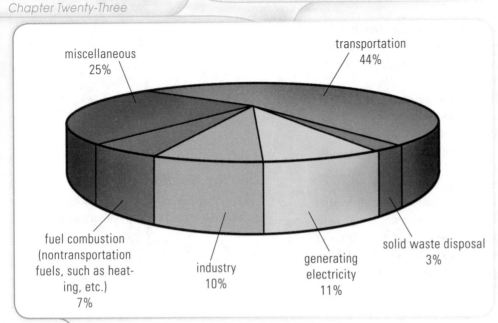

23C-7 Sources of air pollution in the United States

miscellaneous
25%

transportation
44%

fuel combustion
(nontransportation
fuels, such as heat-
ing, etc.)
7%

industry
10%

generating
electricity
11%

solid waste disposal
3%

Paper accounts for 40% of the volume in landfills. Plastics account for 11% of the volume.

ment, others have closed down because they could not afford to meet the clean-air standards.

Since cars and trucks are another source of air pollution, laws have also been made to force manufacturers to design vehicles that produce less pollution. But the antipollution devices in the vehicles can make them more expensive and often cause them to use more fuel.

23C.3 Trash

Solid waste materials that are either useless or unwanted are called **trash**. Some experts estimate that Americans produce over 200 million tons of trash per year. In the past, most cities had *dumps* for trash disposal. Workers burned the trash to make it sterile and to reduce the amount in the dump. But the smoke contributed to air pollution, so many areas passed laws prohibiting burning trash.

Today most cities have **sanitary** (SAN ih TEHR ee) **landfills** for their trash. A sanitary landfill is like a dump, but workers do not burn the trash. Instead, they periodically put a layer of soil over the trash to help control odors and pests. As the layers of trash build up, the sanitary landfill reaches its capacity, and a new dumping area must be found.

Some cities once solved their trash problems by sinking trash into the ocean. The ocean has suffered considerably from this practice. Thousands of animals have died in the "death traps" produced by the trash. U.S. cities are no longer permitted to dump their trash into the ocean. However, the already dumped wastes may have long-term effects.

Another method of dealing with trash is to recycle it. To **recycle** something is to use it again. When the idea of recycling trash first became popular, people hoped to save money and conserve natural resources through this process. Some even believed that they could make a lot of money doing it. But there are only a few materials in trash that are profitable to recycle. Most of the materials may be obtained more cheaply from the natural resource than from collected, sorted, and processed trash.

One material that is worth recycling is aluminum. It is cheaper to pay people for aluminum cans than it is to find, mine, and purify more aluminum.

23C-8 Today trash is put into sanitary landfills and covered with dirt. Can you foresee some problems that may result from this method of trash disposal?

Serving God as an Environmental Engineer

Job Description
Environmental engineers use math, chemistry, and biology to prevent or solve environmental problems. They may have responsibilities dealing with water or air pollution, hazardous wastes, or even recycling. Some environmental engineers work as consultants with industries to correct environmental problems or maintain compliance with state and federal regulations. Usually they spend more time in an office than in the field.

Possible Workplaces
landfills, construction sites, wastewater treatment facilities, government agencies

Education
A minimum of a bachelor's degree in engineering is expected, and most environmental engineers also take ecology and other biology courses. Many engineers continue their study in graduate school to focus on a particular area of study such as groundwater or air quality.

Dominion Opportunities
By developing and implementing plans and systems for improving the quality of the air, water, and soil, environmental engineers apply technology to preserve God's creation and improve the quality of life for mankind.

Paper (newsprint) used to be profitable to recycle. The "paper drive" was a method of raising funds for many groups. During a paper drive people collect newspapers and sell them to a paper recycling company. In recent years, however, the amount of paper collected for recycling exceeded the demand. This made paper drives less profitable.

However, the paper recycling situation is expected to improve. Many states are passing laws that require local newspaper publishers to use paper with 10%, 25%, and even 50% recycled-paper content. This should increase the demand for and profit in recycling paper.

In many communities, recyclable materials must be separated from trash for recycling.

23C-9

Section Review 23C

1. What distinguishes biodegradable pollution from nonbiodegradable pollution?

2. Name the energy pollutant that you think is most excessive in your area. What is its source?

3. What does primary sewage treatment accomplish?

4. What is used to cover trash in sanitary landfills?

The primary intent behind paper recycling is to reduce the amount of landfill space required, not to save trees.

Scientifically Speaking

natural resource

extinct

endangered species

birthrate

death rate

conservation

fossil fuel

pollution

biodegradable pollutant

nonbiodegradable pollutant

trash

sanitary landfill

recycle

Chapter Review

1. List one renewable and one nonrenewable natural resource.

2. What does the term *endangered species* mean?

3. Describe agriculture.

4. List two ways that harvesting crops can reduce soil productivity.

5. What important nutrient do legumes add to the soil?

6. List one advantage and one disadvantage of using gasohol instead of gasoline.

7. What two factors affect a population's growth rate?

8. What kept the human population growth relatively slow in the past?

9. What is conservation?

10. How can clean, warm water be a pollutant?

11. Which does secondary treatment of sewage reduce—biodegradable or nonbiodegradable material?

12. What is the main reason that some cities do not completely treat their sewage?

13. List three common components of air pollutants.

What Did You Learn?

1. Is it possible to overuse renewable resources? Explain your answer.

2. How are domesticated animals different from their wild counterparts?

3. Explain why hunting was responsible for the extinction of passenger pigeons even though hunters did not kill every passenger pigeon.

4. What relationship must exist between the birthrate and death rate of a population for that population to increase?

5. Explain how a hazardous substance dumped on the ground could contaminate the fish for sale at your local grocery store.

6. How do dumps and sanitary landfills differ?

Self Quiz 23

_____ 1. Which of these is a renewable natural resource?

    A. oil
    B. timber
    C. copper
    D. coal

_____ 2. The beaver is an example of a

    A. consumer.
    B. producer.
    C. decomposer.
    D. none of these

_____ 3. Which of these is considered to be extinct?

    A. whooping crane
    B. pronghorn
    C. Wyoming toad
    D. passenger pigeon

_____ 4. Domesticated animals are those that man raises primarily for his own use. (True/False)

_____ 5. Clover, soybeans, and other legumes are important to farmers mainly because they add _____ to the soil.

    A. oxygen
    B. carbon
    C. nitrogen
    D. potassium

_____ 6. If a country's birthrate is increasing while its death rate is decreasing

    A. its population will grow.
    B. its population will shrink.
    C. its population will remain the same.
    D. (not enough information given)

7. _____ is the preservation and wise use of natural resources.

_____ 8. Heat may be a form of

    A. renewable pollution.
    B. energy pollution.
    C. substance pollution.
    D. biodegradable pollution.

_____ 9. Lumber is an example of a nonbiodegradable pollutant. (True/False)

_____ 10. Which of these is *not* a potential source of air pollution?

    A. CO
    B. SO_2
    C. NO
    D. PO_4

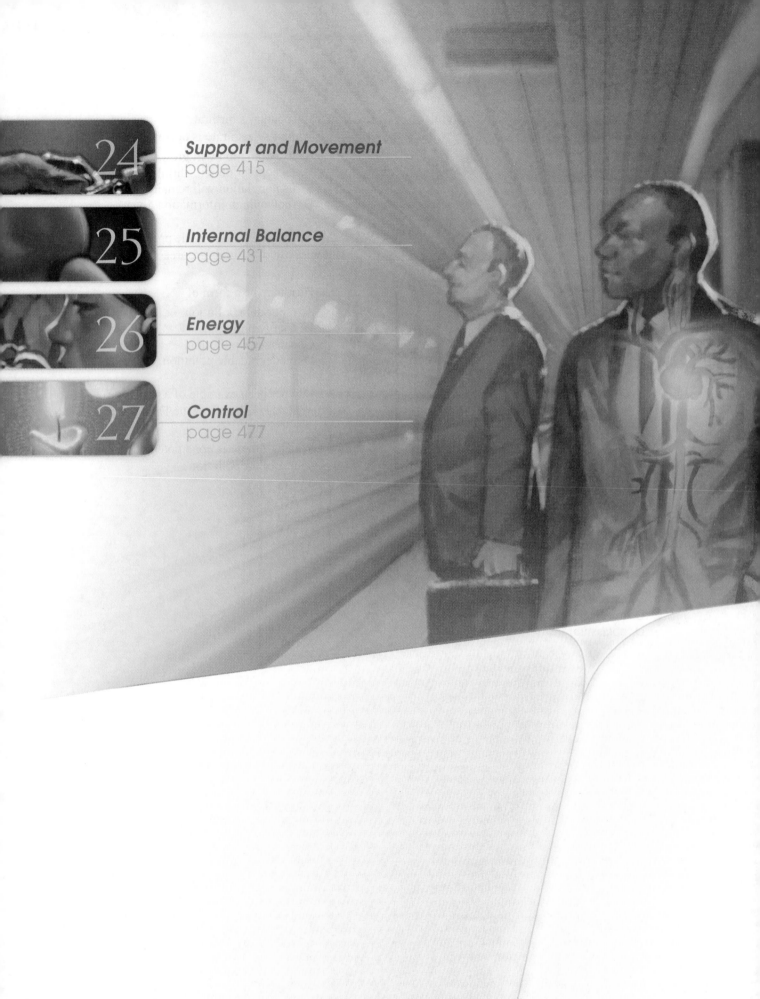

STRUCTURE AND FUNCTION OF THE HUMAN BODY

SUPPORT AND MOVEMENT

An android (AN DROYD) is a human-shaped robot. Androids are not limited to modern science fiction stories. Man's fascination with androids dates back thousands of years. The Greek poet Homer (circa 850 BC) described metallic maidens that helped Hephaestus, the god of fire and metalworking. In 1495 Leonardo da Vinci drew plans for a mechanical man.

About the time the Declaration of Independence was signed, a Swiss watchmaker named Pierre Jacquet-Droz was building beautiful doll-like androids that could do astonishing things. The first android Jacquet-Droz built was Charles the Writer. Charles could be programmed to write up to forty letters in any sequence on a tablet on the desk in front of him.

Today robots are used in hundreds of manufacturing jobs in diverse forms ranging from mechanical arms that weld automobile frames to rovers that have explored the surface of Mars and searched through rubble at disaster sites. For example, search-and-rescue (SAR) robots fitted with cameras and heat sensors were used after the 9/11 attacks to search for survivors in areas that were too dangerous for human rescuers to search.

As fascinating as these robots are, their actions are actually far from human. Android builders face many more problems than robot builders. Androids must look, move, and react like humans. For example, your hand alone contains over thirty-five bone connections. It can be soft and gentle enough to stroke a kitten or to play a quiet note on the piano, but it can be strong enough to force open a jelly-jar lid when necessary. You know how much force to use because you know the difference between a kitten and a jelly jar—you can react to the many situations in your environment.

One of the major design problems for researchers has been human-like mobility. Developing an android that can walk independently—something

What is the difference between an android and a robot? A *robot* is any mechanical device that can perform a task on command or be programmed ahead of time to perform the task. Robots don't have to look like humans!

Would You Believe?

Over 90% of robots are used to perform highly repetitive tasks in factories. Over half are used in the automotive industry.

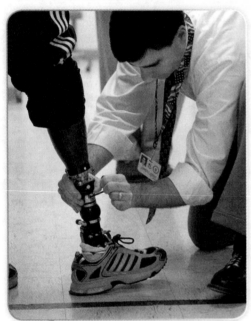

24-1 Even the best artificial limbs cannot restore full function.

Objectives 24A

- Describe the layers of human skin.
- Explain how the skin protects the body and helps regulate body temperature.
- Describe the three kinds of burns.

epidermis: epi- (Gk. EPI, upon) + -dermis (Gk. DERMA, skin)

that humans learn early—has proved to be very difficult for android developers. Currently, the androids that best mimic these human actions are ASIMO (**A**dvanced **S**tep in **I**nnovative **Mo**bility) manufactured by Honda and QRIO (CURE ee OH) manufactured by Sony. Both of these androids can walk, run (approximately 3.5 km/hr), and avoid obstacles in their path. ASIMO has over twenty-six joints that are powered by computer controlled motors. QRIO is able to get up by itself if it falls over. Both ASIMO and QRIO have some basic facial recognition and response capabilities. Although these androids can perform amazing things, they are still little more than technological wonders.

Providing fully functional artificial limbs to replace missing body parts is another use of android technology. Those who were born with deformed arms or legs or have lost them due to injuries or surgery can certainly benefit from advanced artificial limbs. Many artificial limbs are custom-made using computers to analyze the movements of the *amputee* (the person receiving the limb). Some have microprocessors that pick up nerve impulses and cause small motors to move the limb.

Androids have progressed greatly from Charles the Writer; however, even man's best attempts at copying just some of the movements of the body cannot reproduce God's original design. As you study the structures that cover, support, and move your body, keep in mind that God designed, created, and sustains your body in ways no android maker ever could.

24A Human Skin

Your skin is one of your body's major defenses. Unless your skin is cut or damaged, few disease-causing organisms can penetrate it. Although we often think of skin as thin and easily damaged, it is actually quite strong, and it functions well in keeping our insides in and other things out.

24A.1 *Structures of the Skin*

Skin is made up of two layers. The outer layer, called the **epidermis** (EP ih DUR mis), has dead cells at the surface and living cells underneath, and it contains nerve endings such as pain receptors. The dead cells on the surface are continually shed as you wash and as your clothing rubs against your body. The living cells of the epidermis constantly replace these dead cells. As the living cells divide, they form new cells that fill with a protein substance, die, and are pushed outward to be shed.

The inner, thicker layer of the skin is the **dermis** (DUR mis). It contains many blood vessels, nerve receptors, and hair follicles. Sweat glands, oil glands, and wax glands are also found in the dermis. Special cells in this layer make fibers, which are woven around and between all these structures to hold them together.

Hair develops from cells in the hair follicles located in the dermis layer. As these cells divide, the hair grows. The part of the hair deep in the follicle is alive, but the part of the hair above the epidermis is composed of closely packed dead cells.

Oil glands next to each hair secrete oil that keeps the skin and hair soft, flexible, and water resistant. The skin of your ear canals contains other glands that produce a white substance that later turns into dark, sticky earwax. Earwax protects the ear by repelling insects and trapping foreign objects. It also keeps the eardrum and the skin of the ear from drying out.

The skin at the tips of your fingers and toes is soft and sensitive. Before you were born, the epidermis near these spots thickened and then gradually developed nails to protect your fingers and toes.

The **subcutaneous** (SUB kyoo TAY nee us) **layer** below the dermis is not really a part of the skin. It consists of loosely arranged fat cells and fibers. The fat cells help to cushion and insulate your body. The fibers attach the skin to the muscles under the skin.

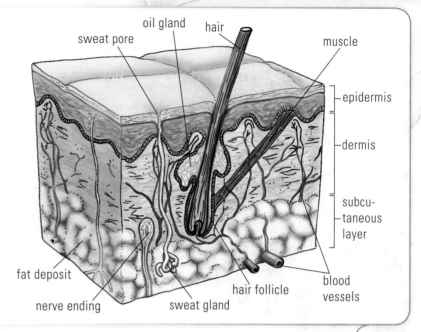

Human skin 24A-1

subcutaneous: sub- (L. SUB-, under) + -cutaneous (L. CUTIS, skin)

melanin: (Gk. MELAS, black)

24A.2 *Skin Color*

A dark pigment called **melanin** (MEL uh nin) causes much of the color of human skin. Special cells in the epidermis produce melanin and pass it on to other cells of the skin. Skin that produces only a little melanin sometimes appears pink because the color of the blood shows through the epidermis. Freckles are clumps of cells that contain more melanin than the rest of the skin. People with darker skin have a greater amount of melanin in their skin. Some other people have more *carotene* (KEHR uh TEEN), a yellowish pigment, in their skin. This combination of pigments results in a yellowish brown skin color.

A little sunlight is good for your skin since

All humans are the same race; they just have different amounts of melanin. 24A-2

invisible ultraviolet rays of the sun aid in producing vitamin D. However, excessive exposure to sunlight may result in sunburn. When you sustain a sunburn, the ultraviolet rays of the sun have killed some of your skin cells. As your body replaces these cells, the increased blood flow to your skin causes redness and soreness. The ultraviolet rays in sunlight can also cause skin cancer. This happens because the

Facets of *the Human Body:* *Fingerprints*

What is dactylography (DAK tuh LAHG ruh fee)? Experts using dactylography can pick you out without ever having seen you. It is a means by which you can be scientifically proven to be you and not just someone who looks like you. Dactylography is the study of fingerprints.

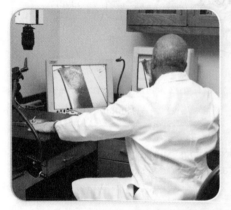

An FBI technician compares fingerprints using AFIS. (photo courtesy of the Bureau of Alcohol, Tobacco, Firearms and Explosives)

Your fingerprints are unique. No one else has ever had, nor ever will have, fingerprints identical to yours. Even identical twins have different fingerprints. Except for growing larger, the patterns of ridges on your hands and feet do not change from the time you are born to the time you die. The footprints taken of a baby in the hospital where he was born remain valid identification in a court of law throughout his life.

Your fingerprint is on the part of your finger called the bulb—between the first knuckle and the tip. The ridges on the bulb are produced by rows of *papillae*, which are ridges of the dermis that extend into the epidermis. The dermis all over your body contains papillae. They are pronounced enough to produce ridges only in the epidermis on your hands and feet.

Papillae keep the same shape throughout your life. Even if your fingers are cut, as long as the dermis is

still alive, the rows of papillae will still produce your characteristic fingerprints when the epidermis grows back.

The U.S. Department of Justice and the Federal Bureau of Investigation (FBI) divide fingerprints into eight groups. Detectives use fingerprints to trace the identity of criminals. Whenever someone touches something with his bare fingers, he leaves imprints of oil that are the same shape as the ridges on his fingers. These imprints, called latent fingerprints, cannot usually be seen (except sometimes on shiny surfaces). Dusting latent fingerprints with dark powders that stick to the oil can make them visible. Afterward, they can be photographed or picked up using a sheet of clear adhesive, mounted onto white paper, and then identified.

The FBI used to identify people by visually comparing a suspect's prints with those filed on paper cards. Today images of fingerprints are scanned into a computer, and the computer electronically compares the suspect's prints with over 40 million prints in the FBI's Automated Fingerprint Identification System (AFIS) file. The computer's identification is then verified by an expert. Many criminals have tried to mutilate their fingertips to avoid being caught by dactylography. They are rarely successful since all ten fingers have to be mutilated by a painful process to destroy the papillae of the dermis.

dactylography: dactylo- (Gk. DAKTULOS, finger) + -graphy (Gk. GRAPHEIN, to write)

Plain arch
The ridges hump in the middle to form a little hill.

Radial loop
The ridges that cross the bulb start at the thumb side, turn at the middle, and go back toward the thumb.

Ulnar loop
The ridges that cross the bulb start at the little finger side, turn, and go back toward the little finger.

Tented arch
In the center of the little hill, a few ridges form a point instead of a curve.

Plain whorl
The bulb's ridges form a circle in the center that spirals out to the sides.

Central pocket loop
The ridges form a loop, but a few ridges form a complete circle within the loop.

Double loop
The ridges look like an S shape.

Accidental
The ridges resemble a hotdog bun partially opened and laid upside down.

ultraviolet rays can cause mutations in the DNA of skin cells. Some of these mutations may cause skin cells to undergo rapid and uncontrolled cell divisions called *cancer*.

When skin is exposed to sunlight, it produces melanin, resulting in a tan. Tanning, however, is the body's way of trying to protect the skin from harmful ultraviolet rays of the sun. Melanin absorbs some of these rays before they can damage the cells. Sunbathers who expose themselves to the sun in an effort to look better force their bodies to use this means of protection and increase their risk of developing skin cancer.

24A.3 *How Your Skin Protects You*

God designed the structures of your skin to protect you. The barrier formed by your skin keeps harmful chemicals and disease-causing organisms out while holding in the fluids and substances of your body. Structures within your skin sense factors in your environment and provide you with information that you need to survive. Other skin structures form under special circumstances to protect you from physical injury.

The nerve receptors of the skin respond to cold, heat, touch, and pressure. In the dermis a nerve loops around the root of each hair. Whenever a hair is bent, the receptor is stimulated, and you sense that the hair has been touched. In this way, your hair helps make you aware of things near your body.

Working with tools such as shovels and rakes exposes your skin cells to friction that can damage skin's delicate structures. The skin that is subjected to friction and pressure responds by producing more cells in that area. The thickened epidermis helps protect the deeper layers of the skin. An area of skin with thickened epidermis is a **callus**. Calluses often form on your feet when you go barefoot or where skin is exposed to rubbing or pressure.

Blisters form when the skin is exposed to excessive friction or intense heat. Friction causes the layers of the skin to separate. Intense heat can damage the dermis and also cause the layers to separate. Fluid, mostly water, collects in the space between the separated layers. Over time, the water is absorbed into the dermis, and new epidermis forms to heal the injury.

24A.4 *Regulating Body Temperature*

Another important function of skin is to regulate body temperature. The blood vessels and the sweat glands in the skin work together to maintain your body temperature. On hot days and at times when you are very active, the blood vessels in the dermis open wide to allow more blood to flow near the epidermis. (See illustration 24A-4 on page 421.) As the warm blood from within your body comes close to the surface, its heat is released through the epidermis. At the same time, the sweat glands secrete *perspiration* (sweat) through tiny pores on the surface of the epidermis. Since sweat is mostly water, it evaporates quickly, cooling the surface of your skin.

(See illustration 24A-4 on page 421.)

Love Thy Neighbor

All humans belong to the same race. God "made of one blood all nations of men" (Acts 17:26). No one should look down on another because that person has different physical features (e.g., skin color, hair color). Jesus made only one distinction between people—those bound for heaven and those bound for hell. We are to love all people as we love ourselves (Luke 10:25–37).

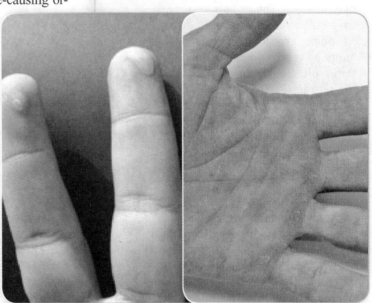

What is the difference between blisters (left) and calluses (right)?

24A-3

Would You Believe?

Although only 1 mm to 2 mm thick, skin is one of the largest organs of your body—6% of the body weight, and covering about 1.9 square meters on an adult. With age the skin becomes dry, scaly, and thin. Certain tissues within the skin will degenerate, resulting eventually in wrinkles.

Facets of *the Human Body:* *Burns*

Remember the last time you had a sunburn? Your skin probably turned red, itched, and maybe even blistered. All burns destroy body tissues. Minor burns, such as sunburn caused by the sun's ultraviolet rays, damage the outer layer of the skin, whereas more severe burns destroy deeper tissues. Touching hot metal or liquids is usually the cause of severe burns, but not always. Some burns have quite unusual causes.

Some chemicals cause burns by reacting with the skin's oil, sweat, or even the skin itself. The intense heat given off by these reactions destroys the surrounding cells. Phosphorous pentoxide, for example, which is used in manufacturing fertilizers, baking powder, and other household products, reacts with the water in sweat to produce phosphoric acid and large amounts of heat.

Most chemical burns should be rinsed with large amounts of water; phosphorus burns, however, should be soaked in water, since rinsing them can cause tissues to slough away. Soaking the burn dilutes the acid enough so that it no longer burns.

Electrical burns occur when a strong electrical current passes through a person's body. The current usually enters at one point and leaves at another small point on the opposite side of the body. Between these two points it fans out, destroying many tissues inside the body. Electrical burns are always much worse than they look.

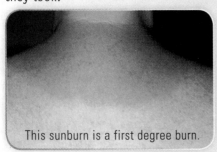

This sunburn is a first degree burn.

Ultraviolet rays, x-rays, or highly radioactive substances can cause radiation burns. A radiation burn interferes with the functions of cells, prevents them from reproducing, and often kills them. The scar tissue that replaces the destroyed cells cannot carry on the functions of the original cells. Sunburn is a mild ultraviolet radiation burn.

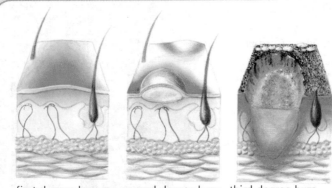

first-degree burn   second-degree burn   third-degree burn

Weather forecasts often include the UV index, which is the amount of UV radiation that is expected at the earth's surface when the sun is highest overhead. It is calculated by determining the elevation of the sun, the amount of ozone in the stratosphere, and the amount of cloud cover. The scale of the UV index ranges from zero (night) to 15–16 (tropics on a cloudless day). Anytime you plan to be outside, you should use sunscreen to protect yourself from UV radiation. It is best to use sunscreen that has an SPF (sun protective factor) of at least 15. Sunscreens help prevent skin damage by absorbing, reflecting, or scattering the UV radiation.

Whether or not a burn is serious depends on two factors: how deep it is and how much body surface it covers.

A **first-degree burn**, such as a mild sunburn, results in redness and sometimes pain.

A **second-degree burn** causes red or pink blistered skin. Touching a second-degree burn turns the skin white and causes pain. As a second-degree burn heals, the skin often be-comes firm and leathery because of water trapped beneath the epidermis. Second-degree burns damage the upper part of the dermis as well as the epidermis. A victim who has second-degree burns over more than 75% of his body has almost no chance of recovering.

A **third-degree burn** destroys both the dermis and the epidermis. The skin, if it is still present at all, is waxy white, red, brown, or black and never turns white when touched. Touching a third-degree burn causes no pain because all the nerve endings in such burns have been destroyed. A victim with third-degree burns over 50% of his body has only a poor chance of surviving.

The best way to treat first-degree burns is to apply cold water (not ice since too much cold could damage tissues) for at least half an hour. This treatment relieves the pain and prevents heat from continuing to damage the tissues. First-degree burns should be covered with clean, dry dressings after treating with cold water. More serious burns should receive medical care as soon as possible.

Serious burns are sometimes treated by applying chemicals that form crusts over the burned area while the tissues heal naturally. They also can be treated by transplanting pieces of skin from other body areas. Synthetic membranes are now used for some temporary transplants. These

cultured skin graft being prepared for use

temporary transplants help reduce pain and stimulate scar tissue formation, but they do not remain part of the body. Another new treatment for severe burns is to cover the burned areas with artificially grown skin. In this treatment a small amount of undamaged skin is taken from the patient. The skin cells rapidly grow and reproduce in a laboratory. The resulting skin is then grafted back onto the patient.

When your body becomes cold and needs to conserve heat, the blood vessels in the skin contract and the pores of the sweat glands close. When this happens, your skin becomes pale, dry, and cold. When you are warm inside but your skin is exposed to cold (like when you are active outside on a cold winter day), blood is sent to your skin to keep the skin warm. This is why your nose and cheeks turn red while you build a snowman. These automatic changes in the skin help regulate the body's temperature.

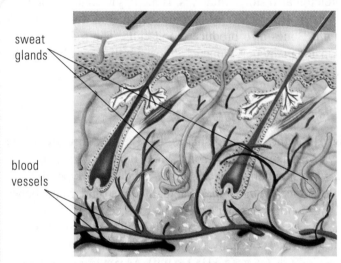

sweat glands

blood vessels

At normal body temperature there is only enough blood supplied to keep the skin cells alive. Sweat glands are minimally active and the skin's blood vessels are not enlarged.

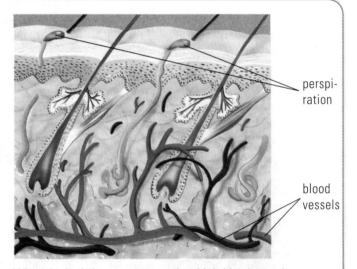

perspiration

blood vessels

When the body becomes warm, the skin's blood vessels enlarge to carry warm blood near the surface for cooling. When perspiration evaporates, it cools the skin.

Regulating body temperature **24A-4**

Section Review 24A

1. List the two layers that form the skin.

2. List two pigments found in human skin.

3. What structure of the skin is responsible for the formation of fingerprints?

4. An area of thickened epidermis is called a _____.

5. Besides perspiration, how else does skin function to keep you cool?

24B-1 Functions of the Skeletal System

A. Framework for support and movement
B. Protection
C. Storage of minerals
D. Production of blood cells

periosteum: peri- (Gk. PERI around) + -osteum (L. OSTEON, bone)

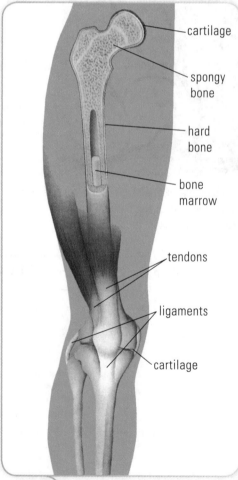

24B-2 Human skeletal and connective structures

cartilage

spongy bone

hard bone

bone marrow

tendons

ligaments

cartilage

24B The Skeletal System

A structure as large as your body must have some means of support. If you were supported by an exoskeleton, like an insect's or a lobster's, you would have to move in a hard, thick, heavy coating that would make a suit of medieval armor seem lightweight and graceful. The lightweight strength of the endoskeleton's bones, along with the flexibility of its various types of joints, permits your muscles to move your body easily.

24B.1 The Functions of the Skeleton

The skeleton provides the supporting framework for the body. Without bones you could not stand or sit upright; your muscles would have no firm structures to move, and your body would have no definite shape.

The skeleton also protects the body's organs. Your skull protects your delicate brain, eyes, and inner ears. Your rib cage protects your lungs and heart. Your vertebrae (VUR tuh bray) protect your spinal cord.

The skeleton also stores minerals. Bone tissue contains calcium and phosphorus. Bone cells secrete these minerals to give bones their strength. Bones also produce blood cells. The red bone marrow found inside many bones makes almost a billion new blood cells every day.

24B.2 Bones of the Body

Bones have different sizes and shapes, but they are also similar in several ways. Very few bones are solid. Many bones have a hard, solid outer layer with spongelike spaces on the inside. This type of bone, although it is named *spongy bone*, is actually quite rigid. Many bones contain a long, central chamber called a marrow cavity. Marrow cavities and the spaces in spongy bone are filled with **bone marrow**.

A bone's surface is usually covered with a tough, white tissue called the *periosteum* (PEHR ee AHS tee um). As you grow, the periosteum forms new bone tissue. Joined to the periosteum are ligaments and tendons. **Ligaments** are tough, flexible bands of connective tissue that attach bones to other bones at joints. **Tendons** are bands of connective tissue that connect muscles to bones.

The outer surface of a bone is not always smooth and solid. There are openings and grooves in bones that serve as passageways for blood vessels and nerves. Projecting parts and rough humps on many bones provide places for tendons and ligaments to attach.

24B.3 The Structure of Bones

When you think of the skeletal system, you probably think of a skeleton you have seen in a museum or classroom. The bones in your body, however, are much different from dead, dry bones. Your bones contain living bone cells, blood vessels, and nerves.

Two main types of tissue, bone and cartilage, make up the skeleton. **Bone** tissue consists of living bone cells and the nonliving material they secrete. This nonliving substance is made up of calcium,

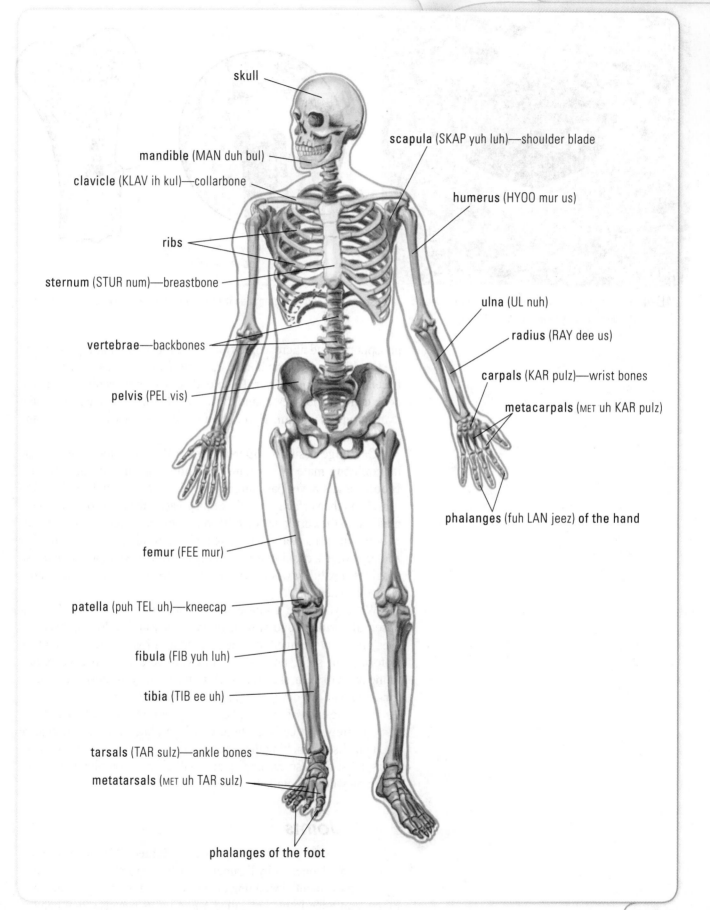

skull

scapula (SKAP yuh luh)—shoulder blade

mandible (MAN duh bul)

clavicle (KLAV ih kul)—collarbone

humerus (HYOO mur us)

ribs

sternum (STUR num)—breastbone

ulna (UL nuh)

radius (RAY dee us)

carpals (KAR pulz)—wrist bones

vertebrae—backbones

metacarpals (MET uh KAR pulz)

pelvis (PEL vis)

phalanges (fuh LAN jeez) of the hand

femur (FEE mur)

patella (puh TEL uh)—kneecap

fibula (FIB yuh luh)

tibia (TIB ee uh)

tarsals (TAR sulz)—ankle bones

metatarsals (MET uh TAR sulz)

phalanges of the foot

Human skeletal system | **24B-3**

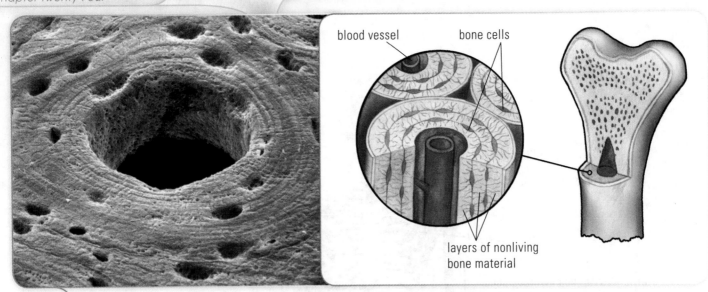

blood vessel   bone cells

layers of nonliving
bone material

24B-4   Osteon as seen through a scanning electron microscope (left) and diagrammed (right). (photo © Dr. Richard Kessel and Dr. Randy Kardon/Tissues & Organs/Visuals Unlimited)

phosphorus, and microscopic fibers, and forms circular layers around the tiny blood vessels in bones. Each circular layer has bone cells between it and the next layer. The blood vessel supplies nutrients to the bone cell. A blood vessel and the layers of nonliving material around it make up an **osteon**. Hard, strong bone sections consist of many osteons side by side.

Cartilage tissue is softer and more flexible than bone because its nonliving material contains very little calcium and phosphorus. Blood vessels never pass through cartilage. Nutrients from blood in vessels on the surface of cartilage pass easily through soft, nonliving material to the cartilage cells. In your body, cartilage covers the ends of bones in joints, helping them to slide smoothly against one another and providing a cushion for the hard ends of the bones. Cartilage also provides flexibility where it is needed, such as in the tip of your nose and your outer ear.

When you were a tiny embryo, your entire skeleton was composed of cartilage and similar tissues. As you developed, these tissues gradually changed to bone. The bones of your head did not fuse to form your solid, bony skull until you were about two years old. Some parts of your skeleton, such as the tip of your nose, your outer ears, and part of your kneecaps, never change to bone.

Near the ends of the long bones of your body are cartilage plates. As you grow, the cells in these cartilage plates divide and change into bone tissue, making these bones longer. During your high school years, most of these cartilage plates will change completely to bone. When they do, you will stop growing.

24B.4 *Joints*

A **joint** is a place where two or more bones meet. The bones of most joints are held together by ligaments. Different joints permit different types of movement, depending on the shapes of the bones in the joint. Elbow and knee joints are called *hinge joints* because they bend in only one direction, like a door hinge. The joints between the vertebrae of the back are *gliding joints*, which allow the vertebrae to slide and

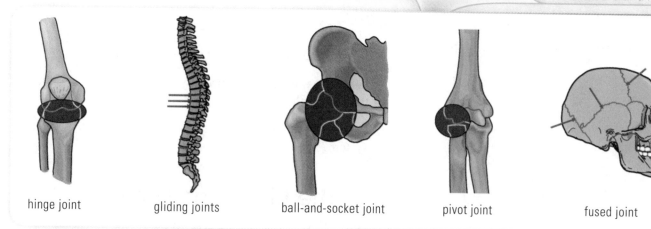

hinge joint   gliding joints   ball-and-socket joint   pivot joint   fused joint

Types of joints   **24B-5**

twist. The *ball-and-socket joints* of the shoulder and hip provide free movement within a limited area. The joint between the two bones of the forearm near the elbow is a *pivot joint*. Circular movement occurs between these bones whenever the arm twists. *Fused joints*, such as those between the bones of the skull, do not allow any movement since the bones have become permanently fused together.

Facets of *the Human Body:* Broken Bones

Scientifically speaking, a broken bone is a *fractured bone*. The type of break that occurs determines what type of fracture it is. When a bone breaks completely in two, the break is called a *complete fracture*. An *incomplete fracture* occurs when there is only a crack, not a break, in the bone. Bones that break cleanly in one place are *simple fractures*; fractures that splinter the bones are called *comminuted* (KAHM uh NOO tid) *fractures*.

Fractures heal properly only if they are set properly. Physicians set fractures by aligning the pieces of bone in their proper positions and securing them, if necessary, with a cast on the outside or metal screws

and plates on the bone itself. Sometimes traction (pulling on the end of a bone) is also required to keep the bone in place as the fracture heals.

A broken bone begins to heal as its cells produce fibers and secrete jellylike substances into the cracks of the fracture. This material, which is the same cartilage-like material from which the bone formed in the first place, fills the cracks much like glue. As minerals are deposited in this "glue," it gradually hardens into bone.

Most fractures heal in several weeks to several months, depending on the type of fracture. However, fractures that move after they have been set take longer to mend. Movement at the fracture site "unsets the glue," forcing the bone to secrete more "glue" and start the hardening process all over again. Large lumps of bone sometimes form at such a fracture site.

The fractures of children and teenagers heal much faster than the fractures of older people. The bone cells of an elderly person are slower to manufacture the gluelike material needed for healing fractures. Fractures that heal in a few weeks in children

and teenagers can sometimes take years to heal in an elderly person.

Although you may have seen more people your age with casts than elderly people, the longer a person lives, the more brittle his bones are likely to become. Why? The body removes the minerals from the bone, making them thinner and much easier to break. If this condition becomes severe, it is called *osteoporosis* (os tee oh puh ROE sis).

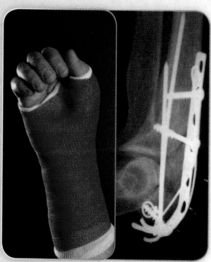

Broken bones are maintained in proper alignment with a cast or plates and screws.

complete

incomplete

comminuted

1. What is the technical name for the thigh bone?

2. What two minerals are especially important in giving bones their strength?

3. Besides bone, what other tissues are important in the skeletal system?

24C The Muscular System

Your body moves when your muscles contract. Since contracting involves becoming shorter and thicker, your muscles can move your body only by pulling, never by pushing. Muscles, however, cannot move the body by themselves. Nerves are necessary to stimulate most muscles to contract. Joints provide smooth surfaces and sturdy connections between bones. Thus, the muscles, nerves, bones, joints, and other structures work together to move the body.

24C.1 *Types of Muscles*

Muscles that you can control at will are called **voluntary muscles**. The muscles that move your skeleton, called **skeletal muscles**, are voluntary muscles. A view of skeletal muscle tissue through a microscope shows a pattern of dark and light bands. These bands, called striations (STRY AY shunz), appear where layers of different kinds of protein molecules meet. As the muscle contracts, the protein molecules move past each other, and the striations appear to move. Striations are most obvious in skeletal muscle, but they also appear in heart muscle. Therefore, both skeletal muscle and heart muscle may be called **striated muscle**.

Muscle tissue that you cannot control at will is **involuntary muscle**. The muscles of the heart, stomach, intestines, blood vessels, and other internal organs are involuntary muscles. The nervous system automatically controls involuntary muscles. Your heart continues to pump blood, and your stomach continues to churn food, even when you are asleep or otherwise unconscious. Involuntary muscles generally contract more slowly than voluntary muscles, but they can function longer before tiring. Most involuntary muscles do not have striations and are known as **smooth muscles**. The heart muscle is an exception. Its muscle tissue, called **cardiac muscle**, is both involuntary and striated.

24C.2 *How Muscles Move*

Skeletal muscles usually work in pairs. When the biceps (BY seps) muscle of your arm contracts, your arm bends at the elbow. At the same time the triceps (TRY seps) muscle in the back of your arm stretches as it relaxes. When the triceps contracts, the arm straightens and the biceps stretches as it relaxes. With your left hand, feel the movements of the muscles in your right arm as you flex your arm (pick up an object by bending only at the elbow) and extend your arm (push down on your desk with the back of your hand).

Objectives 24C

- Differentiate between voluntary and involuntary muscles.
- Differentiate between striated and nonstriated muscles.
- List three functions of the muscular system.

24C-1 Microscopic views of striated muscle tissue (top) and smooth muscle tissue (bottom)

cardiac: (Gk. KARDIA, heart)

Many of the skeletal muscles that move your body extend across at least one joint and attach to two different bones. Normally the joint the muscle crosses is the joint that moves when the muscle contracts. For example, the sartorius (sar TOR ee us) muscle, the longest muscle in your body, attaches at the upper part of the pelvic bone, extends across both the hip and the knee joints, and attaches on the inner side of the tibia (TIB ee uh) near the knee joint. You use this muscle to cross one of your legs in front of the other, as you would when kicking a soccer ball in a lateral pass.

Some skeletal muscles do not extend across joints. Instead they cause movement of the skin or other muscles to which they attach. For example, the muscles around the eyes and mouth change the size of these openings. Also, the tongue and throat muscles that help you swallow do not extend across joints.

24C.3 Other Functions of Muscles

Skeletal muscles do more than provide movement. They also maintain your bodily posture. The muscles along your back and neck keep your backbone in an erect position when you are active as well as when you are standing or sitting. When muscles contract, they produce heat. This heat warms the body and helps maintain the body's constant temperature. Strenuous exercise, especially on hot days, can produce too much body heat, which the body must eliminate. When you are inactive on a cold day, you may begin to shiver. Shivering is actually a result of involuntary muscle contractions that produce heat and raise the body temperature. Another involuntary muscle contraction causes "goose bumps." How do you think muscle contractions cause "goose bumps"?

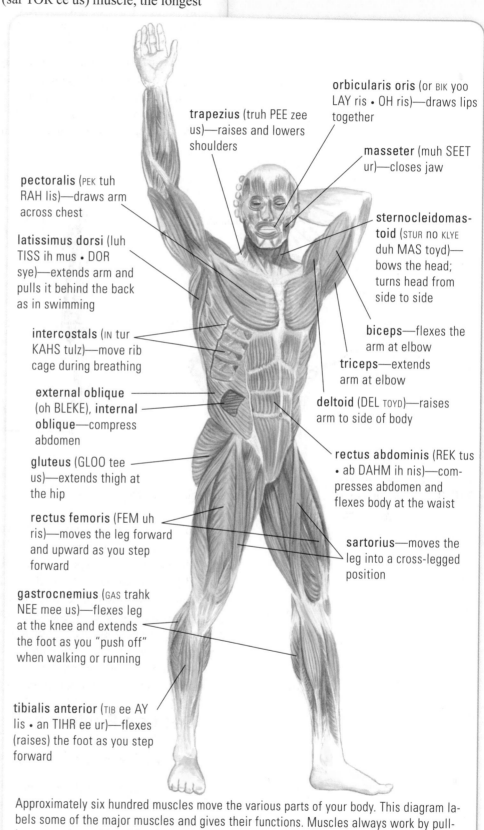

orbicularis oris (or BIK yoo LAY ris • OH ris)—draws lips together

trapezius (truh PEE zee us)—raises and lowers shoulders

masseter (muh SEET ur)—closes jaw

pectoralis (PEK tuh RAH lis)—draws arm across chest

sternocleidomastoid (STUR no KLYE duh MAS toyd)—bows the head; turns head from side to side

latissimus dorsi (luh TISS ih mus • DOR sye)—extends arm and pulls it behind the back as in swimming

biceps—flexes the arm at elbow

triceps—extends arm at elbow

intercostals (IN tur KAHS tulz)—move rib cage during breathing

deltoid (DEL toyd)—raises arm to side of body

external oblique (oh BLEKE), internal oblique—compress abdomen

rectus abdominis (REK tus • ab DAHM ih nis)—compresses abdomen and flexes body at the waist

gluteus (GLOO tee us)—extends thigh at the hip

rectus femoris (FEM uh ris)—moves the leg forward and upward as you step forward

sartorius—moves the leg into a cross-legged position

gastrocnemius (GAS trahk NEE mee us)—flexes leg at the knee and extends the foot as you "push off" when walking or running

tibialis anterior (TIB ee AY lis • an TIHR ee ur)—flexes (raises) the foot as you step forward

Approximately six hundred muscles move the various parts of your body. This diagram labels some of the major muscles and gives their functions. Muscles always work by pulling, never by pushing. Muscles normally come in pairs that pull in opposite directions.

Human muscular system   **24C-2**

24C.4 **How Muscles Work**

To function, muscles need a supply of readily available energy. Stored energy comes to muscles in the form of glucose (sugar) carried by the blood. Muscles release the energy stored in glucose by breaking down the glucose. The process that muscles use is called aerobic cellular respiration (see pp. 68–69). This process requires oxygen. The blood carries oxygen from the lungs to the muscles. As muscles use oxygen to break down glucose, the energy that is released is available to make the muscle cells contract.

When you work or play hard, you begin to breathe rapidly and deeply to supply your muscles with the oxygen they need to continue

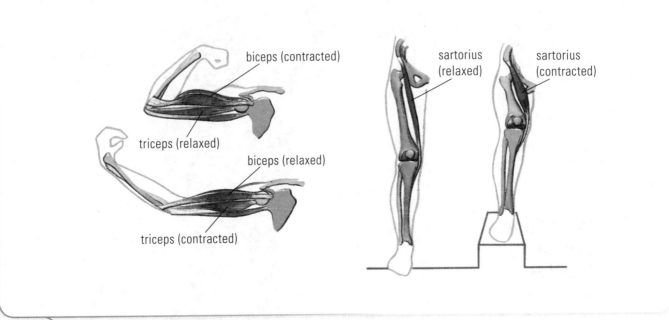

biceps (contracted)

triceps (relaxed)

biceps (relaxed)

triceps (contracted)

sartorius (relaxed)

sartorius (contracted)

24C-3 A typical muscle pair (left) and a muscle that extends across joints (right)

to operate. Occasionally, when you are active, your muscles break down glucose without oxygen. This process, called lactic acid fermentation, is the type of anaerobic cellular respiration (see pp. 69–70) that produces lactic acid. Muscles carry on anaerobic respiration when they do not get enough oxygen to perform aerobic respiration.

Have you ever wondered why your muscles are sore after exercising or playing hard? One theory suggests that the buildup of lactic acid in the muscle tissue causes them to be sore. Other theories based on more recent research hold that the soreness may be a result of microscopic damage to the fibers and resulting inflammation.

Section Review 24C

1. What organ has involuntary, striated muscle?

2. Explain the difference between voluntary and involuntary muscles. Give an example of each.

3. When muscles _____, they produce heat.

Chapter Review

1. Explain why skin is considered a major defense against disease.

2. What is the dark pigment that causes the skin to have color?

3. Which layer of skin contains hair follicles?

4. What is the best way to treat first-degree burns?

5. How does your bone marrow affect your blood?

6. What is the name of the tough white tissue that forms new bone tissue?

7. What do you call the bands of tissue that connect muscle to bone?

8. What kind of joints do not allow movement?

9. Which kinds of muscles are striated?

10. What metabolic processes supply the energy for muscles to contract?

What Did You Learn?

1. If your skin produced no pigment, what color would it be? Why?

2. List three ways your skin may respond to ultraviolet light in sunshine.

3. How does the Bible say you should treat someone whose looks or physical features are different from yours?

4. How could you tell if a burn was first-degree or second-degree?

5. After vigorous exercise, your friend looks both red and sweaty. Explain how the processes that cause both of these conditions help your friend cool down.

6. Describe how ligaments and tendons are similar and how they are different.

7. Why might your muscles be sore after strenuous exercise?

Scientifically Speaking

epidermis
dermis
subcutaneous layer
melanin
callus
blister
bone marrow
ligament
tendon
bone
osteon
cartilage
joint
voluntary muscle
skeletal muscle
striated muscle
involuntary muscle
smooth muscle
cardiac muscle

Self Quiz 24

_____ 1. The dermis contains all of the following *except*
   A. dead cells.
   B. hair follicles.
   C. blood vessels.
   D. sweat glands.

Label the numbered structures of the skin using the lines below the diagram.

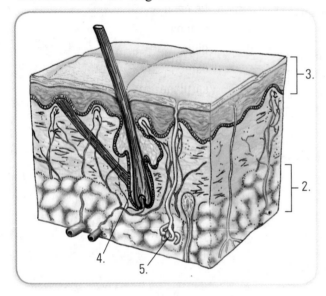

2. _____

3. _____

4. _____

5. _____

_____ 6. Special cells in the dermis produce a skin pigment called melanin. (True/False)

7. List three functions of the skeleton.

_____ 8. Ligaments are tough bands of tissue that connect muscles to bones. (True/False)

9. A unit of bone tissue that contains a blood vessel surrounded by circular layers of non-living bone is called a/an _____.

10. A _____ is where two or more bones meet.

_____ 11. All muscles attach to at least one bone. (True/False)

_____ 12. To function, muscles need
   A. oxygen.
   B. water.
   C. energy.
   D. light.

INTERNAL BALANCE

It's 10:30 a.m.; you are finally awake; you feel good after sleeping through study hall; it's time for P.E.—basketball today! You jump, stretch, run, dribble, and block. Your heart pumps faster; you can feel it throbbing. Beads—no, buckets—of sweat pour from your body. Fifty minutes later, hot, sweaty, and tired, you head for the showers. Your stomach begins to rumble. It is just a half hour until lunch.

The conditions inside your body need to be maintained within a safe range. This is true whether you are sitting in class or playing basketball. Your heart should beat only so fast or so slow, your temperature should vary by only a few degrees, and you can breathe only so deeply or shallowly. If your body does not maintain these conditions, you will probably feel sick and might even die.

As your activities keep changing, your body must adjust. For example, when you are resting, you normally have enough sugar and oxygen in your blood to supply your cells. But when you exercise vigorously, your cells need more sugar and oxygen. To keep the proper amounts of these substances in supply, your heart beats faster, forcing more blood through your blood vessels. Your cells then receive more oxygen and sugar because of the greater amount of blood that passes by them. When you stop exercising, and the extra sugar and oxygen are no longer needed, your heart adjusts by slowing down.

Maintaining the internal balance of a living organism is called **homeostasis** (HO mee oh STAY sis), a term which literally means "staying the same." Your body maintains homeostasis by trying to keep internal conditions "the same" or, more accurately, by keeping them as they should be. You are healthiest when your body maintains the proper homeostatic levels. You may become ill when something upsets your body's ability to maintain these levels. Things that may affect homeostasis include parasites, viruses, bacteria, poor nutrition, and the "breakdown" of a body part that helps maintain homeostasis.

The *circulatory system* is one of the main systems for maintaining homeostasis. Your circulatory system consists of your heart, blood vessels, and blood. The chief function of the circulatory system is to transport substances such as food, oxygen, hormones, and enzymes to the cells of your body and to remove carbon dioxide and other waste products.

The body's *defense system* also helps maintain homeostasis. The skin helps prevent disease-causing organisms and substances from entering the body. But when organisms and substances break through its protective barriers, the immune system begins to defend the body using special blood cells to rid the body of invaders.

Another system important in the maintenance of your body's homeostasis is the *excretory system*. The kidneys filter waste substances out of the blood and help restore the proper amounts of other substances to the blood.

25A The Heart and Blood Vessels

This year approximately one million people in the United States will die of *cardiovascular* (KAR dee oh VAS kyuh lur) malfunctions. Heart disease alone accounts for over one-third of all deaths in the United States. For various reasons the heart and blood vessels begin to wear out or become clogged.

Cardiovascular difficulties are often related to diet, exercise, and stress. A proper diet supplies the proper nutrients for good health. Regular vigorous exercise is necessary to keep the cardiovascular system functioning well. Many studies, however, point to stress as a major cause of cardiovascular problems in humans. To understand how stress causes problems in the cardiovascular system, you will need to learn more about the heart and blood vessels.

25A.1 *The Structure of Blood Vessels*

Humans have a *closed circulatory system*. Under normal circumstances blood travels from the heart and returns to the heart without ever leaving the blood vessels. Materials do enter and leave the blood, but most of the blood itself remains in the circulatory system.

Arteries always carry blood away from the heart. They branch and rebranch until they become microscopic. The smallest vessels are called **capillaries**. Capillary walls are only one cell thick. Dissolved gases and small molecules can easily move through the capillary walls. While the blood is in the capillaries, materials are exchanged between the blood and the body cells.

Objectives 25A

- Define *homeostasis*.
- Compare the structure and functions of arteries, veins, and capillaries.
- Identify the anatomic structures of the heart.
- Trace the flow of oxygenated and deoxygenated blood through the heart.

cardiovascular: cardio- (Gk. KARDIA, heart) + -vascular (L. VASCULUM, vessel)

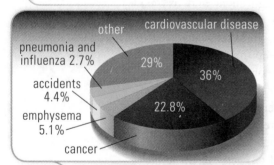

25A-1 Cardiovascular disease, which includes heart disease and stroke, is the leading cause of death in the United States today (National Vital Statistics Report, Vol. 53, No. 5, Oct. 2004)

Capillaries merge to form larger vessels called **veins**, which return blood to the heart. Veins do not have walls as thick as arteries, but they do have one-way valves. These valves allow the blood to flow in only one direction—toward the heart. The pumping action of the heart forces the blood through the arteries and on into the capillaries. After it has passed through the capillaries, there is little pressure to push it along in the veins. The return of the blood to the heart is aided by body movements. As the muscles contract, they squeeze the veins, forcing the blood to move. The valves of the veins ensure the blood flows toward the heart.

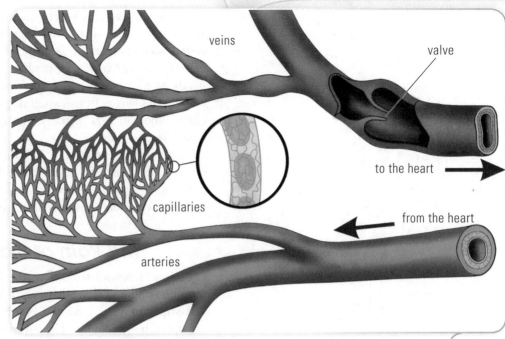

The relationship between arteries, capillaries, and veins keeps the blood confined in a closed circulatory system.

25A-2

Standing still for a long time may cause your feet to swell. Why? When there is no bodily movement, the blood in your vessels slows down and can begin to lose fluid into the surrounding tissues. This misplaced fluid causes swelling. Moving your legs helps to prevent swelling. Muscles squeeze the veins, forcing the blood to return to your heart before the blood has a chance to lose its fluid.

25A.2 *The Structure of the Heart*

The **heart** is a muscular organ about the size of your fist. Its only function is to pump blood. When most of your body is resting, your heart continues to beat about sixty to eighty times per minute, depending on your age and your physical condition. A person who is in good physical condition normally has a slower heart rate because his body is operating more efficiently. Inside the heart a special tissue called the *pacemaker* causes the heart to beat automatically at your normal resting rate. When you are active, your heart beats faster because your brain and spinal cord send messages that increase your heart rate. When you are asleep, nerves can slow down the rate of your heart.

Not only is the heart a strong muscle, but it also has more endurance than any other muscle. Beating, on average, seventy-two times per minute, your heart will beat 2,650,838,400 times by your seventieth birthday. All this movement could build up a lot of heat from friction (rubbing). Yet there is little friction because the heart is in a fluid-filled sac called the *pericardium* (PEHR ih KAR dee um).

The heart has four hollow spaces called chambers. The upper, thin-walled chambers are called **atria** (*sing.*, atrium). The larger, thick-walled chambers are **ventricles**. Blood that comes into the heart enters one of the atria. Blood leaves through one of the ventricles. The right side of the heart is separated from the left by a muscular wall called the **septum** (SEP tum).

Would You Believe?

Capillaries are so small that you need a microscope to see them. However, if all of the capillaries from an adult were placed end-to-end, they would be between 25,000 and 60,000 miles long!

pericardium: peri- (Gk. PERI, around) + -cardium (Gk. KARDIA, heart)

Four valves in the heart direct the flow of blood. The atrium and ventricle on each side of the heart are separated by one-way valves called **atrioventricular** (AY tree oh ven TRIK yuh lur) **valves (AV valves)**. The AV valves are made of flaps of tissue attached by strong bands of tissue to the inner surface of the ventricles. These bands prevent the valves from swinging back into the atria. The AV valves allow blood to flow in only one direction—from the atria to the ventricles.

The **semilunar** (SEM ee LOO nur) **valves** are located at the beginning of large vessels that carry blood away from the heart. The semilunar valves are also one-way valves. They allow the blood to leave the ventricles but prevent it from returning.

25A.3 *The Path of Blood*

Blood from all regions of the body (except the lungs) returns through two large veins that empty into the right atrium of the heart. The **superior vena cava** (VEE nuh • KAY vuh) returns blood from the upper body regions. The **inferior vena cava** returns blood from the lower body regions.

The blood coming from the body is low in oxygen content and high in carbon dioxide content. It is called **deoxygenated blood**, and

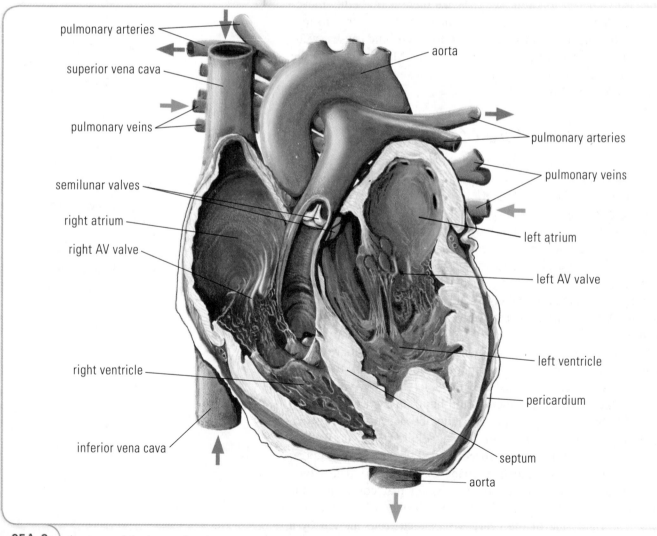

25A-3 Anatomy of the human heart

in most diagrams it is colored blue. The actual color of deoxygenated blood is a dull purplish red.

After the right atrium fills with blood, it contracts and sends the blood through the right AV valve into the right ventricle. As the right ventricle contracts, the right AV closes to prevent the blood from flowing back into the atrium. The blood moves through the semilunar valve into the **pulmonary** (PULL muh NEHR ee) **arteries**.

The pulmonary arteries carry deoxygenated blood to the lungs. As the blood flows through the lungs, carbon dioxide is released from the blood into the lungs to be exhaled. At the same time, oxygen moves from the air in the lungs into the blood. The oxygen-rich blood is called **oxygenated blood**, which is usually diagrammed red. The oxygenated blood returns to the left atrium through the **pulmonary veins**.

When the left atrium is filled with blood, it contracts. The blood flows through the left AV valve into the left ventricle. As the left ventricle contracts, the left AV valve closes, and the blood rushes through the semilunar valve into the **aorta** (ay OR tuh). The aorta is the largest artery in the body. It branches to supply blood to all of the body.

pulmonary: (L. PULMO, lung)

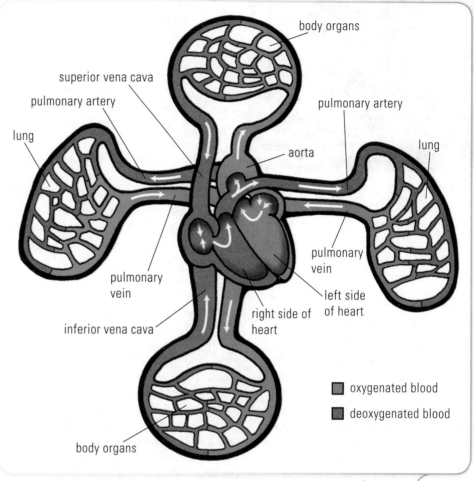

Path of blood in the human body **25A-4**

As the blood passes through the capillaries, it delivers oxygen to the cells and absorbs carbon dioxide from them. By the time the blood enters the veins, it is deoxygenated. The veins collect the deoxygenated blood and return it to the heart. Scientists estimate that one drop of blood may circulate through the body at the rate of once every twenty-three seconds.

25A.4 *The Working of the Heart*

The walls of the left ventricle are about three times thicker than the walls of the right ventricle. The right ventricle has to pump blood only to the lungs, but the left ventricle has to push blood to all other body regions.

The muscle of the heart receives almost no nourishment from the blood that flows though its chambers. The heart's nourishment is supplied primarily by two **coronary arteries**. These arteries branch off the aorta and enter the heart muscle. In time, the blood from the heart muscles enters a vein on the back side of the heart and flows into the right atrium.

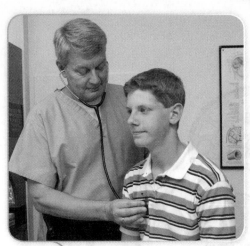

25A-5 The way your heart sounds can reveal its health.

When the heart contracts, both atria function together, and then both ventricles function together. Both the right and left atria receive blood at the same time. When they contract, both AV valves open and blood flows into the ventricles. After a brief pause both ventricles contract, the AV valves close, and the semilunar valves open. The blood is then pumped into the pulmonary artery and aorta at the same time.

A physician uses a *stethoscope* (STETH uh SKOPE) to listen to your heart. The normal sounds of a heartbeat are a soft *lubb-dubb*. The *lubb* is produced as the ventricles contract and the AV valves close. The sound is that of AV valves shutting. Shortly after this, the semilunar valves close, producing the *dubb*. The first sound is longer and louder than the second.

Unusual heart sounds may indicate a heart disorder. A *heart murmur* is an abnormal sound usually caused by defective heart valves. If the valves do not close properly, blood may leak backward, causing a gurgling sound or murmur. *Arrhythmia* is another problem that can often be detected by listening to the heart. Arrhythmia occurs when the heart beats out of rhythm.

Facets of *the Human Body:* *Sweat Drops of Blood*

In the garden just before He was betrayed, Jesus prayed, "Father, if thou be willing, remove this cup from me: nevertheless not my will, but thine, be done" (Luke 22:42). Jesus was willing to do the Father's will, but thinking about the suffering and death He would endure on the cross was very trying. The Father sent an angel to strengthen Him.

Then "being in an agony he prayed more earnestly: and his sweat was as it were great drops of blood falling down to the ground" (Luke 22:44).

There are several interpretations of the passage in Luke describing Christ's sweating blood. Some Bible scholars state that the words in Luke 22:44 do not necessarily mean that blood was lost through the sweat glands. The meaning of the words "as it were" leaves room for several interpretations. Other people believe that Jesus perspired very heavily and that the large, frequent sweat drops appeared to be drops of blood.

Many others believe that the agony Jesus suffered caused Him actually to lose blood through the pores in His skin. There are recorded cases of blood leaving the body through the sweat glands. Aristotle, who lived three hundred fifty years before Christ's birth, spoke of a person's bleeding through the skin when experiencing great suffering and mental agony.

The historian Mezeray wrote about several individuals who had been observed sweating blood. One case described a town governor who was condemned to die. When he saw the scaffold, he began to sweat large amounts of blood. Mezeray also

(*Christ in Gethsemane*, Unknown Spanish (follower of Vincente Juan Macip, called Juan de Juanes), from the Bob Jones University Collection)

wrote about a nun who was captured by ruthless bandits. She was so terrified that blood oozed from her sweat pores. Another case involved a military commander who was captured and threatened with death by a conquering general. The commander responded to the extreme anguish by perspiring blood.

Physicians say that it is theoretically possible to sweat blood if there is a violent disturbance of the nervous system. This may force the blood pressure in the blood vessels near the sweat glands to increase. If the walls of the blood vessels and sweat ducts break from the pressure, it becomes possible for blood to escape through the sweat pores.

When people sweat blood, a network of tiny blood vessels can be seen on the skin's surface. Before the blood comes through the sweat pores, the person usually feels a prickly and itching sensation.

The agony that Jesus suffered may have caused Him literally to sweat blood. Although Luke 22:44 does not state clearly whether or not Jesus sweated blood, it does reveal one important fact: Christ was willing to obey his Father even when His obedience involved extreme suffering and death.

Section Review 25A

1. What is the greatest cause of death in the United States?

2. The smallest blood vessels in your body are

   called _____.

3. Which chamber of your heart first receives blood returning from your body?

4. What two organs do the pulmonary arteries and pulmonary veins connect?

5. What arteries nourish the heart?

25B The Blood

Your body contains about 3–5 L (3–5 qt) of blood. If you place a sample of blood in a test tube and spin it in a machine called a centrifuge, it will separate into three layers (see photos on p. 439). The straw-colored top layer is the blood plasma. The plasma makes up a little more than half the substance of the blood. Next would be a thin white layer. This layer contains the white blood cells and platelets. The lowest layer, the red blood cells, takes up a little less than half the volume of the sample.

Objectives 25B

- Describe the anatomy and functions of erythrocytes and leukocytes.
- Discuss the process of blood clotting.
- Describe the composition of blood plasma.
- Compare the causes of high blood pressure and low blood pressure.
- List several problems encountered with blood transfusions.

Facets of *the Human Body:* Beating Heart Attacks

Each year more than seven hundred thousand people in the United States die of heart attacks. Anyone at any age may have a heart attack. Physical exercise or emotional problems do not necessarily cause heart attacks. Many people suffer heart attacks when they are relaxing or sleeping.

The most common warning sign of a heart attack is a squeezing type of pain in the center of the chest. This painful sensation also may spread to the shoulders, neck, and arms. It may last for two minutes or longer, and it may come and go. Usually the pain is neither severe nor sharp and stabbing. The person may not appear ill, but he may feel weak, nauseated, short of breath, and sweaty.

The first thing a person suffering a heart attack should do is lie down and try to relax. It is important to put as little strain as possible on the weakened heart. A person suffering a heart attack should receive medical attention immediately.

So what exactly is a heart attack? The term actually means that something has gone wrong rather suddenly with the heart, stopping it from working properly. Heart attacks are caused by a decreased supply of blood to the hard-working heart muscle.

Coronary arteries, which supply the heart muscle with oxygen-rich blood, are sometimes clogged by clots called *emboli* (EM buh LYE) floating in the blood. This kind of heart attack is called a *coronary embolism*. The heart muscle fed by the blocked coronary artery no longer receives its share of blood. The area quickly becomes damaged and stops working. The rest of the heart may continue working, but the damaged section reduces the heart's efficiency.

Coronary atherosclerosis (ATH uh roh skluh ROH sis) is a common disease in which fatty deposits develop in the coronary artery walls. This causes the walls of the arteries to thicken, making

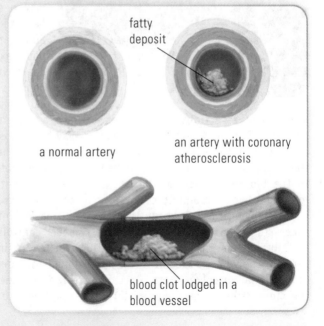

fatty deposit

a normal artery

an artery with coronary atherosclerosis

blood clot lodged in a blood vessel

Beating Heart Attacks (cont.)

the opening inside smaller. Smaller passageways reduce the amount of oxygenated blood pumped to the heart muscle. If the blood flows too slowly, a clot can form that completely blocks the artery. This kind of heart attack is called a *coronary thrombosis* (thrahm BOH sis). Without enough oxygen the muscle tissue may function irregularly, eventually die, and be replaced by scar tissue.

Sometimes the heart itself can repair some of the damage caused by a coronary embolism or thrombosis. Nearby blood vessels can grow into the damaged section to resupply the area with blood. The damaged area is replaced with new tissues, but a section of nonfunctioning scar tissue will usually remain. The blood can work to dissolve clots. If a clot is small, it may be completely removed.

It is possible for surgeons to remove blood clots from arteries. They

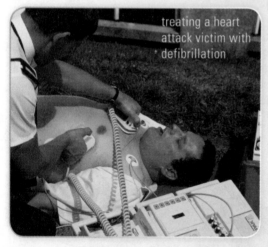
treating a heart attack victim with defibrillation

also can take sections of blood vessels from another part of the body and use them to restore circulation to the heart. Such sections are attached to the blocked vessels of the heart, forming a bypass around the clot.

A nonsurgical treatment that is successful in many cases is the use of "clot busters." Given to a patient through the veins, a clot buster is an enzyme that dissolves clots. Once in the blood stream, the drug circulates

to the blocked artery. It dissolves the clot quickly, allowing oxygenated blood to flow to the affected part of the heart. Patients treated in this way have a higher survival rate and usually recover faster. In fact, a few patients recover so quickly that in just a few minutes they seem totally recovered.

Some sudden heart attacks may result in irregular heartbeats. A heart that is not beating properly is said to have an *arrhythmia* (uh RITH mee uh). *Ventricular fibrillation* (FIB ruh LAY shun) is an arrhythmia in which the ventricles quiver vigorously but do not pump blood.

Ventricular fibrillation and some other arrhythmias can be restored to a normal rhythm by a *defibrillator* (dee FIB ruh LAY tur), which shocks the heart with a direct electrical current. This causes the heart to contract all at once and temporarily stops its electrical activity. When the heart's natural pacemaker begins functioning again, the heart should beat normally.

Some heart attacks damage the heart's natural pacemaker, often causing a slow heartbeat (less than sixty beats per minute). An artificial pacemaker may need to be implanted to help the heart beat regularly. Sometimes only a temporary pacemaker is needed to help the heart while it recovers. If the heart is severely damaged and cannot maintain a normal heart rate, a permanent artificial pacemaker may be necessary.

Permanent pacemakers are usually small battery-powered units implanted under the skin. An electrode runs from the unit through a vein and passes into the heart. The pacemaker controls the rate of the heartbeat by sending out regular electrical impulses. Some models may last for three to fifteen years before the batteries need to be replaced.

Years ago pacemakers were preset to beat at a fixed rate. A patient using this type of pacemaker was unable to participate in much physical exercise. The preset heart rate did not pump enough blood to supply the body's increased needs. Today's pacemakers are able to sense increased body movement and increase the heart rate to deliver more blood to the body. There are also implantable

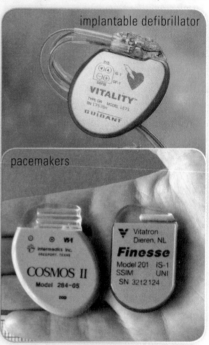
implantable defibrillator

pacemakers

defibrillators that can detect an arrhythmia and deliver a shock to the heart if needed.

If a person is going to die of a heart attack, death usually occurs in the first few hours following the attack. If the victim survives, the heart gradually repairs itself. Many victims are able to increase physical activity in one to three weeks, depending on the amount of damage to the heart. Most are then started on a regimen of physical therapy to increase the strength of the heart. By carefully following the exercises and diet prescribed by doctors, over 70% of all heart-attack victims recover.

25B.1 *Erythrocytes—Red Blood Cells*

The proper name for red blood cells is **erythrocytes** (ih RITH ruh SITES). Actually, erythrocytes are not complete cells. They are formed by special cells in the bone marrow. These cells first divide and then begin to produce hemoglobin. When they are filled with hemoglobin, the nuclei dissolve, and the erythrocytes take on their usual shape: a disc, dented on both sides. Erythrocytes cannot move themselves. They are carried along by the flow of the blood.

Since erythrocytes lack a nucleus, they cannot reproduce or make new cellular parts. About one hundred twenty days after the erythrocytes are formed, their cell membranes wear out and they begin to fall apart. These worn-out cells are constantly sorted out by the liver, spleen, and bone marrow. Most of the materials from these old red blood cells are used to make new erythrocytes. To keep enough healthy red blood cells in circulation, your body must produce several million new erythrocytes every second.

Hemoglobin is the iron-containing pigment that makes erythrocytes appear red. Each molecule of hemoglobin can carry four oxygen molecules. These molecules are released when the blood passes through areas that need oxygen. Whether the blood is *oxygenated* or *deoxygenated* depends upon how much oxygen is attached to the hemoglobin in the erythrocytes.

A person has *anemia* (uh NEE mee uh) if his blood cannot carry enough oxygen to his body cells. Usually anemia is caused by a lack of hemoglobin or by hemoglobin that does not work properly. The result is that too little oxygen is delivered to the cells. A person can suffer anemia-like effects from breathing carbon monoxide. Carbon monoxide is a colorless, odorless, tasteless gas that is produced by incomplete burning of fuel. This gas easily combines with hemoglobin at the same place that oxygen does. The carbon monoxide attaches to the hemoglobin more tightly than oxygen. Once hemoglobin attaches to carbon monoxide, it cannot carry oxygen.

If only a small amount of hemoglobin combines with carbon monoxide, deeper breaths usually supply the body with enough oxygen. In time, the contaminated erythrocytes will be replaced with new ones, and the person will no longer suffer from any symptoms. If a large amount of hemoglobin combines with carbon monoxide, the tissues will not receive enough oxygen. Decreased oxygen to vital organs,

erythrocyte: erythro- (Gk. ERUTHROS, red) + -cyte (Gk. KUTOS, hollow vessel or cell)

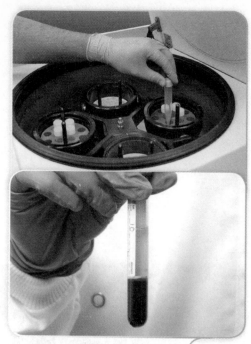

Blood can be rapidly separated by spinning in a centrifuge (top). The erythrocytes are at the bottom of the test tube (bottom). **25B-1**

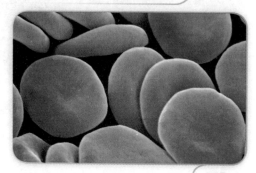

Erythrocytes **25B-2**

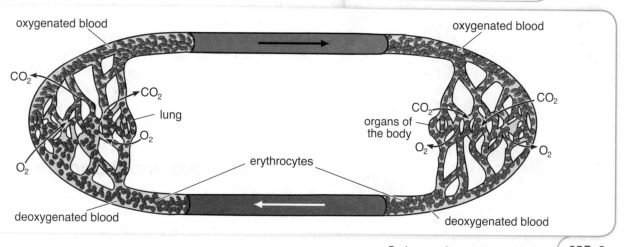

oxygenated blood

oxygenated blood

CO_2

CO_2

lung

O_2

O_2

CO_2

CO_2

organs of the body

O_2

O_2

erythrocytes

deoxygenated blood

deoxygenated blood

Exchange of gases in capillaries **25B-3**

such as the brain, can result in permanent damage. If too much hemoglobin combines with carbon monoxide, the person might die.

Other factors can also cause anemia. If a person does not have enough iron in his body, he cannot make enough hemoglobin—a condition called *iron-deficiency anemia*. As a result, his blood cannot carry enough oxygen. Eating foods that contain iron or taking mineral tablets usually corrects this kind of anemia.

leukocyte: leuko- (Gk. LEUKOS, clear or white) + -cyte (Gk. KUTOS, cell)

25B.2 *Leukocytes—White Blood Cells*

White blood cells are properly called **leukocytes** (LOO kuh SITES). Leukocytes are considerably larger than red blood cells. Unlike erythrocytes, leukocytes have nuclei and can move by themselves. To move, leukocytes change their shape like amoebas.

There are several different types of leukocytes. Two of their most important functions are destroying foreign substances and producing antibodies.

Some leukocytes *destroy bacteria and other foreign matter* in the body by engulfing and digesting them. Chemicals released by injured cells or cells attacked by foreign organisms attract these leukocytes. The leukocytes travel to injured areas by leaving the blood capillaries and entering the body tissues. (Red blood cells leave the capillaries only when you are bleeding.) Once in the area of infection or injury, white blood cells destroy any invading organisms and clean up the cell fragments in the wounded tissues.

Other white blood cells *produce antibodies*. **Antibodies** are chemicals that attack invading organisms or poisons. These two functions of leukocytes are a major part of the body's defense against disease, which will be discussed further in Section D.

Some white blood cells form in the bone marrow, and others develop in the spleen, tonsils, and thymus gland. Most of them have a rather short life span—usually about one to twelve days. One type of white blood cell, however, may live for about ten months.

Although there are normally few leukocytes in the body (red blood cells outnumber them six hundred to one), more are produced when a person has an *infection*. Physicians often check the number of leukocytes in a sample of a person's blood. If the number is large, the physician suspects that the person has an infection. This is helpful in diagnosing infections that are difficult to find, such as those in the liver, kidneys, and other internal organs.

25B-4 Leukocytes (blue) and erythrocytes (red)

25B.3 *Platelets and Blood Clotting*

Platelets are very small cell fragments that help in blood clotting. Platelets come from large cells in the bone marrow. Platelets are irregular in shape and about one-third the size of red blood cells. They do not have a nucleus and live only about one week.

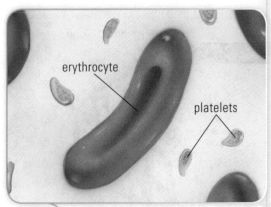

erythrocyte

platelets

25B-5 Platelets are small fragments of cells.

Facets of *the Human Body:* *Transfusion Confusion*

The first recorded blood transfusion was performed in England in 1666. Blood from one dog was passed to another through the quill of a feather. The next year a Frenchman transfused blood from a sheep to a boy and from a calf into a man. The boy recovered, but the man died, and the physician was charged with murder. Although the charge was dropped, laws were established banning blood transfusions.

James Blundell

About one hundred fifty years later, James Blundell, a London physician, performed the first recorded human-to-human blood transfusion. The patient was a woman who had lost a large amount of blood when her baby was born. He did transfusions on nine other women with similar problems, but six of them died. Since Blundell knew nothing about blood types and did not practice sterile techniques, it is surprising that any of the women survived.

Early blood transfusions were done directly between the *donor* (person giving blood) and the *recipient* (person receiving blood). Usually a short tube was used to carry the blood from one person to another, but occasionally the donor's and recipient's blood vessels were sewn together.

The problem with using this direct blood-transfusion method was that doctors did not know how much blood was being given to the recipient. As a result, physicians developed syringes (like hypodermic needles used to inject medicines today) to measure and transfuse blood. Doctors also used flasks to collect and measure blood. The flasks were set on a shelf above the recipient. Then gravity moved the blood through a tube into the recipient's arm.

Injuries, illnesses, surgery, and other problems cause many people to lose blood. In the past, people often died from the loss of blood rather than from the original injury or illness. For this reason physicians began devising methods to transfuse blood from a healthy person to a person who had lost blood.

In spite of the progress in blood-transfusion methods, major problems still existed. For example, as blood is taken out of the body, it clots quickly. For this reason physicians often found their syringes and tubes clogged by clots. Then in 1868 a physician found that chemicals could be added to prevent blood from clotting. Later it was discovered that containers with smooth surfaces slowed clotting. Soon wax-lined containers were used during blood transfusions.

Since the red blood cells in stored blood break down quickly, physicians also needed to find a way to store blood. They discovered that by adding certain chemicals they could prevent red blood cells from breaking down so quickly. Better chemicals were developed, and by 1957 blood could be stored for about twenty-eight days and still be usable in transfusions. Today blood is refrigerated at 1°C–10°C. At these temperatures it can be kept for thirty-five days.

Even with these techniques there were still problems to be overcome before transfusions became safe. Around 1900, Dr. Karl Landsteiner collected samples of blood from various people working in his lab. He mixed the blood in all the possible combinations and noticed that some blood samples mixed well but other combinations *agglutinated* (uh GLOOT n AY tid), or formed clumps.

In the agglutinated blood samples, the red blood cells became sticky and clumped together. These tiny clumps of cells were large enough to plug small blood vessels. From this, researchers understood why some blood transfusions were successful and others were not.

Karl Landsteiner

Later, blood samples were grouped in A, B, AB, and O groups, based on whether or not they contained chemicals called *antigens* (AN tih junz), which caused agglutination. Today blood is carefully matched so that people with type A blood usually receive type A blood in transfusions, and so on.

There are other blood antigens that are important in transfusions. The Rh factor is an antigen located on red blood cells, similar to the A and B antigens. Since the Rh factor also can cause agglutination, it must be checked before blood is transfused. Physicians use a plus sign to indicate the presence of the Rh factor in the blood and a minus sign to indicate its absence. There are many other blood factors, but they usually do

Transfusion Confusion (cont.)

not cause complications during blood transfusions.

Because blood is not always available, sometimes a technique called *autotransfusion* is used. The blood a person loses during surgery is collected, filtered, and cleaned. Then it is replaced into the patient's own bloodstream. The advantage of autotransfusion is that it eliminates the problems of matching blood types. This is especially important if the person has a rare type of blood.

If a patient needs more blood, a salt solution similar to plasma can be added to the blood before it is returned to the patient. If a patient

Modern methods of blood storage

knows far enough in advance that he is going to have surgery, he can have his own blood taken and saved for use during the surgery.

In spite of all these developments, about 2% of all transfusions have some undesirable effects on the recipient. To remedy this problem, scientists have tried to develop "artificial blood." Many substances have been tested and several show promising results; however, none have been approved for use in the United States.

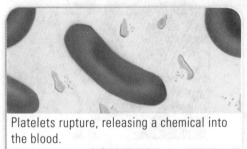

Platelets rupture, releasing a chemical into the blood.

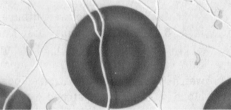

The chemical triggers the formation of protein fibers.

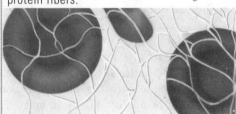

The protein fibers trap blood cells, forming a clot.

25B-6 Blood clotting

When blood vessels are broken, platelets first stick together, forming a temporary plug to stop blood loss. Some of the platelets then burst and release a substance that triggers a series of reactions that produce long fibers in the blood. A **blood clot** consists of a microscopic net of these fibers, which has trapped some blood cells. The clot then serves as a plug, stopping blood loss until the blood vessel can heal.

If a blood vessel breaks, a blood clot is necessary. If, however, a blood clot forms inside a blood vessel, it may block the blood supply to some area of the body. If the clot stops the flow of blood to a vital organ, the condition can be deadly. Your blood contains chemicals that slowly break down blood clots as the wound heals. These same chemicals also break down clots that are floating in the blood. If a physician suspects a problem with clots in the blood, he can inject such chemicals into a patient's bloodstream.

25B.4 *Blood Plasma*

The fluid portion of the blood is called the **blood plasma**. It is about 90% water. The remaining 10% of the materials in the blood plasma fall into two groups.

Substances that are transported by the blood. This group includes dissolved foods, wastes, minerals, hormones, and various other substances that cells need or produce.

Substances that regulate the blood. This group includes proteins and other substances that keep the blood chemicals balanced. The substances carried in the plasma enter and leave the plasma through the capillaries. The function of the blood is to transport those sub-

Serving God as a Phlebotomist

Job Description

A phlebotomist (fli BOT uh mist) is a person who draws blood for tests, research, transfusions, and donations. He also performs diagnostic tests on blood in a lab setting, often in co-operation with other lab technicians. Phlebotomists may be involved in analyzing the results of blood tests. In addition to having social skills, phlebotomists must also work accurately and safely to reduce the risk of infection from blood-borne diseases.

Possible Workplaces

hospitals, commercial labs, doctors' offices, public health departments, blood banks

Education

In addition to a high-school diploma, most phlebotomists are trained and certified after completing a one- or two-semester program involving classroom and on-the-job training. Four different national organizations offer certification, which is required by some states.

Dominion Opportunities

By collecting blood to be used in diagnosing diseases and disorders, a phlebotomist can help preserve and improve the

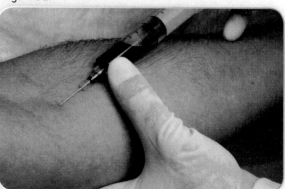

quality of life for humans. Those who work in blood banks, where blood is removed, stored, and then used to help others, demonstrate a high level of care for others.

stances, but if the blood is not carefully regulated, the substances the blood transports are of little value.

For example, a certain blood-clotting substance comes from platelets, but the other clotting substances are found in the plasma. If the concentration of some of these substances is too high, the blood may clot too much. This could result in dangerous clots in the blood vessels. If there is too little of these substances, the blood may not clot when a vessel is cut. Regulators in the body work to keep the concentration of the blood-clotting substances in the blood plasma at the proper levels. This is another example of the body working to maintain homeostasis.

25B.5 Blood Pressure

As the heart pumps, the blood passes into the arteries with such force that they swell slightly. You feel this force when you take your **pulse**. By pressing an artery against a bone, you can feel the force of blood pushing against the pressure caused by your finger. Your pulse rate tells you how fast your heart is beating.

The pressure of circulating blood against the walls of the arteries is called the **blood pressure**. Even between heartbeats there is some pressure in the arteries. This pressure forces the blood through the arteries and on into the capillaries of the body.

Often a person with low blood pressure does not have enough blood passing through his capillaries to nourish his cells properly. If the blood pressure goes too low, the person may become unconscious.

Facets of *the Human Body:* *Blood and Water from Jesus's Side*

Jesus was crucified on the day of preparation for Passover. Jewish law and custom prohibited execution on Passover day (Mark 15:42; John 19:31). To avoid breaking Jewish law, a Roman soldier was sent to break the legs and thereby hasten the deaths of Jesus and the two criminals executed with Him.

Why would broken legs speed death during crucifixion? A victim of crucifixion had to alternate between pushing up with his legs and pulling up with his arms to breathe. It was usually at least thirty-six hours before the exhausted victim could no longer lift himself to breathe and died by suffocation. Once a crucified person's legs were broken, he could lift himself only by his arms and died more quickly.

However, the soldiers did not break Jesus's legs. John 19:33–34 tells us, "When they came to Jesus, and saw that he was dead already, they brake not his legs: but one of the soldiers with a spear pierced his side, and forthwith came there out blood and water."

Jesus actually died before the soldiers came to break his legs in fulfillment of the Old Testament prophesies: "he keepeth all his bones: not one of them is broken" (Ps. 34:20) and "they shall look upon me whom they have pierced" (Zech. 12:10). Also in this passage the apostle John is no doubt drawing a connection between the Passover lamb described in Exodus 12, about which the Lord said "you shall not break any of its bones." Jesus was the perfect sacrificial Lamb, the perfect fulfillment of Old Testament law.

The blood inside the blood vessels of a dead body does not normally separate into clotted blood and watery plasma. However, a long, violent struggle that ends in death can involve severe internal bleeding and the pooling of blood in the chest and abdomen. This blood could separate and thus account for blood and water flowing from a wound.

Christ may have had such internal bleeding, but this is somewhat unlikely because it takes blood a long time to collect around internal organs. Besides, Jesus did not put up a violent struggle. He humbly endured the torture before His death. He was "brought as a lamb to the slaughter, and as a sheep before her shearers is dumb, so he [opened] not his mouth" (Isa. 53:7).

Many people believe that Christ's heart ruptured (broke). There are records of strong emotions causing other people to die of a ruptured heart. If one of the heart chambers or large blood vessels near the heart had ruptured, blood probably would have flooded into the pericardium (sac around the heart). Here the blood could have rapidly separated into clotted blood cells and watery plasma.

The Roman soldier, surprised to find Christ already dead, may have aimed his spear toward the heart. If he pierced the pericardium, clotted blood and watery plasma could have drained from the wound in Christ's side.

Jesus's physical death on the cross was real. He did not swoon or faint and then revive in the tomb. Blood and water could have flowed from His body only if He had been physically dead. But the important aspect of the death of Christ is not the specific injuries to His physical body. What is important is that the Son of God died for the sins of all mankind. Christ gave Himself on the cross that we might be saved: "It is fin-

ished," He said and "gave up the ghost" (John 19:30).

No one and nothing on earth could kill Jesus because He is God. Earlier in His life Christ declared, "I lay down my life, that I might take it again. No man taketh it from me, but I lay it down of myself" (John 10:17–18). Jesus died because He chose to give His life "a ransom for all" (1 Tim. 2:6).

Death, however, was not the end for Christ; He rose again on the third day, conquering death. He now lives in a glorified, eternal body (Phil. 3:21). Those who trust in Him for salvation will also die (or be raptured) and receive a glorified, eternal body like His (1 Cor. 6:14; 2 Cor. 4:14; 1 John 3:2).

(*The Crucifixion*, Pieter Vlerick (attr. to), from the Bob Jones University Collection)

When you exercise, your cells use more nutrients and oxygen and produce more wastes. By increasing the blood pressure, your body forces more blood through the capillaries. This increases the food and oxygen supply to the cells and removes the extra amounts of wastes.

One way the body increases blood pressure is by having the heart pump more blood. This is what happens when your heart beats faster. Another way to increase blood pressure is to make the diameter of the blood vessels smaller. Smooth muscles in artery walls contract, reducing the diameter of the vessel. Increasing the blood pressure is beneficial when your body needs it. However, continually high blood pressure can overwork the heart and blood vessels and cause them to wear out sooner.

normal blood pressure

arteries' decreasing in diameter increases blood pressure

heart's pumping more blood increases blood pressure

heart's pumping more blood and arteries' decreasing in diameter increases blood pressure

Blood pressure **25B-7**

Various diseases of the heart, liver, and kidneys can cause high blood pressure. These diseases should be treated by a physician. Several other factors, including old age, lead to high blood pressure. As blood vessels get older, they lose their ability to expand. If they are unable to expand as blood is pumped into them, the blood pressure increases.

One of the major factors that contributes to high blood pressure is tension. Tension is often caused by worries, frustrations, guilt, anxiety, and similar problems. In a fallen world plagued with wars, social and economic problems, and every variety of sin, it is easy to see how tension can become a major problem, especially for non-Christians. Christians, however, should be different. Although Christians should expect testings and trials, the Lord Jesus Christ will protect, defend, guide, and strengthen His own (Phil. 4:6, 13). Christians are expected to be concerned enough about the world to try to influence the world toward a Christian worldview. As they do what they know is right, Christians must rely on the Lord and trust Him to work out everything (James 5:7–8).

What Do You Think?

After reviewing Figure 25B-7, what effect do you think an increase in blood vessel diameter would have on blood pressure?

Section Review 25B

1. What organelle does an erythrocyte lack?

2. What molecule in erythrocytes carries oxygen?

3. Who donates blood to the recipient in an autotransfusion?

4. Why is it important for you to have platelets?

5. How can tension affect your blood pressure?

Objectives 25C

- Describe the nonspecific defense mechanisms.
- Define *antigen*.
- Explain the difference between T cells and B cells.
- Define *immunity*.

pathogen: path- (Gk. PATHOS, suffering) + -gen (Gk. GENES, born)

25C The Body's Defense System

At the end of the sixth day when God had finished His creation, He saw "everything that He had made, and behold, it was very good" (Gen. 1:31). All that God had created lived in harmony. There was no disease and no death. Many people who hold a Christian worldview believe that although there were bacteria, viruses, and other microbes, none of them were harmful. However, two events changed the relationship between man and all other organisms.

The first event is the disobedience of Adam and Eve and the consequent event is the Curse that God placed upon them and the earth. Though Adam and Eve were placed in the Garden of Eden "to dress it and to keep it" (Gen. 2:15), now the earth would resist them and their efforts to survive. Adam and Eve's disobedience also resulted in death. God had said, "Thou shalt surely die," and in addition to the spiritual death all men and women suffer, everyone has physically died since Abel (with the exception of Enoch and Elijah).

The environment changed as a result of sin. Death and disease became commonplace. Many bacteria, viruses, and other organisms that originally caused no harm are now pathogens (PATH uh junz), which cause sickness and death. After the Flood, man raised animals for food and clothing. Some people believe that organisms and substances originally found only on animals eventually infected humans and sometimes caused illness or death. But God knew that the human body would be attacked in a sin-cursed world, and from the beginning He designed humans with bodily defenses to help them survive in this flawed environment.

Christians can look forward to the restoration of creation. When the results of man's sin are reversed—there will be no death or suffering (Rev. 21:4), the lion and lamb will live together, and the child and asp (a kind of poisonous snake) will play together (Isa. 11:6–8).

25C.1 *Nonspecific Defenses*

The body's first line of defense against invaders is its covering—the skin and mucous membranes. As you learned in Chapter 24, the skin provides a protective covering for the outside of the body. Although thin, the connections between the cells are very strong. The skin also produces some chemicals that kill microorganisms on its surface. Usually the only way an organism can get through is when the skin is cut or scraped.

Mucous membranes are similar to skin, but usually not as thick. They line the inside of the body. For example, your mouth and nose are lined by mucous membranes. Mucous membranes produce sticky mucus that traps foreign organisms. Some mucous membranes have tiny fingerlike projections called *cilia* that can move back and forth. These wavelike movements move the mucus and trapped organisms to the throat where it is swallowed. The hydrochloric (HYE druh KLOR ik) acid produced by the stomach kills the organisms. As in the case of the skin, organisms can

trapped organism
cilia
mucus
mucous membrane

25C-1 Mucous membranes are an important part of the body's first line of defense.

usually penetrate this barrier only through small cuts or scrapes.

Once an organism gets through the skin, the next line of defense is activated—inflammation. **Inflammation** is a local response to invaders. When cells are damaged, they release special chemicals that cause changes in the blood vessels. First, the diameter of the blood vessels in the area increases in size to supply more blood to the area. Second, the walls of the capillaries become "leaky" so that plasma can reach the site. If the area where the inflammation is occurring is close to the surface of the skin, the area may be swollen, red, painful, and slightly warmer than the surrounding skin. The plasma brings nutrients and other substances to fight the invaders. Third, special white blood cells called *macrophages* slip through the capillary walls. The macrophages attack the foreign organisms and kill them. How do the macrophages know what to attack? Any foreign substance or organism contains antigens. **Antigens** are molecules that the macrophages recognize as not belonging in the body.

If more help is needed, the body responds by causing a fever. A **fever** is an increase of the normal body temperature of 37°C (98.6°F). You probably think that a fever is bad; however, the increase in temperature often slows the rate of bacterial reproduction and increases many of the body's defenses to fight the invaders. Special chemicals released at the site of inflammation travel to the brain, which triggers the increase in temperature.

25C.2 *Specific Defenses*

The body's final line of defense is the **immune system**. The cells in the immune system can respond to and attack specific pathogens. The white blood cells used by the immune system are called *lymphocytes* (LIM fuh SITES). There are two major kinds of lymphocytes—T cells and B cells.

Millions of T cells circulate in the blood. Their primary job is to recognize antigens. Once a macrophage identifies an antigen, the macrophage releases a chemical that causes the T cells to spring into action. First, they rapidly multiply to make more T cells that recognize the antigen. Some of the T cells called *helper* T cells activate *killer* T cells. The killer T cells begin to attack the antigen-containing pathogen or cells that have been infected with the pathogen. Helper T cells also seek out B cells to notify them that an antigen has been found.

Once the B cells have been notified, or activated, by the helper T cells, they begin producing plasma cells. The plasma cells, in turn, begin producing antibodies. *Antibodies* are proteins that react against a specific antigen. The antibodies destroy the pathogen or inactivate it so that other cells can destroy it.

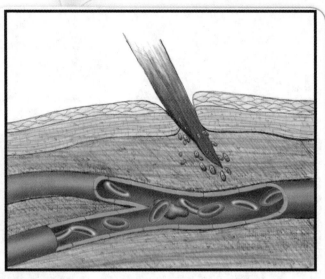

Bacteria (green) enter the body on the end of a splinter.

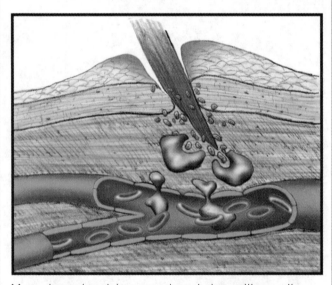

Macrophages (purple) squeeze through the capillary walls.

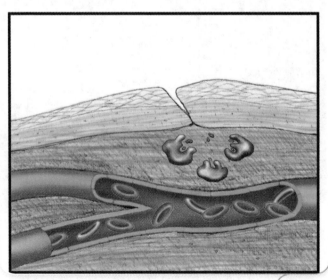

As the wound heals, the macrophages finish destroying the bacteria.

25C-2

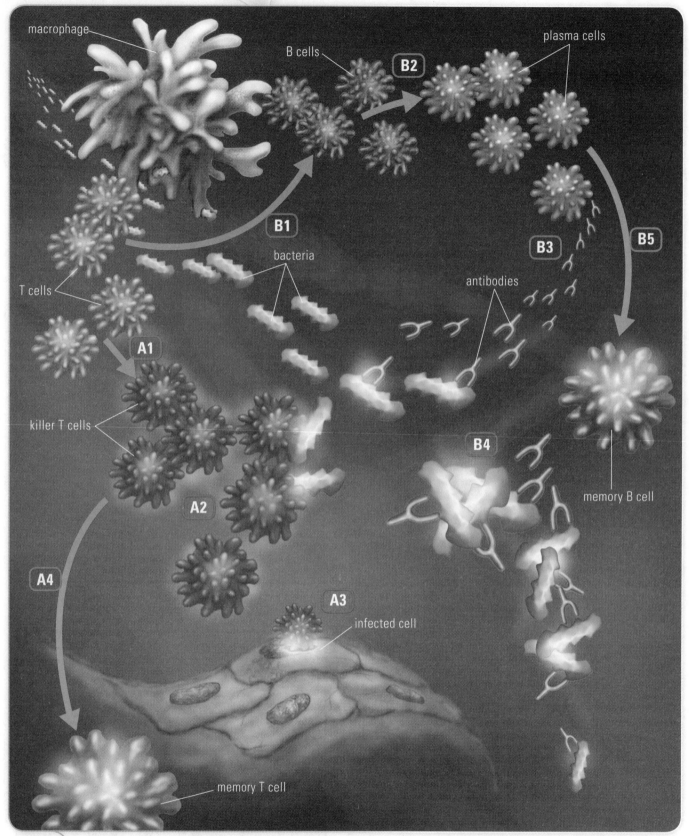

25C-3 The immune response: When macrophages identify a foreign substance (bacteria), two series of events begin to happen simultaneously. T cells activate killer T cells (A1) as well as B cells (B1). Some killer T cells attack the bacteria (A2), and others attack infected cells (A3). Meanwhile, the activated B cells produce plasma cells (B2), which in turn produce antibodies (B3). The antibodies attack the invading bacteria (B4). After the bacteria have been destroyed, some T cells (A4) and some B cells (B5) become memory cells to guard against future infections. Leftover antibodies also remain in the bloodstream, enhancing the body's immunity.

Once the pathogen has been destroyed, the leftover antibodies remain in the bloodstream in case they are needed again. Also, some of the T cells and B cells are able to "remember" the antigen so that if it ever returns, the body can quickly respond. These remaining B and T cells are called *memory cells*. The body's ability to remember a specific antigen and respond to it is called **immunity**.

When your body produces antibodies itself, it is called *active immunity*. Active immunity occurs when there has been an infection and the immune system has responded. Another way to develop active immunity is by receiving a vaccine (vak SEEN). A *vaccine* contains a weakened form of the virus or bacterium that still contains the antigens. Your body responds in the very same way, producing antibodies and memory cells that are ready in case they are needed.

Passive immunity occurs when you receive ready-made antibodies. A newborn baby receives antibodies from his mother. Since these antibodies do not last as long as those produced by active immunity, infants need to be vaccinated so they can develop their own antibodies. Antibodies can also be produced by animals or other organisms. These antibodies are injected just like a vaccine. Since these antibodies do not last long, booster injections are needed.

25C.3 *Defense Malfunctions*

Although God designed a marvelous immune system that works almost perfectly, problems can occur. Sometimes the immune system overreacts to substances that are not pathogens. Some pathogens cause the immune system to react against normal body tissues, while other pathogens prevent it from working effectively.

Allergies. Has freshly mown grass ever caused your nose to run or your eyes to itch? Do some foods make you break out in a rash? If so, you probably have an allergy. An **allergy** is an overreaction of the immune system to a foreign substance that is normally not a pathogen. The substance that causes such a response, such as pollen or mold, is called an *allergen*. The response may be just a runny nose, or it can cause life-threatening breathing difficulties.

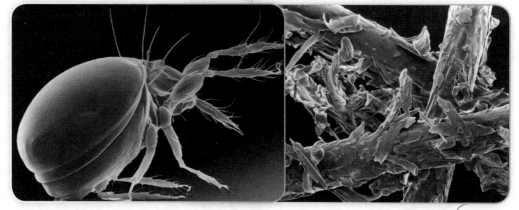

Dust mites and pet dander (flakes of dried skin on hair) can cause allergic reactions. **25C-4**

Autoimmune diseases. In an **autoimmune disease**, the immune system is unable to tell the difference between pathogens and some of its normal cells. When this happens, the immune system attacks the pathogen and the normal cells. Doctors and scientists are not sure why this occurs. Examples of autoimmune diseases include rheumatoid arthritis, lupus, multiple sclerosis, and some types of diabetes.

Facets of *the Human Body:* *Organ Transplants*

Occasionally people are born with defective organs that surgery cannot repair. In other cases, injury or disease makes an organ useless. Often drugs can destroy an organ's ability to function. For people in these circumstances, organ transplants may be necessary if they are to lead normal lives.

The major problem with organ transplants is rejection. The human body's immune system produces white blood cells and antibodies to fight off infection caused by foreign substances—normally bacteria and viruses. If the immune system recognizes an antigen on the transplanted organ as foreign, it produces antibodies that attack it, and the body then rejects the organ.

One method of reducing the rejection of transplanted organs is to slow or stop the activity of the immune system. However, drugs used to inhibit the immune system cause the body to tolerate not only the foreign organ but also foreign bacteria and viruses. Sometimes the patient dies not because the transplanted organ is rejected, but because of an infection his body could easily have fought off

if his immune system had been working properly.

Because of new techniques, rejection is becoming less of a problem. Anti-rejection drugs such as cyclosporine, Imuran, and Rapamune help the body retain a transplanted organ by blocking some actions of the immune system.

In 1954 a kidney became the first organ ever to be successfully transplanted in humans. The kidney was donated by a young boy to his twin brother, who was dying of kidney failure. Because the boys had the same genetic makeup, there was little problem with rejection. Both boys grew up to be healthy men. Since 1954, kidney transplants have added years to the lives of many people.

The techniques for transplanting kidneys are not as complicated as those for transplanting other organs. In a kidney transplant only one artery, one vein, and one ureter must be cut and attached. The ideal kidney donor is a close, living relative of the patient. Most donors, however, are people who have just died and have willed their bodies to be used for organ transplants. A kidney taken

from a dead donor must be transplanted within a few days; otherwise, the rejection rate increases.

People suffering from kidney disease usually prefer to have a kidney transplant. The alternative is to be attached to an artificial kidney machine three times a week for several hours at a time. This process is called dialysis. If a kidney transplant is successful, it allows a patient to lead a nearly normal life.

Sometimes rejection is immediate, and the person dies soon after the transplant is completed. In other instances, the organ functions well for several years; then it gradually slows down as the immune system destroys it.

Both dialysis and organ transplants are expensive. Transplants and additional medications typically range from $100,000 to $504,000 during the first year after the transplant. Understandably most patients are unable to pay all the costs. In the past, many patients were rejected for treatment due to inability to pay. In 1972 an amendment to the Social Security Act authorized the federal government to pay almost all expenses related to kidney machines and kidney transplants. This has not reduced the costs but has merely shifted the payment of these costs to all Americans by way of taxes.

Many other organ and tissue transplants are now possible. Livers, bones, cartilage, tendons, intestines, eardrums, middle-ear bones, corneas, bone marrow, and even lungs, pancreases, and hearts have been transplanted successfully.

Frequently Transplanted Organs (U.S. Hospitals)

Cornea. A cornea transplant is the most frequent transplant operation. Few corneas are rejected by the recipients' bodies. Cornea transplants improve the vision of over 90% of the people who have this operation.

1. organ transplanted

2. organ produces foreign chemicals

3. body produces antibodies

4. organ dies

Kidney. Over 14,000 kidneys are transplanted each year. Approximately 96% of these still function after one year. This is the most frequent organ transplant. (The cornea is only part of an organ.) If the transplanted kidney fails, the person can survive by using a dialysis machine.

Liver. Approximately 5400 liver transplants are attempted each year. About 88% of the people who receive a transplant are alive after one year.

Heart. Approximately 2300 people receive heart transplants each year. About 85% of heart-transplant patients remain alive a year after the transplant. About 70% are alive after five years.

Heart–lung. Patients needing only a lung transplant often receive a heart–lung transplant. The combined transplant operation has a better suc-cess rate than lung transplants alone. Less than a hundred such operations are attempted each year. About 60% of the patients receiving heart–lung transplants are alive after one year.

Pancreas. About 700 pancreas transplants are performed each year. About 90% of those are successful. A person whose transplanted pancreas fails can receive injections of insulin to remain alive.

Bone marrow. The success rate for marrow transplants varies greatly (between 10% and 90%). Survival depends on which disease the patient has and how well matched the donor and patient are. Bone marrow produces the cells used by the immune system. Thus, sometimes the marrow transplant rejects the body, rather than the body rejecting the transplant.

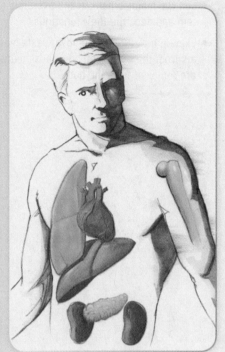

HIV infections and AIDS. An infection by the human immunodeficiency virus (HIV) destroys the ability of the immune system to respond to pathogens. HIV infects and destroys helper T cells. Without helper T cells, the killer T cells and the B cells are not activated and cannot respond to HIV or other pathogens that might infect the body. The result is that many HIV-infected people develop AIDS (Acquired Immune Deficiency Syndrome). Since their bodies cannot properly respond to infections, they often die from infections that a healthy immune system could easily overcome.

Section Review 25C

1. What two major events changed God's creation?

2. Which affects the entire body, inflammation or fever?

3. Explain the similarities and differences between T cells and B cells.

4. Which kind of immunity is caused by an injection of pre-formed antibodies?

5. List two immune system malfunctions.

6. How is rejection in a bone marrow transplant different from rejection with other transplants?

Love Thy Neighbor

HIV infections have spread rapidly over the world primarily through improper sexual relations. Before HIV was fully understood, however, infections were sometimes spread through blood transfusions. Sadly, many innocent people were infected. In 1985 a screening test was designed to test donated blood for the presence of HIV. Since that time, blood collection centers screen donated blood for HIV. How should a Christian respond to this situation? What does this information tell us about the effects of sin?

25D The Excretory System

The primary functions of the excretory system are to remove wastes from the blood and to eliminate them from the body. The main organs of the excretory system are the **kidneys**. The kidneys are reddish brown, bean-shaped organs about 10 cm (4 in.) long and 6.5 cm (2.5 in.) wide. They are located in the lower back, one on each side of the vertebral column.

Attached to each kidney is a ureter. The **ureters** (*yoo* REE turz) are tubes that carry the wastes and water filtered out of the blood down to the urinary bladder. The **urinary bladder** is a muscular bag that temporarily stores the fluid wastes from the kidneys. From the urinary bladder a muscular tube called the **urethra** (*yoo* REE thruh) leads to the outside of the body.

25D.1 Functioning of the Kidney

Inside each kidney are about one million nephrons (NEF rahnz). A **nephron** is the unit in the kidney that filters the blood. The filtering takes place in two steps. First, a large portion of the water from the plasma leaves the blood capillaries and enters the nephrons. This water contains many dissolved substances. The water then flows along the nephron tubule.

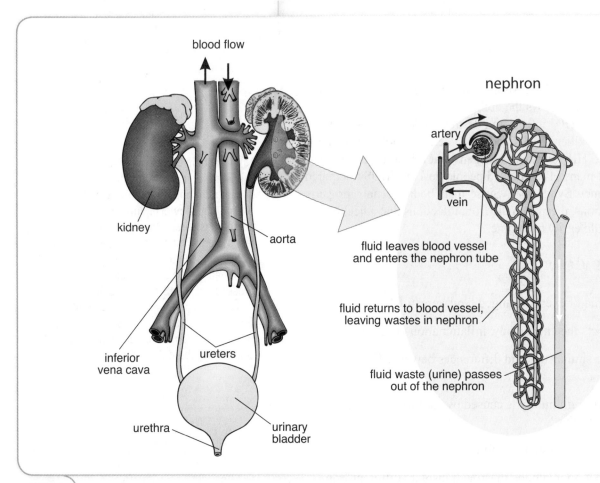

blood flow

nephron

artery

vein

kidney

aorta

inferior
vena cava

ureters

urethra

urinary
bladder

fluid leaves blood vessel
and enters the nephron tube

fluid returns to blood vessel,
leaving wastes in nephron

fluid waste (urine) passes
out of the nephron

25D-1 Human excretory system

The second step involves the return of substances to the blood. Most of the water and normal substances of the blood plasma, such as salts, calcium, vitamins, hormones, pigments, and amino acids, return to the blood through capillaries that surround the nephron tube. If the plasma has too much of any of these substances, some will remain in the nephrons. Also, substances that are not normal to the blood, such as drugs and waste products, remain in the nephron tube. The fluid that remains in the nephrons is called **urine**. The urine from the nephrons collects in the kidney and then passes into the ureter.

25D.2 *Usual and Unusual Substances in Urine*

Normally urine contains a small amount of each of the substances found in the blood plasma. However, urine may contain larger quantities of these substances if unusually large amounts of them are present in the blood. For example, if you consume more vitamin C than your body can use, your urine will contain some vitamin C.

Urine contains mostly water and waste products. Protein digestion produces ammonia as a waste product. Ammonia is changed to another waste product, **urea** (*yoo* REE uh), by the liver. When blood containing urea passes through the kidney, much of the urea is left in the nephron. Thus the blood is much "cleaner" after it passes through the kidneys.

One of the key regulators of blood sugar is the pancreas. (See pp. 493–95.) If this organ fails, there may be too much sugar in the blood. This condition is called *diabetes mellitus*. The excess sugar in the blood will cause the kidney to filter out sugar and put it in the urine. Various other diseases and disorders account for the presence of unusual substances or abnormal amounts of substances in a person's urine. Urine analysis (a process for determining what is in urine) can often tell a physician a great deal about a patient's health.

25D.3 *Artificial Kidneys*

Occasionally a person's kidneys will fail to operate properly. This failure may be caused by injury, disease, or overworking of the kidneys. If one kidney stops operating, there is usually little problem. People can function normally with one kidney. People also can function with only a part of one kidney working, but they must be under careful supervision. However, if a person loses the use of both kidneys, a *dialysis* (dye AL ih sis) *machine* (often called an artificial kidney) can help filter his blood.

An artificial kidney contains thin tubes submerged in warm, circulating fluid. After a patient's blood vessels are connected

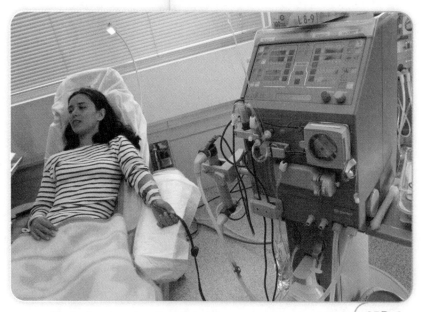

Student undergoing dialysis to filter wastes from her blood **25D-2**

to the artificial kidney, his blood flows through these tubes. As the blood flows through the tubes, wastes are removed in much the same way that they are in a nephron. The cleansed blood then returns from the dialysis machine into the patient's blood vessels through other plastic tubes.

Section Review 25D

1. What is the structure in the kidney that filters wastes from the blood?

2. List two substances *normally* found in urine.

3. What does sugar in the urine indicate?

Chapter Review

1. Name the three components of the circulatory system.

2. To what body system do the kidneys belong?

3. What are clot busters?

4. What kind of energy does a defibrillator use to restore normal heart functions?

5. What is the function of your natural pacemaker?

6. Through which blood vessels does blood enter the heart from the body?

7. Name the largest artery in the body.

8. How much blood does a human body normally have?

9. What is the usual life span of an erythrocyte?

10. Which type of blood cell transports oxygen?

11. What is the proper name for white blood cells?

12. What are the nonspecific methods the body uses to protect itself?

13. Name the two types of lymphocytes used by the immune system.

14. Name the body structure that temporarily stores urine.

15. Name the microscopic units in the kidney that filter wastes from the blood.

16. What is a common waste substance in urine that is produced from protein digestion?

17. What is another name for an "artificial kidney"?

What Did You Learn?

1. Describe the relationship of arteries, veins, and capillaries.

2. Why are the walls of the ventricles in the heart thicker than the walls of the atria?

3. How does the body defend itself against infections?

4. If you were bleeding, how would the blood itself help stop the bleeding?

5. What causes your pulse?

6. Why is the immune system described as a *specific* defense system?

Scientifically Speaking

homeostasis
artery
capillary
vein
heart
atria
ventricle
septum
atrioventricular valve (AV valve)
semilunar valve
superior vena cava
inferior vena cava
deoxygenated blood
pulmonary arteries
oxygenated blood
pulmonary vein
aorta
coronary arteries
erythrocytes
hemoglobin
leukocyte
antibody
platelet
blood clot
blood plasma
pulse
blood pressure
inflammation
antigen
fever
immune system
immunity
allergy
autoimmune disease
kidney
ureter
urinary bladder
urethra
nephron
urine
urea

Self Quiz 25

_____ 1. Homeostasis is
   A. maintaining the internal conditions of your body.
   B. a chemical reaction that occurs when two different blood types are mixed.
   C. a balance that exists between the right atrium and the left atrium.
   D. (none of these)

_____ 2. Arteries carry blood to the heart. (True/False)

_____ 3. The chamber of the heart that pumps blood to the entire body is the
   A. right atrium.
   B. right ventricle.
   C. left atrium.
   D. left ventricle.

4. _____ separate the atria from the ventricles.

5. _____ contain hemoglobin and transport oxygen.

_____ 6. Which of the following does _not_ describe white blood cells?
   A. produce antibodies
   B. outnumber red blood cells
   C. attack bacteria
   D. larger than red blood cells

7. _____ help form blood clots.

8. _____ are molecules that alert the immune system to foreign substances.

_____ 9. Helper T cells do all of the following _except_
   A. activate killer T cells.
   B. produce antibodies.
   C. activate B cells.
   D. produce T cells that recognize an antigen.

10. _____ are special proteins that react against a specific antigen.

11. The structure that filters the blood in the kidney is called the _____.

12. What are the primary functions of the excretory system?

ENERGY

Do you seem to have more energy while playing basketball or playing an instrument? What happens to your "energy level" when you do homework on a sunny afternoon? This lack of motivation, however, really has nothing to do with your "energy level." Actually, your body uses energy all the time to perform the processes that keep you alive. All these processes together are called **metabolism** (muh TA buh LIZ um). Even when you sleep, your body's metabolism continues to work and use energy.

The measurement of how much energy you use is called your **metabolic** (MET uh BAHL ik) **rate**. If you were running a race, your metabolic rate would be high. If you stopped running and began walking slowly, your metabolic rate would decrease.

Normally your metabolic rate is lowest when you rest quietly. This low rate is called your **basal** (BAY sul) **metabolic rate**. It changes as you grow older. The basal metabolic rate of a one-year-old baby is higher than that of a six-year-old child. Your basal metabolic rate is higher now than it will be when you reach age eighteen. From age eighteen to old age, your basal metabolic rate will drop gradually.

Where does your body get energy for metabolism? From food. In your lifetime you will probably consume more than 50 tons of food. Not all of what you eat will supply energy for metabolism. For example, you probably consume a half gallon of water each day (some as fluid, some in foods). You must have water to live, but water does not supply energy. You eat some materials that your body cannot digest. These materials leave your body as wastes and do not supply you with energy. Your body uses some food to build tissues. Not very much of your food, however, is used as body-building material. We know this because the average adult weighs only about 68 kg (150 lb), which is considerably less than 50 tons!

26-1 Your basal metabolic rate slows down as you get older.

Most of what you eat supplies your body with the energy it needs to function. A good way to understand how the body uses food is to compare your body's metabolism to a fire. To have a fire, you must have oxygen and something to burn, such as wood, coal, or oil. Similarly, your body must have oxygen and something to burn (food) to carry on metabolism. In this chapter you will study the two systems that provide the raw materials for metabolism. The *respiratory* (RES pur uh TOR ee) *system* supplies the oxygen, and the *digestive system* supplies the energy.

26A The Respiratory System

The primary function of the **respiratory system** is to exchange carbon dioxide for a fresh supply of oxygen from the air. The **lungs** are the main organs of the respiratory system. They deliver oxygen to the blood and remove carbon dioxide. The air you *inhale* (breathe in) is the source of oxygen, and the air you *exhale* (breathe out) contains the carbon dioxide produced by cellular respiration.

Chapter 5 explains *aerobic cellular respiration*, the process of combining an energy source (sugar) with oxygen to release energy in a form that cells can use. The sugar *glucose* is your body's most common energy source. The blood is the transport system for the body. It carries glucose and oxygen to the cells for aerobic respiration and removes carbon dioxide. Carbon dioxide is a waste product of aerobic cellular respiration. The blood carries it to the lungs where it is removed from the body.

26A.1 *Structures of the Respiratory System*

The simplest way to describe the parts of the respiratory system is to follow the way air flows past them as you inhale. Air enters your body through the *nostrils* or through the *mouth*. Membranes that line the nose secrete a thick, sticky substance

Objectives 26A

- Define *metabolism, metabolic rate,* and *basal metabolic rate.*
- Name the structures of the respiratory system and describe their functions.
- Outline the process of breathing.

cilia

26A-1 Your respiratory system is swept clean by the cilia of its membrane cells.

called **mucus**. Similar membranes line the rest of the respiratory system and parts of the digestive tract.

The humid air inside the nose warms and moistens the outside air you inhale. The sticky mucus traps particles of dust and other substances that may be floating in the air. Cilia on the cells of the membrane that line the respiratory tract move the mucus toward the throat, where it is swallowed. Digestive juices in the stomach destroy the mucus and the trapped particles.

At the back of the mouth and nose is the part of the throat called the **pharynx**. The pharynx leads downward to the esophagus and the larynx. The **esophagus** is an elastic tube that is located behind the larynx and that carries food and liquids to the stomach. Normally the esophagus opens only when you swallow. The **larynx** (LAR ingks) is a boxlike structure composed of several pieces of cartilage. The top of the larynx opens into the pharynx, and the bottom leads to the other structures of the respiratory system.

Between the pharynx and the larynx is a flap of tissue called the **epiglottis** (EP ih GLAHT is). When you swallow, the epiglottis bends down and covers the opening to the larynx, preventing food or liquids from entering the lungs.

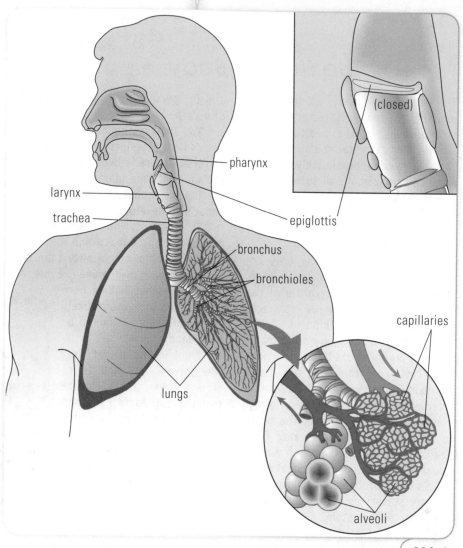

Human respiratory system **26A-2**

Inside the larynx is a "last chance" stop for food or liquids that go "down the wrong tube." A pair of folds inside the larynx can pull together and completely cover the opening.

The space between these folds is called the **glottis** (GLAHT iss). If something other than air tries to pass through the glottis, the folds immediately close. Then the body begins *coughing* to get the substance out of the larynx before it causes damage.

The folds around your glottis are the *vocal cords*. If you draw your vocal cords together and then force air through them, you can make them vibrate much like the

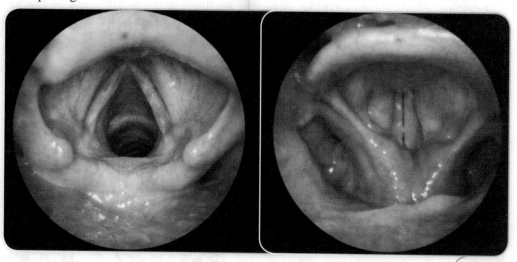

Vocal cords—open and closed position **26A-3**

Facets of *The Human Body:* *Smoking—A Habit That Kills*

The results of many studies have established that cigarette smoking is hazardous to the health of the smoker. For example, scientists know that each year approximately 399,000 American smokers die of some type of health problem related to their smoking. Studies have also shown that 90% of the people who die of lung cancer are smokers.

The lungs are not the only organs affected by smoking. Doctors have linked smoking to cancer of the larynx, mouth, esophagus, stomach, pancreas, bladder and kidneys.

Besides cancer, many other major physical problems are linked to smoking. Fatty substances often build up inside a smoker's arteries. As the arteries harden, the smoker's blood pressure increases, forcing the heart to work harder. The death rate from heart disease is twice as high among smokers as it is among nonsmokers.

Smoking probably affects the respiratory system more than it affects any other body system. Although the respiratory system has various structures to protect itself, cigarette smoke can still cause lots of much damage.

An important means of defense for most of the respiratory system is the protective lining made up of mucous membrane and cilia (tiny hairlike structures). The mucous membrane produces mucus, which traps dust and other particles in the air you breathe. The cilia constantly wave in an upward direction, moving the mucus and trapped materials up and out of the respiratory system.

People who smoke, however, often damage their cilia and lose this cleaning action. A light smoker may do temporary minor damage, but a heavy smoker may permanently destroy the cilia. Without cilia to clean the air passageways, mucus and trapped materials build up in the lungs. Soon the alveoli fill up with these materials and the person experiences shortness of breath.

The smoker's cough is one of the body's final attempts to get rid of this material before it becomes lodged in the lungs. If the material remains in the lungs, emphysema and other diseases may develop.

If pregnant women smoke cigarettes, their babies weigh less and usually develop more slowly than babies of nonsmoking women. Evidence also shows that babies born to smokers are more likely to be born too early or to be born dead.

Smokers harm not only themselves but also those around them. The cigarette smoke breathed in by someone not smoking is called *secondhand smoke*. Young babies in homes of parents who smoke suffer from bronchitis, asthma, ear infections, and pneumonia more often than babies in homes with nonsmoking parents. Cigarette smoke in the home also increases the likelihood of Sudden Infant Death Syndrome (SIDS).

Older children in smokers' homes often suffer from severe headaches, allergic coughing and sneezing, and extreme eye irritations. In addition to these harmful effects, the same type of damage that occurs in the smoking parents' lungs often occurs in the lungs of their children.

In a study of couples in which the husband smoked but the wife did not, there was a high occurrence of lung cancer among the wives. The more cigarettes the husband smoked, the more likely it was for his wife to develop cancer. Scientists have also completed studies of the effects of cigarette smoke on work environments. These studies indicate that nonsmokers who work in areas where others smoke are more likely to develop lung cancer as

SURGEON GENERAL'S WARNING: Smoking Causes Lung Cancer, Heart Disease, Emphysema, And May Complicate Pregnancy.

well as coronary heart disease than if they worked in a smoke-free area.

In fact, secondhand smoke has been officially labeled as a known human carcinogen. Scientists estimate that secondhand smoke causes thirty-eight hundred lung cancer deaths and thirty-five thousand to forty thousand heart-disease deaths each year in the United States. Or more simply, for every eight smokers that die of smoking-caused disease, one nonsmoker also dies of the same disease.

For many years the tobacco industry advertised that smoking tobacco was fun and not really harmful. Cigarette ads with pictures of attractive, healthy looking people seemed to say, "You too can smoke and stay healthy and beautiful."

No telling what that smoke is doing to our Health!

Today most Americans know about the harmful effects of smoking. By law the Surgeon General's warning must appear on every package of cigarettes and in all cigarette advertisements. The warning has helped to make smokers more aware of the risks they are taking. Today a smaller percentage of Americans smoke than thirty, twenty, or even ten years ago. The warning has even affected those who still smoke. The average smoker nowadays smokes fewer cigarettes per day than the average smoker ten did years ago.

Some cigarette companies produce "low tar" and "slim-light" cigarettes, hoping to minimize the harmful effects of smoking. However, low tar cigarettes are no less harmful than regular cigarettes.

Tobacco supporters point out that tax on tobacco products helps pay for parks and roads. They also emphasize that the tobacco industry employs thousands of Americans. If the government passed legislation that hurt the industry, many people would be out of jobs. These arguments in favor of tobacco are strong and have kept a harmful product on the market. Even though the tobacco industry accounts for billions of dollars in the U.S. economy, it also contributes to untold human suffering, medical costs, loss of income, and needless waste.

Knowing all these scientific facts, Christians should oppose smoking. Smoking defiles the body, which is the temple of the living God (1 Cor. 6:19–20). It also may shorten a Christian's lifetime of service for the Lord. To a Christian, being like someone else or gaining economic benefits is not important when the choice is between doing right or wrong. Although the Bible does not specifically mention smoking, biblical principles must guide the lives of Christians.

Healthy lung tissue

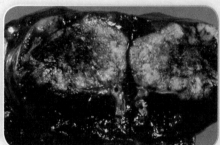

Cancerous lung tissue

strings on a violin. Your pharynx, mouth, and nose modify these vibrations to produce your voice. Since the larynx contains the vocal cords, it is often called the *voice box*.

The bottom of the larynx opens into the **trachea** (windpipe). The trachea is an open tube made up of a series of cartilage rings. In the chest, just above the heart, the trachea branches to form two similar but smaller air passages called the **bronchi** (BRAHNG KYE). Each bronchus carries air to a lung. Inside the lungs the bronchi branch and rebranch to form **bronchioles** (BRAHNG kee OALZ). The trachea, bronchi, and bronchioles together look something like the trunk, branches, and twigs of an upside-down tree.

26A.2 *Air in the Alveoli*

The air passing through the bronchioles finally enters tiny dead-end sacs called **alveoli** (al VEE uh LYE). The alveoli look like clusters of grapes on the end of each bronchiole. Their walls are only one cell thick. Many tiny *capillaries* surround the alveoli. The capillary walls are also one cell thick. Despite their tiny size, the area of contact between alveolar cells and capillaries in one human lung is 70–80 square meters. That is about forty times the surface area of the skin.

How does the air in your lungs reach your blood? Gases in the air pass through the one-cell-thick walls of both the alveoli and the

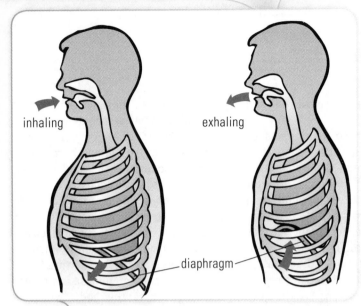

26A-4 Breathing involves movement of the diaphragm and the ribs.

capillaries to enter the blood. Gases in the blood can pass just as easily into the alveoli. This exchange of gases does not depend on how "hard" you breathe but operates on the principle of *diffusion*. (See p. 51.) There is a much higher concentration of oxygen in the air you breathe than there is in deoxygenated blood. Therefore, the oxygen you inhale diffuses through the walls of the alveoli and into the blood. There is much more carbon dioxide in deoxygenated blood than there is in the air in your lungs. This concentration causes the carbon dioxide in the blood to diffuse into the air in the alveoli.

26A.3 **Breathing**

Breathing is the process of inhaling and exhaling air. The air is not actually moved by the lungs, but by muscles surrounding the lungs.

You inhale by making your chest cavity, or **thorax** (THOR AKS), larger. This works much like sipping a beverage through a straw. When you make the back of your mouth cavity larger, something must go into your mouth to fill the space. Since the straw forms the only opening, whatever is at the end of the straw rushes in to fill the space.

You make your thorax larger by contracting your diaphragm. The **diaphragm** is a dome-shaped muscle that attaches to the lower ribs, the backbone, and the sternum. It forms a flexible wall between the thorax and the abdomen. When the diaphragm contracts, the dome flattens, pushing the organs in your stomach area down and making the thorax larger. Air then rushes through the trachea into the lungs, causing the alveoli to swell and fill the thorax. Muscles that raise and expand the rib cage also help make the thorax larger.

You exhale by making your thorax smaller. You might think that the diaphragm pushes upward to force the air out, but it does not. The diaphragm simply relaxes. When it relaxes, the muscles of your abdomen push in. As the organs in your stomach area are pressed inward and upward, they push the diaphragm up into its dome shape, making the thorax smaller. You use the large muscles of the abdominal area when you exhale with force (for singing or for talking loudly).

When resting, a person usually inhales and then exhales about 500 mL of air with each breath. The maximum amount of air a normal pair of lungs can hold is about 5500 mL. A person uses this extra capacity when breathing

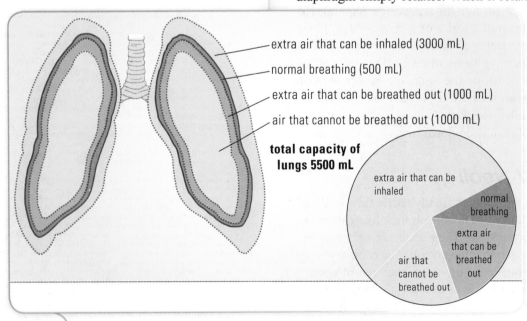

extra air that can be inhaled (3000 mL)

normal breathing (500 mL)

extra air that can be breathed out (1000 mL)

air that cannot be breathed out (1000 mL)

total capacity of lungs 5500 mL

extra air that can be inhaled

normal breathing

extra air that can be breathed out

air that cannot be breathed out

26A-5 Lung volumes

heavily during exercise or when taking a deep breath to sing. If the alveoli become diseased and do not work properly, a person will become short of breath more quickly than normal.

Pneumonia (noo MONE yuh) is a disease that causes the alveoli to fill with fluid. Yet, even if fluid filled one-fourth of a person's lungs, he could still take normal breaths (500 mL) without any trouble. Only when he begins to exercise would he find that he could not get enough air into his lungs. A person who has *tuberculosis* (too BUR kyuh LO sis) has bacteria growing in his alveoli. As the bacteria

Facets of *The Human Body:* *The Common Cold Cured? No Way!*

Sneeze! Sniffle! "Ugh, I don't feel very good." These are the familiar symptoms that announce the onset of a common cold. When a person with a cold sneezes or coughs, he helps to spread the cold virus.

A virus is not a living organism. It is a tiny strand of DNA or RNA surrounded by a coat of protein. Some viruses (such as those that cause rabies, smallpox, warts, and hepatitis) can be spread by contact (touch). These viruses can enter the body through breaks in the skin. Cold and flu viruses, however, usually float in the air and enter the nose and mouth. These viruses can penetrate the mucous membrane cells that line the nose and throat.

Normally each type of virus can affect only a certain kind of cell. For example, a cold virus attacks the cells that line the respiratory system. Skin cells, muscle cells, bone cells, and other cells in the body seem to be unaffected by a cold virus.

A viral infection often begins with a virus entering a suitable cell. Once inside the cell, the virus may lie unnoticed for years or it may immediately begin using the cell's organelles to produce more viruses just like itself. Within an hour there could be enough new viruses to fill the cell.

Eventually the viruses kill the cell. When it dies, it breaks open, releasing hundreds of viruses. These new viruses then enter the surrounding cells and repeat the process. If viruses infect and kill only a small number of your cells, you may never notice. But if this happens to a large number of your cells, you usually feel sick.

A cold or flu usually begins with a headache, sore throat, and occasionally a fever. For several hours or days a person with a cold may have muscular aches and a general feeling of illness. These same symptoms also signal the beginning of other viral diseases such as measles, mumps, or polio. Almost all viral infections begin with similar symptoms. However, after the beginning stage, viral diseases produce their own characteristic symptoms.

Whether or not you treat your body for a viral infection seems to make no difference in how long the infection will last. It's a good thing that most viral infections limit themselves. The common cold, for example, may make a person miserable for a few days, but eventually the body stops the viruses and the cold goes away.

Your body uses its immune system to fight viral infections. The T cells recognize the virus and activate the B cells to produce antibodies. The antibodies combine with viruses to help make them harmless. The body then removes the harmless viruses as waste material. If enough of the specific antibodies are present in the blood, they can stop the viruses from entering any new cells.

Once you have survived a viral infection, your body is immune to that specific virus and can quickly make the needed antibodies. This ability to respond quickly will prevent another infection by the same type of virus—you are now immune to that virus. Immunities to chicken pox, measles, and some other viral infections can last a lifetime.

Cold and flu viruses are exceptionally hard to control because they frequently mutate. When a virus mutates, its protein coat changes, forming a new antigen. Antibodies formed before the virus mutates may not recognize the virus with its new antigen. If the virus mutates, the antibodies may not work against it. The body must suffer through an infection of this "new virus" while producing antibodies against it.

Because flu and cold viruses mutate frequently, the vaccines and antibodies produced from this year's viruses may not work against next year's viruses.

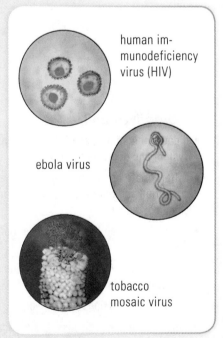

human immunodeficiency virus (HIV)

ebola virus

tobacco mosaic virus

Viruses have many different shapes and sizes.

multiply, they damage the lung tissue. The damaged tissues cannot exchange gases. As more alveoli are affected, breathing becomes more and more difficult.

Emphysema (EM fih SEE muh) is another smoking-related lung disease. Chemicals from cigarette smoke cause the alveolar walls to become stiff and less elastic. As a person has to cough harder and harder to move out mucus, the increased pressure causes some of the alveoli to burst. As more alveoli are affected, exhaling becomes more and more difficult, and the capillaries and the alveoli exchange less and less gas.

A lung collapses when the alveoli lose most of their air. A *collapsed lung* usually results from a hole in the thorax (chest). The hole may be a wound that opens to the outside of the body. In that case, inhaling is like trying to drink through a straw with your mouth open. Fluid that gets into the thorax also can cause a collapsed lung. The fluid prevents the lungs from expanding. In this case, inhaling is like trying to drink through a straw when your mouth is already full. To treat a collapsed lung, a physician must seal any holes and remove any excess air or fluid in the thorax.

Section Review 26A

1. What is the primary function of the respiratory system?

2. What is secondhand smoke?

3. What are the air passages in your lungs called?

4. Name the microscopic respiratory structure where gases are exchanged.

5. What process causes oxygen in your lungs to enter the blood?

6. What is the maximum amount of air that a typical person can inhale in one breath?

26B The Digestive System

Physically speaking, you are what you eat. This is not literally true, of course. A strong man's arms are not filled with steak. The hamburger you ate the other day is not still a hamburger somewhere inside you. The meat of the hamburger did not necessarily become muscle, and the ketchup did not become blood.

Then how can we say, "you are what you eat"? When you eat food, your body takes it apart and uses the resulting substances to build body tissues. The body's process of taking foods apart is **digestion**. The process of building living tissues from the digested foods is **assimilation** (uh SIM uh LAY shun). Your **digestive system** contains the organs that break down your hamburger into sugars, amino acids, fats, vitamins, minerals, and water. Then your blood carries these substances to various parts of your body, where your cells assimilate the materials to form tissues. Through these processes much of the substance of the hamburger may now be part of you. There are two methods of digestion that your body uses: mechanical digestion and chemical digestion.

Objectives 26B

- Identify the structures of the digestive system and describe their functions.
- Differentiate between digestion and assimilation and between mechanical and chemical digestion.
- List and describe the four types of human teeth.
- Give examples of foods that contain carbohydrates, proteins, and fats.
- List several functions of the liver.
- Define *calorie* and discuss its significance in relation to metabolism.

Mechanical digestion involves grinding food and mixing it with digestive juices. The teeth and stomach do most of the mechanical digestion, but other structures in the digestive system help with the process.

Chemical digestion involves chemically breaking down the food into soluble substances that the body can use. The action of *enzymes* and other substances in the *digestive juices* accomplishes chemical digestion.

The organs of the digestive system are generally divided into two groups. These two groups are the alimentary canal and the accessory organs.

The **alimentary** (AL uh MEN tuh ree) **canal** is a tube about 9 m (30 ft) long that runs from the mouth to the anus. The main sections of the alimentary canal are the *mouth, pharynx, esophagus, stomach,* and *intestines*. Food is moved along the alimentary canal by waves of **peristalsis** (PEHR ih STAHL sis), a type of muscular contraction. These waves pass along the walls of the alimentary canal and push the food through the tube.

The **accessory organs** of the digestive system are organs that are attached to the alimentary canal by ducts (tubes). The main accessory organs are the *liver* and the *pancreas*. These organs produce the substances necessary for digestion. The ducts carry these substances to the alimentary canal.

26B.1 *Structures of the Digestive System: Mouth*

Mechanical digestion begins in the mouth as the tongue moves the food between the teeth for chewing. The human mouth contains four types of teeth: incisors, canines, premolars, and molars.

Incisors (in SY zurz) are the eight teeth in the front of the mouth (four on the top and four on the bottom). These teeth have flat, narrow, bladelike surfaces for cutting and biting food. The next tooth towards the back of the mouth is the *canine*. There are four canine teeth, one next to each of the outermost incisors. These teeth were originally named canines because they often resemble the fangs of dogs. (Dogs are sometimes called canines.)

Are you what you eat?

alimentary: aliment- (L. ALIMENTUM, to nourish) + -ary (L. -ARIUS, relating to)

peristalsis: peri- (Gk. PERI, around) + -stalsis (Gk. STELLEIN, to wrap)

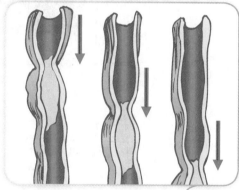

Peristalsis is a series of coordinated muscular contractions in the alimentary canal.   26B-1

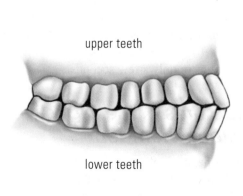

upper teeth

lower teeth

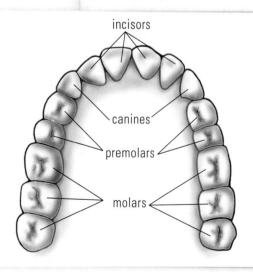

incisors

canines

premolars

molars

Human teeth   26B-2

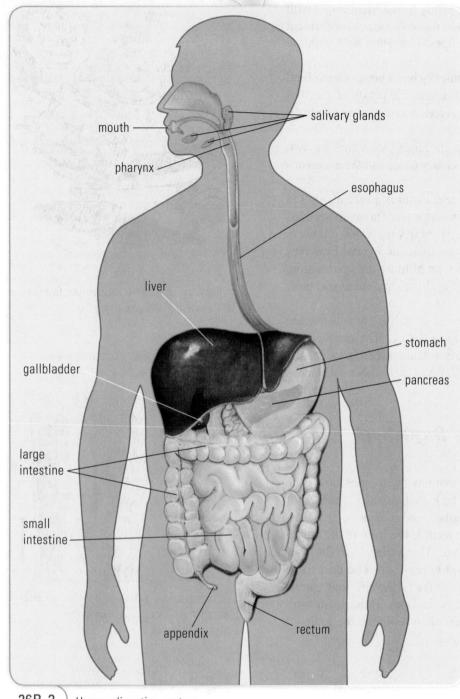

mouth

salivary glands

pharynx

esophagus

liver

stomach

gallbladder

pancreas

large
intestine

small
intestine

appendix

rectum

26B-3 Human digestive system

Next are the *premolars*. There are eight all together, two behind each canine. These teeth have broad tops for crushing food. The backmost teeth in the jaw are the *molars*. Molars have broad tops for grinding food. Most adults have three molars behind each set of premolars—a total of twelve. Junior high-aged students have only one or two molars behind the premolars, depending on their age.

The four molars at the back of the jaws are often called *wisdom teeth*. This name comes from the notion that a person does not become wise until these teeth appear in his mouth. Wisdom teeth usually come in when a person is between the ages of seventeen and twenty-one. Some people's wisdom teeth never become visible. There is no evidence that adults who lack back molars are actually any less wise than those who do have wisdom teeth.

Around the mouth are three pairs of **salivary** (SAL uh VEHR ee) **glands**. These glands produce **saliva** (suh LYE vuh), a watery fluid that contains a digestive enzyme. Ducts carry the saliva to the mouth, where the fluid mixes with food as it is chewed. The enzyme in saliva begins chemical digestion. Saliva also helps make food moist and slippery.

The tongue then moves the chewed food into the *pharynx* at the back of the mouth, where swallowing starts. Swallowing begins the peristalsis that pushes the food through the *esophagus*. The esophagus is a muscular tube about 25 cm (10 in.) long that leads to the stomach. Peristalsis pushes food through the esophagus in only a few seconds.

26B.2 Structures of the Digestive System: Stomach

When food enters the stomach, mechanical and chemical digestion continue. Closed valves at each end of the stomach keep the food inside while muscles in the walls of the stomach carry on peristalsis. The stomach churns food for up to four hours, depending on the type of food. A steak, for example, takes longer to digest than a soft food such as pudding.

Microscopic glands in the stomach lining produce fluids that contain enzymes and hydrochloric (HYE druh KLOR ik) acid. The hydrochloric acid helps to digest certain foods and also kills some microscopic organisms that enter the stomach. In addition to hydrochloric acid, the stomach also produces enzymes that continue the digestive process. The acid and enzymes do not digest the stomach itself because it is protected by a thick layer of mucus. As the acid and enzymes break down the mucus, more is produced. Because mucus is continually produced, the acids and enzymes do not actually contact the stomach lining.

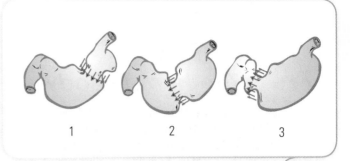

Peristalsis in the stomach causes the thorough mixing of chyme.

26B-4

26B.3 *Structures of the Digestive System: Intestines*

In the stomach, the mixture of food, enzymes, and acid becomes a semiliquid called **chyme** (KIME). The stomach then gently squirts small amounts of chyme through a valve and into the **small intestine**. Most of the chemical digestion process takes place in this organ, which is 7 m (23 ft) long.

The lining of the small intestine produces many substances that help digest food. One group of glands produces a fluid that contains *sodium bicarbonate* (SO dee um • bye KAR buh NATE), the substance found in baking soda. The acid in the chyme must be neutralized so that it does not damage the intestinal walls. The sodium bicarbonate produced by the glands combines with the hydrochloric acid and forms harmless substances. Other glands in the lining produce enzymes that help chemical digestion of sugars, proteins, and fats.

As peristalsis moves the digesting food along, the small intestine performs another function: *absorption*. The inner surface of the small intestine has many folds lined with microscopic fingerlike structures called **villi** (VIL eye). These folds and villi provide a large internal surface area for absorbing digested food. Most of the digested foods are absorbed through the thin villi walls into capillaries inside the villi. Blood then carries the food to other places in the body.

At the end of the small intestine, the remaining undigested foods and fluids enter the **large intestine**. The large intestine is only about 1.5 m (5 ft) long, but it has a much larger diameter than the small intestine. Little or no digestion occurs in the large intestine. Its primary function is to absorb water and minerals. Many bacteria normally live and reproduce in the large intestine. Usually these bacteria do not cause diseases; instead they produce certain vitamins and digest food that humans cannot digest. The material that is left after the large intestine absorbs most of the water is called *feces* (FEE seez). Peristalsis moves feces from the large intestine through the *anus*, the last valve of the alimentary canal.

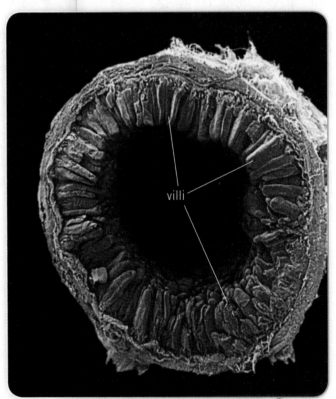

villi

This scanning electron micrograph shows villi inside the small intestine. (Dr. Richard Kessel & Dr. Gene Shih / Visuals Unlimited)

26B-5

Facets of *The Human Body:* *Appendicitis—Ouch!*

The appendix is a small tubular organ attached to the large intestine. It is located near the area where the large and small intestines join. Normally the appendix is about 8 cm (3 in.) long and about 1 cm (0.4 in.) in diameter, but it may be larger.

From childhood through young adulthood, the appendix functions to help the body fight infections. The appendix of a young person contains *lymphatic* (lim FAT ik) *tissue*. Lymphatic tissue makes white blood cells that are used by the immune system. In time, however, the lymphatic tissue of the appendix wastes away and stops functioning. Once these tissues are gone, the appendix has no known function.

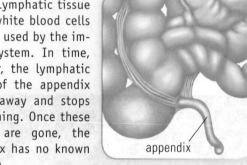

appendix

Normally the appendix holds only mucus and fluids. The muscles in the walls of the appendix contract and push the fluids through a valve and into the large intestine. Occasionally the large intestine may force some of its contents into the appendix. The weak muscles of the appendix cannot move these solid materials back into the intestine. As these materials decompose inside the appendix, they produce gases and poisons. These gases and poisons irritate the lining of the appendix, causing it to swell and become painful. This condition is called *appendicitis*.

When appendicitis begins, the person usually does not know he has it. He may have a low fever, and the number of his white blood cells may increase. These are normal body reactions to infection. Once appendicitis starts, however, it usually continues. The appendix becomes more irritated, and the swelling reaches the point at which the person feels a great amount of pain. When this occurs and the appendix is about to burst, the person is said to be suffering from *acute appendicitis*.

At the beginning of an attack of acute appendicitis, most people feel pain in the right upper abdominal (stomach) area. Some patients, however, describe the pain as "all over" the abdomen. Later the pain becomes more intense in the lower right abdominal area. The muscle layers of this area become tense and rigid when they are touched.

Because normal breathing is too painful, the patient's breathing becomes shallow. Vomiting, nausea, and fever are also common symptoms. A person with acute appendicitis usually has a fever ranging from 37°C to 38°C (99°F to 101°F).

In most cases of acute appendicitis, the physician will recommend removing the appendix as soon as possible. By performing surgery quickly, he hopes to remove the appendix before it ruptures. If the appendix ruptures, its contents will spill into the body cavity and affect other organs. Sores may develop on the tissues that line the body cavity and cover the organs. This infection is usually severe and may cause death.

If an appendix has ruptured, the body cavity is cleaned and the person receives antibiotics. Before the development of antibiotics, a ruptured

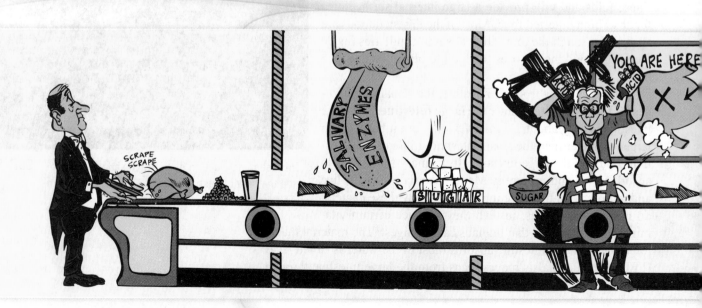

appendix almost always resulted in death.

There are many symptoms of appendicitis. Sometimes other problems produce some of the same symptoms. When this happens, a doctor may make a mistake in his diagnosis and perform surgery to remove an appendix when it is actually healthy. In one study of 5800 surgical cases of appendicitis, 18% had healthy appendixes.

However, when a patient seems to be suffering from appendicitis, it is often wiser to go ahead with surgery than to wait for more proof. Removing a healthy appendix is usually better than delaying surgery and having a patient suffer from a ruptured appendix.

26B.4 *Food*

Food may contain traces of drugs, artificial colorings, preservatives, and even poisons. These substances are found primarily in prepared foods. They may improve the food's appearance, taste, or shelf life but do not usually provide any nourishment for the body. Most of the substances in food do help the body and belong to one of the following groups: carbohydrates, proteins, lipids, vitamins, minerals, and water.

Most of the *carbohydrates* we eat are *sugars* or starches. Foods such as bread, cereal, potatoes, and sweets are high in carbohydrates. Although tasty, treats that are almost pure sugar provide little nourishment. Eating too many sugars can result in tooth decay and other health problems.

Proteins, which are made up of *amino acids*, serve as enzymes or building blocks for many tissues and organs in the body. Most proteins come from meats; however, nuts and seeds also contain proteins. *Lipids* are the fats and oils in foods. Since fried foods are cooked in lipids, they usually contain many of them. Foods that are good natural sources of lipids include eggs, whole milk, meat, and butter.

Let Them Have Dominion

In 2005 the Centers for Disease Control and Prevention (CDC) issued a study claiming that lack of exercise in a person's life is as harmful as smoking! Proper exercise and healthy living choices should be a very real consideration for every person. What sort of healthy practices should a Christian be involved in, and why?

Vitamins are substances that are made by living organisms and are essential to the normal functioning of the body. Different foods provide different vitamins. *Minerals* are vital substances that are usually not made by living things. The body uses minerals to build certain materials, such as calcium and phosphorus in bones. A variety of minerals are found in different foods.

Although water does not provide any nutrients, it is essential for life. You probably drink just a few glasses of *water* each day; however, you actually consume much more water than you think. With the exception of dry foods such as crackers, almost everything you eat contains water.

Of the substances listed, carbohydrates, proteins, and lipids require chemical digestion before they enter the blood stream. Vitamins, minerals, and water can enter the blood stream without further chemical digestion.

Facets of *The Human Body:* Peptic Ulcers—That Burning Sensation

An ulcer is any open sore that discharges pus and fluid and does not heal normally. It may be on the outer surface of the skin or on the inner surface of an internal organ, such as the stomach or intestine.

A peptic (PEP tik) ulcer is the most common type of internal ulcer. It usually occurs in the linings of the esophagus, the stomach, or the first part of the small intestine, called the duodenum (DOO uh DEE num). Of all peptic ulcers, 80% occur in the duodenum. These ulcers are most common in men ranging in age from twenty to fifty. Peptic ulcers in the stomach (sometimes called gastric ulcers) are more common in older men.

Until just a few years ago most physicians thought that peptic ulcers were caused by digestive fluid eating away at the inner surface of the stomach wall. Although excess digestive fluid is responsible for much of the pain and damage of a peptic ulcer, it is not the underlying cause. Most peptic ulcers are caused by a bacterial infection in the stomach. A species of bacteria called *Helicobacter pylori* destroys the protective mucus lining of the stomach; then the digestive fluids attack the stomach wall. Without the bacterial infection the stomach would remain unharmed by the digestive fluids.

Most of these ulcers are small, but if a peptic ulcer continues to grow, it may become so severe that it bleeds continuously. Eventually the ulcer may form a hole in the organ's wall. This condition could be fatal when food and digestive fluids flow through the hole and injure other organs in the body cavity.

Peptic ulcers also may develop when the valve between the stomach and the small intestine becomes weak. This happens to some elderly people. The weakened valve allows intestinal enzymes and acids to seep back into the stomach. Over time this backward movement may cause ulcers in the stomach area near the valve.

The symptoms a person feels when he has an ulcer may vary. The pain is probably due to the acid's irritating the exposed nerve endings and muscle cells in the stomach or small intestine wall. People who have peptic ulcers usually feel a "heartburn" sensation and have indigestion. Those with peptic ulcers in the duodenum (duodenal ulcers) also may experience a burning feeling in the back of the throat.

The symptoms associated with ulcers usually occur about two hours after a meal, when the stomach is empty. They

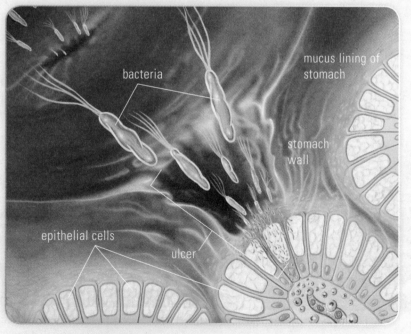

bacteria

mucus lining of stomach

stomach wall

epithelial cells

ulcer

26B.5 *Chemical Digestion*

The chemical digestion of carbohydrates actually begins in the mouth. An enzyme in saliva breaks down carbohydrates into *sugars*. This enzyme can only begin to digest the carbohydrates in your food. When the food reaches your stomach, the stomach's acid quickly stops the enzyme's action. In the small intestine, enzymes from the pancreas and from glands in the intestinal wall finish digesting carbohydrates to smaller sugars, such as glucose. These sugars are transported through the walls of the villi and into the blood.

The chemical digestion of proteins starts in the stomach. Here the stomach acid activates enzymes produced by glands in the stomach lining. These enzymes break down proteins into short amino acid chains. In the small intestine these chains are broken down into individual amino acids by enzymes from the pancreas and from glands in the intestinal lining. The amino acids enter the blood through the villi.

also may occur after a person drinks a beverage that increases acid production or irritates the stomach lining. Drinks containing alcohol, caffeine (such as coffee and many soft drinks), or acids (such as orange juice) may affect the stomach in this way.

God has designed the human body to prevent the development of ulcers in two main ways. First, each organ of the digestive tract contains cells that constantly produce a thick layer of mucus that protects the tissue underneath. Second, each organ of the digestive tract has a lining of special cells that protects its muscle layers from digestive acids and enzymes. The cells that make up this lining are attached so tightly to each other that almost nothing can pass between them. As these cells grow old and worn, the body continually replaces them with new cells through cell division. The stomach, for example, completely replaces the cell lining every one to three days.

Physicians are not sure how a person gets the bacteria responsible for peptic ulcers. They do know that how a person treats his body has an affect on the development of ulcers. People who drink alcoholic beverages and regularly use certain stomach-irritating drugs (such as aspirin, ibuprofen, or caffeine) frequently develop ulcers. These sub-stances often kill the cells in the stomach lining or reduce mucus production.

Another factor affecting ulcers is emotional stress, such as worry. Stress can cause the stomach to produce acid even when it contains no food to digest. Thus, stress may indirectly affect a peptic ulcer.

Often the ulcers irritated by stress are minor. For example, many students develop tiny "stress ulcers" before a major test. After the test, the stress is gone and the ulcers heal in a few hours. If, however, stress or worry continues for a long time (usually weeks or months), a person may develop a serious peptic ulcer.

Physicians often treat peptic ulcers with antibiotics to eliminate the ulcer-causing bacteria. Someday there may even be a vaccine for peptic ulcers. In addition to antibiotics, physicians also use drugs to either neutralize stomach acid or to decrease the secretion of acids and enzymes in the stomach. Finally, rest helps the ulcer to heal sooner.

In rare instances, surgery may be necessary. One surgical procedure helps decrease the amount of acid the stomach can produce by cutting a certain nerve. If a peptic ulcer has developed into a bleeding ulcer, the patient often needs more complicated surgery. The physician must remove the damaged area of the stomach or intestine and then suture (sew) the edges together.

Although medical treatment helps prevent some of the causes of ulcers, it does not eliminate stress. Your reaction to stress (which may be revealed by a stress-irritated peptic ulcer) may indicate that you do not have a proper relationship with the Lord. Dedicated Christians may have peptic ulcers from other causes, but they should not have stress-irritated ulcers. If Christians trust in the Lord (Prov. 3:5–6), lean on His "everlasting arms" (Deut. 33:27), and "fret not" (Ps. 37:1), stress will be a minor problem.

Many in our culture like to needlessly attribute their problems to chemical or biological causes. They think they should take drugs for everything from depression to bad behavior. What is a Christian response to this attitude?

The chemical digestion of lipids begins in the small intestine. Lipids tend to stick to each other, like the oil in oil-and-vinegar dressing. **Bile** is made by the liver and stored in the *gallbladder* until it is needed to aid in fat digestion. In the small intestine, bile breaks up the lipids into droplets. This action, called *emulsification*, allows the lipids to mix with water. This is necessary so that the enzymes from the pancreas and the small intestine can more easily get to the lipid molecules and digest them. If the lipids remained clumped together, digestion would be a slow process. After digesting the lipids, enzymes are absorbed into the body through the villi.

26B.6 *The Liver*

Scientists usually classify the **liver** as one of the accessory digestive organs. The bile that the liver produces is carried to the small intestine by a duct. However, the liver does much more than make bile to help digest food. It actually performs more than five hundred functions. For this reason, the liver is sometimes called the "master chemist of the body."

The liver receives a rich supply of blood from the **portal vein** and various arteries. Blood coming to the liver from the portal vein carries food and other substances absorbed by the small intestine. As this blood passes though the liver, the liver adjusts the contents of the blood to meet the body's needs.

One of the most important ways the liver adjusts the blood is by regulating the sugar content. For example, after a meal the blood in the portal vein contains large amounts of sugar. If the blood carried all that sugar to the body's cells, the overdose of sugar would cause dizziness and fainting. If the sugar content of the blood continued to rise, the person would go into a coma and might die. The liver helps prevent this problem by removing extra sugar from the blood and storing it.

Later, when the body completes digestion, the blood coming into the liver may not contain enough sugar. A lack of sugar in the blood is also dangerous. When the blood sugar is too low, the liver releases some of its stored sugar into the blood. The liver stores or releases sugar in response to various hormones.

Most substances absorbed from the digestive system into the blood are carried by the portal vein directly to the liver. Thus, before these substances reach the body cells, the liver has a chance to filter out poisons and many other harmful substances. The liver can deactivate some of these substances so that they are no longer harmful to the body.

When a person takes in excessive amounts of harmful substances, the liver cannot always completely deactivate the substances or filter them out effectively. For instance, when a person consumes alcohol, much of it is converted to a substance that, until it is broken down into other substances, is actually more toxic than alcohol. If the toxic substance overpowers the liver's ability to convert it into a safer substance, it begins to damage liver cells as well as other cells in the body. Even when the liver cells do convert the toxin, they are less able to properly function. Continued exposure to the toxin may result in permanent liver disease. Any toxin that gets past the liver may affect other organs and cause health problems.

The liver makes many other adjustments in the blood that passes though it. For example, it filters out old red blood cells, breaks down their contents, and recycles much of their material. The liver also secretes many substances into the blood plasma, including some materials used in blood clotting. It slowly releases its waste products into the blood in nonpoisonous forms that the kidneys can filter out.

26B.7 *The Pancreas*

The pancreas is the other major accessory digestive organ. It produces *pancreatic juice* that contains several enzymes that are important in the digestion of proteins, carbohydrates, fats, and nucleic acids. It also produces fluids that contain high levels of sodium bicarbonate to help neutralize the acidic chyme. Just as with the liver, the digestive enzymes produced by the pancreas are carried to the small intestine by a duct.

26B.8 *Food and Energy for Metabolism*

The food you eat supplies not only the *materials* to build your body but also the *energy* necessary for your body to function. The energy in food is measured in units called **calories** (**Cal**). Although we usually think of sugars as our source of energy, lipids and proteins also supply energy. In fact, a teaspoon of oil, which is a lipid, contains twice as much energy as a teaspoon of sugar.

You probably use between 2200 and 2500 Cal per day. The number of calories you use will vary. On a day when you play volleyball or mow the lawn after school, you may need more calories. If you spend a day quietly reading a good book, you will probably need fewer calories. Your body size, basal metabolic rate, and whether you

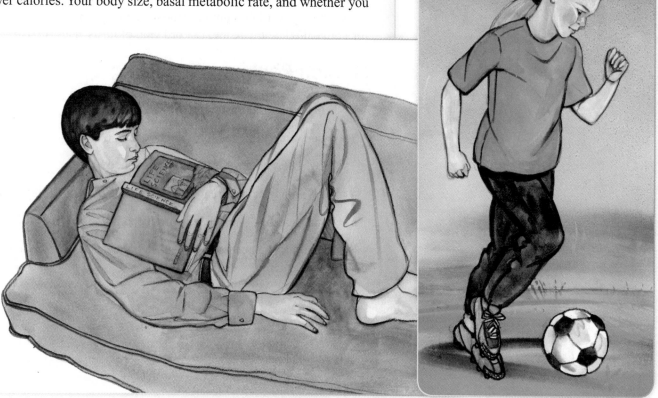

Which of these people do you think is using more calories? 26B-7

are a boy or girl also affect the number of calories you need each day.

If you take in fewer calories than you need, your body will draw energy from the fat it has stored. If you continue to use more energy than you consume, you begin to starve. *Starvation* is becoming weak or dying from lack of food energy. If you eat more calories than you use, your body may store the extra energy as fat.

Your basal metabolic rate is the measure of the amount of energy your body uses to stay alive under nonstressful conditions. Trying to measure the actual amount of energy you use would be practically impossible. Scientists can indirectly measure the amount of energy you "burn." Your body obtains usable energy from sugar primarily by aerobic cellular respiration. Aerobic cellular respiration is the only process in your body that uses the oxygen you breathe. Therefore, by measuring the amount of oxygen you use, scientists can figure the amount of energy you use and compute your metabolic rate.

Physical energy is important, but it is not the only kind of energy humans need. We also need spiritual "energy," and that means getting spiritual "food." The Word of God is spiritual food; it refers to itself in exactly those terms. To grow in Christ, Christians must begin by "drinking" the "milk of the word" (1 Pet. 2:2) and continue until they can "eat" the "meat" of the Word (1 Cor. 3:2). The Word of God gives principles that help structure life, and strength (energy) to make those principles work.

Do you have the spiritual energy you need? One way God can measure your spiritual life is by inspecting your attitude toward Him. If God were to measure your spiritual metabolism, would He find an active Christian life or one suffering from spiritual starvation? If you are starving spiritually, the cure is to read and study your Bible. Then you can say with Jeremiah, "Thy words were found, and I did eat them; and thy word was unto me the joy and rejoicing of mine heart: for I am called by thy name, O Lord God of hosts" (Jer. 15:16).

Section Review 26B

1. What kind of teeth are used to crush food?

2. Where are villi located? What do they do?

3. To what organ is your appendix attached?

4. Why do physicians treat some peptic ulcers with antibiotics?

5. What digestive substance is produced in the liver?

6. Name the two accessory digestive organs and give the function of each.

Chapter Review

1. When is your metabolic rate the lowest? What is it called at that lowest rate?

2. List two functions of mucus in your respiratory system.

3. What is the function of your epiglottis?

4. Name the microscopic structures in your lungs where gas exchange occurs.

5. What muscle do you use to inhale? What does it do to aid inhalation?

6. What is another name for the tube called the digestive tract?

7. Which tube in your throat is used to swallow?

8. Which is longer, the small intestine or the large intestine?

9. Give two examples of food items that you think would be rich in proteins, lipids, and carbohydrates.

10. Why do active people need more food than inactive people?

What Did You Learn?

1. List the following structures in the order that an inhaled breath of air would pass through: alveoli, bronchi, bronchioles, pharynx, trachea.

2. How is a baby born to a smoker likely to differ from one born to a nonsmoker?

3. What is secondhand smoke, and why is it important?

4. Explain the difference between digestion and assimilation.

5. In general, what is the end product of chemical digestion?

6. Why can the liver and pancreas be considered digestive organs even though food never passes through them?

Scientifically Speaking

metabolism
metabolic rate
basal metabolic rate
respiratory system
lungs
mucus
pharynx
esophagus
larynx
epiglottis
glottis
trachea
bronchi
bronchioles
alveoli
thorax
diaphragm
digestion
assimilation
digestive system
mechanical digestion
chemical digestion
alimentary canal
peristalsis
accessory organs
salivary glands
saliva
chyme
small intestine
villi
large intestine
bile
liver
portal vein
calories (Cal)

Self Quiz 26

1. _____ is the combination of all bodily processes.

____ 2. The body gets energy from
A. water.
B. vitamins.
C. food.
D. oxygen.

____ 3. The major function of the epiglottis is to
A. protect the lungs.
B. produce the voice.
C. direct air into the lungs.
D. produce mucus.

4. _____ are the microscopic sacs where gases are exchanged in the lungs.

5. When you breathe in, the diaphragm

_____.

____ 6. All of the following are accessory digestive organs *except*
A. the liver.
B. the stomach.
C. the pancreas.
D. the mouth.
E. B and D
F. A and C

____ 7. No digestion occurs in the esophagus. (True/False)

____ 8. Hydrochloric acid is produced by the
A. small intestines.
B. stomach.
C. large intestine.
D. liver.

____ 9. The primary functions of the large intestine include all of the following *except*
A. absorb water.
B. remove feces.
C. absorb minerals.
D. absorb digested food.

10. Bile is important for digestion of fats and is produced by the _____.

____ 11. Which is *not* a function of the liver?
A. filtering out harmful substances from the blood
B. removing worn-out red blood cells
C. performing mechanical digestion
D. helping regulate blood sugar

____ 12. Food energy is measured in units called
A. calories.
B. ounces.
C. grams.
D. kilograms.

CONTROL

Awkward situations often result from a lack of coordination. Without coordination between coaches of separate athletic teams, sports games can be disastrous. One team might come ready for a game, while another team is still at practice. Even worse, if two teams wear the same color jerseys, one of the players could get confused and his spectacular play might actually score points for the opposing team!

One of the marvelous things about your body is its coordination. When you were a baby, your movements were jerky. When you reached for toys, you often missed them. However, as you matured, your nervous system developed enough that you could coordinate the sight of an object with various structures of your body. Now you are able to reach and grasp things in one smooth motion.

Your body's coordination system is very flexible. It allows you to perform many different activities. For example, you use many of the same structures to see printed notes and play them on a piano as you do to see a ball and hit it with a bat.

The internal functions of the body are also well coordinated, but people do not have to learn to control these functions. Consider how the body reacts to cold. When a person first starts to get chilled, the muscles in thousands of blood vessels near his skin's surface relax. This reaction causes the vessels to become larger and allows them to carry more warm blood to the cold skin. In people with light skin, the extra supply of blood causes the cold exposed skin to turn a bright pink while the warm skin under their clothing remains its normal color. People

27-1 Red skin is one of the body's initial responses to being cold.

with darker skin may feel cold, but their skin does not change colors as drastically.

If, however, the person remains in a cold area, his body reverses the process. As his insides begin to get cold, the muscles in his skin's blood vessels contract. This contraction causes the diameter of the vessels to become smaller and less blood reaches the skin. The warmth is kept inside the body, and people with light-colored skin turn pale. Why does this reversal occur? Some internal organs cannot function if the body temperature drops even a few degrees, and the person might die if these organs stopped functioning.

The internal coordination of the body is a testimony to the fact that God designed it. A reaction such as your body's response to cold involves coordination among many body systems. For that one response to evolve by chance is beyond imagination. Now consider the thousands of processes your body performs every minute to maintain life and respond to changes in its surroundings. What type of worldview claims that the coordination and control of the human body are not a direct creation of God?

There are two main systems that control and coordinate the body's various activities. The first is the nervous system, which includes such structures as the brain, eyes, ears, and nerves. The second is the endocrine (EN duh krin) system, which is a system of glands that produce hormones.

27A The Nervous System

The human nervous system controls bodily movements and many internal functions. It is also responsible for our awareness, emotions,

Objectives 27A

- Name the two systems that control and coordinate the body's activities.
- Differentiate between the central nervous system and the peripheral nervous system.
- Describe a neuron and the functions of its various parts.
- Characterize a nerve impulse and explain how it crosses a synapse.
- Explain how a reflex occurs.
- Define *psychoactive drugs*.

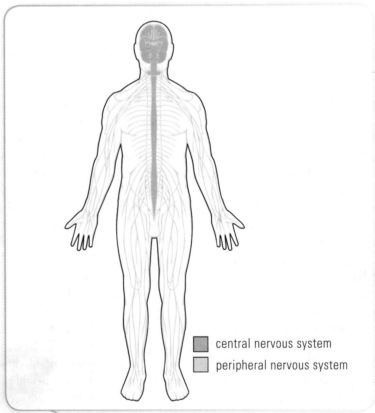

central nervous system
peripheral nervous system

27A-1 Human nervous system

and will. The nervous system is made up of two main divisions: the central nervous system and peripheral (puh RIF ur ul) nervous system. The **central nervous system** is made up of the *brain* and *spinal cord*. The **peripheral nervous system** includes the *sense organs* (eyes, ears, and so on) and the *nerves* that branch off the central nervous system.

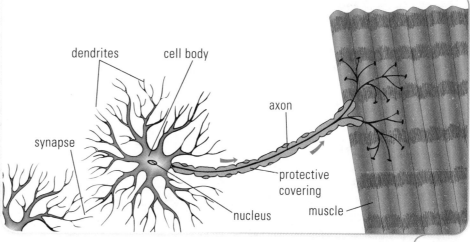

Anatomy of a neuron — 27A-2

27A.1 *Neurons and Nerve Impulses*

The nervous system is composed of several different kinds of neurons. **Neurons** are cells that can transfer an impulse. Although they have different shapes and sizes, all neurons have the same basic parts. The largest part of a neuron is the cell body, which contains the cytoplasm, the organelles, and the nucleus.

Branching off the cell body of the neuron are extensions called **dendrites** (DEN DRYTS) and **axons** (AK SAHNS). These structures are filled with cytoplasm. Dendrites are short, branchlike extensions that carry impulses *toward* the cell body. Axons are usually much longer than dendrites and carry impulses *away* from the cell body. Most neurons have several dendrites but usually only one axon. The axons of some neurons in your spinal cord may be as long as 45 cm (18 in.). The axons of many neurons in the brain, however, are microscopic in length.

Not all neuron parts are located within the brain and spinal cord. Those outside the central nervous system are bundled together in protective coverings. These long, thin branches of the nervous system are called **nerves**. Nerves go to sensory organs, muscles, and many other structures of the body. Because nerve coverings are composed of fatty materials, nerves usually appear a yellowish white color.

A nerve *impulse* involves the exchange of substances through the cell membrane of a neuron. A nerve impulse passes along the membrane at a rate of about 100 m (328 ft) per second. After the impulse has moved on and the substances are exchanged back, the membrane is soon ready for another impulse.

Normally an impulse begins along a dendrite, travels to the cell body, and then moves along the axon. At the end of the axon is a swollen area that looks like a tiny knob. Inside the knob are tiny *vesicles*, which contain a *transmitting chemical*. When a nerve impulse reaches the knob, the tiny vesicles rush to the membrane and burst open, releasing the transmitting chemical. The chemical serves to transmit the impulse across the space between the end of the axon and the next neuron. This junction of two neurons is called a **synapse** (SIN APS).

A nerve impulse can be compared to a bucket brigade. The bucket would be the impulse, and the "space" between the boys would be the synapse.

27A-3

synapse: syn- (Gk. SUN-, together) + -apse (Gk. HAPTEIN, to fasten)

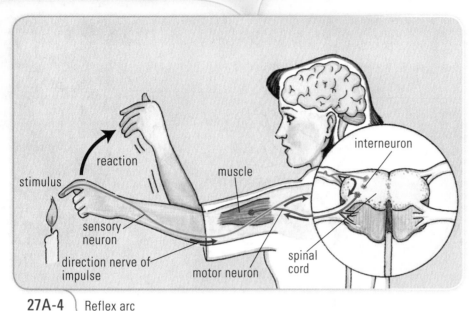

27A-4 Reflex arc

stimulus

reaction

muscle

sensory neuron

direction nerve of impulse

motor neuron

interneuron

spinal cord

27A.2 **Reflexes**

A **reflex** is an immediate inborn (not learned) reaction to a *stimulus*. Reflexes in your body are controlled by **reflex arcs**. A reflex arc is a series of neurons that receive a stimulus and then cause the body to react to it. If, for example, your finger accidentally touches a hot iron, the neuron endings in your finger sense the heat. This sensation triggers impulses to travel along the sensory neuron to the spinal cord. The **sensory neuron** is responsible for sensing stimuli and carrying impulses to the central nervous system.

When the impulses from the sensory neuron reach the spinal cord, they are passed to an interneuron. The **interneuron** acts as the go-between for the sensory neuron and the motor neuron. When the interneuron receives the impulses from the sensory neuron, it transfers them to the **motor neuron**. As the impulses travel along the motor neuron, they move away from the spinal cord and toward a muscle. The motor neuron is responsible for producing movement.

When the muscle receives the impulses, it contracts, pulling your finger away from the hot iron. The entire action of this reflex arc, from sensing the heat to moving your hand, takes only a fraction of a second.

Reflexes such as responding to a hot iron take place without thought. Before you are aware of what has happened, your body has already responded to the stimulus. You may think that you felt the pain at the same time you moved your hand. Actually, some impulses from the interneuron were sent to your brain, but they arrived after the muscle had moved your arm. The impulses that go to the brain interrupt what you are thinking, even though your body has already corrected the problem.

Your body has many reflexes. When the doctor taps you on the knee to make your leg jerk, he is testing a reflex. When he flashes a light into your eye to see how quickly your eye responds, he is testing another reflex. If you are in an accident, a physician may test your reflexes to see if your nervous system has been damaged. By knowing where the neurons of certain reflex arcs are located, a physician can find the damage even though it may not be visible with x-rays.

27A.3 **The Cerebrum of the Brain**

The human brain weighs only about 1.3 kg (3 lb), but it has over ten billion neurons. Twelve pairs of *cranial nerves* branch from the brain to various structures of the head, neck, and internal organs. The brain is divided into three main parts: the cerebrum, the cerebellum (SEHR uh BEL um), and the brain stem.

The **cerebrum** is the largest portion of the brain. It is divided into two dome-shaped halves called *hemispheres*. A thick layer of white fibers joins the two cerebral (suh REE brul) hemispheres together. The outer layer of the cerebrum is called the **cerebral cortex**. The natural color of the cerebral cortex is a grayish red. Because of its color the cerebral cortex is sometimes called *gray matter*. The gray is the color of the neurons, and the red is the color of the blood that nourishes the brain. The cerebral cortex has many wrinkles and folds. Deep folds divide each hemisphere into four *lobes*: the frontal lobes, the parietal (puh RYE uh tul) lobes, the temporal lobes, and the occipital (ahk SIP uh tul) lobes. Each lobe is responsible for different functions.

The *frontal lobes* are the front portion of each hemisphere. They control your

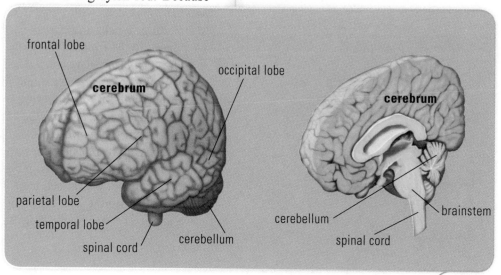

Human brain, side view (left) and cross section (right)   27A-5

Just a Thought?

Have you ever thought about thinking? What is it? How do you think thoughts? How do you store thoughts and bring them back to consider later? What happens to a forgotten thought?

No one knows all the answers to these questions. Scientists do know that when you think, nerve impulses are created in your brain. They even know which part of your brain you use to think about different thoughts. One of the machines used to measure brain activity (nerve impulses) is called an electroencephalograph (i LEK tro en SEF uh luh GRAF), or EEG. The impulses appear on a monitor or strip of paper as wavy lines. Different mental activities cause different patterns of waves. The impulses produced during thinking, sleeping, and unconsciousness all result in different types of "brain waves." Wave patterns can sometimes show if parts of a person's brain are not working properly.

Although thinking creates brain waves, the waves are not really thoughts. A thought is more than just the impulses scientists can record. In fact, thinking involves spiritual aspects. The Bible tells us that as a man "thinketh in his heart, so is he" (Prov. 23:7). This does not mean that thinking that you are a great basketball player or a fine musician makes you either one—you must practice! But what about our thoughts? The Bible tells us what type of thoughts we should think (Phil. 4:8) and what type of thoughts we should not think (Matt. 15:19). We are to guard our thought life carefully (2 Cor. 10:5). For example, coveting is continually thinking about and desiring something that is not yours. You can desire someone else's possessions or abilities without ever saying a word or moving a muscle. But a covetous thought breaks one of the Ten Commandments (Ex. 20:17).

Scripture also tells us that if we choose to think lustful thoughts, we sin just as if we had actually performed those sinful actions (Matt. 5:28). Since a thought can be right or wrong, it is spiritually significant and has eternal consequences.

Using an EEG, a physician can learn a great deal about a person's brain.

consciousness and your primary body movements. Impulses for the body actions you control start in the frontal lobes. Your awareness of what is happening, your personality, and your reasoning ability are some of other the functions of these lobes.

The *parietal lobes* are immediately behind the frontal lobes. The parietal lobes deal with general sensations such as pain, pressure, temperature, touch, and part of taste. Once registered, these senses are relayed to the frontal lobe so that you are aware of them.

The *temporal lobes* are located under the parietal lobes. They receive impulses from the ear and interpret them as sound. They are also responsible for remembering sounds.

The *occipital lobes* are in the back of the cerebrum. They receive impulses from the nerves of the eye and interpret them as vision. These lobes are responsible for remembering things you see.

Although the sense organs receive stimuli from the environment, the stimuli are not interpreted until the nerve impulses reach the cerebrum. In other words, your eyes only catch the light and change it into nerve impulses. You actually "see" in your cerebrum.

Facets of *The Human Body:* *Psychoactive (Mind-Altering) Drugs*

Normally drugs are taken to treat or prevent a physical disease or disorder. For example, penicillin (an antibiotic) is taken to kill bacteria that have invaded the body. When the body does not make enough insulin, extra insulin may be taken as a drug to control blood-sugar problems. The vaccines you received before entering the first grade were drugs designed to prevent disease.

However, many people take drugs not to correct a physical problem but to alter their state of mind. Drugs that have their primary effect on a person's mental or emotional condition are called *psychoactive* (SYE koh AK tiv) *drugs*. Psychoactive drugs are usually classified into four groups.

Depressants are drugs that slow mental activities.

Stimulants increase a person's mental activities.

Hallucinogens (huh LOO suh nuh junz) cause the mind to make up things.

Narcotics (nar KAHT iks) dull the senses and cause a feeling of happiness.

Alcohol is one of the oldest and most widely used psychoactive drugs. Alcohol is a powerful depressant. Even a small amount of alcohol can cause a person to react more slowly than he normally would. Driving under the in-fluence of alcohol is the major cause of automobile accidents.

The more alcohol a person drinks, the more slowly his mind functions. If a person consumes only a little alcohol, he loses his ability to concentrate. As he consumes more alcohol, his ability to think clearly and react quickly to things around him continues to decrease. Soon the person becomes drowsy and falls asleep. If a large amount of alcohol is consumed and causes the person to fall asleep, the ability of the brain to function can slow so much that the person can go into a coma and die.

Drinking alcohol also causes many other physical effects. It irritates the lining of the stomach and intestine, and this irritation can cause ulcers and internal bleeding. Alcohol increases the workload of the heart. It also damages the liver and will eventually destroy it if the person continues to drink significant amounts of alcohol. These are just a few examples of how alcohol is harmful to the body.

Other depressants include *sedatives* and *barbiturates* (bar BICH ur its), which are commonly used in sleeping pills.

Tranquilizers are usually given to calm a person and to help him "cope with life." But they do not help the situation because they do nothing to solve his problem. They merely make the person unable to deal with the problem by preventing him from concentrating.

Certain stimulants (sometimes called "pep pills") contain *amphetamines* (am FET uh MEENS). These pills cause the mind to work more quickly but not better. A person taking amphetamines normally feels excited and energetic. Even though his body may be tired, he is ready to keep going.

Alcohol is involved in 39% of all traffic-related deaths (NHTSA, 2005).

Cocaine is probably the most notorious stimulant; it is also a hallucinogen. Cocaine produces feelings of confidence, excitement, and happiness, but it has many harmful effects. Anxiety, depression, fearful delusions, and psychotic reactions are common results of cocaine use. Cocaine addiction can become so strong that the cocaine user may feel almost helpless without the drug. Cocaine pushes the body past its normal limits and eventually causes it to break down. Heart attacks, arrhythmias, strokes, and pulmonary problems are associated with cocaine use.

One of the most familiar hallucinogens is LSD. Even tiny amounts of

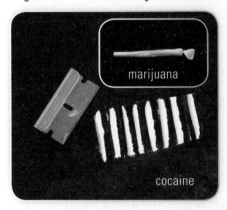

marijuana

cocaine

this drug can cause a person to hallucinate. The chemicals in a hallucinogen affect the nerves of the brain, causing visions and feelings the person cannot control.

Marijuana (MEHR uh WAH nuh) is a weak hallucinogen. It does not cause hallucinations (visions), but it does affect the way a person thinks. Recent scientific investigations have revealed several physical and mental problems linked with the use of marijuana. A sampling of these problems includes cancer, heart disease, susceptibility to other diseases, reproductive problems, birth defects, chromosomal mutations, abnormal brain cells, abnormal brain waves, depression, and psychosis.

Most narcotics, often called "hard drugs," come from the sap of the opium poppy. Examples of narcotics include morphine, heroin, and codeine. These

drugs dull the senses and have been used to relieve pain. Even today, doctors prescribe morphine and codeine for pain relief.

Narcotics cause the mind to go into a state of happiness and well-being, no matter what the circumstances are. As a result, some people use them to escape bad situations or strong feelings of guilt resulting from sin.

Narcotics, barbiturates, alcohol, and some other drugs cause physical addiction. One effect of physical addiction is that each time an addicted person takes a drug, he must take a larger amount to get the same results. Just to "feel good," an addicted person would need to take a dose that could knock out or even kill a person who has never taken the drug.

Another effect of physical addiction is physical withdrawal. Physical withdrawal includes the symptoms the person feels when he stops taking the drug. The strength of the withdrawal symptoms depends upon how much of and how long the drug has been taken. One withdrawal symptom of a person who occasionally drinks too much alcohol is a headache the day after he drinks. If, however, the person drinks large amounts of alcohol for a long period of time, he may experience such symptoms as chills, cramps, sleeplessness, indigestion, shakes, and hallucinations. The physical withdrawal symptoms of narcotics are similar to those of alcohol but are often much stronger.

Since taking psychoactive drugs causes so many problems, why would anyone want to take them? Some people do not know the harmful effects of drugs and are easily persuaded to try them. Often young people begin taking drugs because they want to be accepted. Their friends put pressure on them to be like everybody else. It would be much better to get a new set of friends, however, than to start taking drugs just to please others.

Some people take drugs to help them cope with life. They are deceived

into thinking that a drug will help them solve their problems. But drugs do not solve problems. Other people take drugs to "escape" their problems. The drugs change their moods, so their worries and troubles do not seem as great. Yet when the effects of the drug wear off, the problems are still there.

If you are a Christian, drinking alcohol or using other psychoactive

drugs to change your mood or to escape from your problems is wrong. In the first place, drugs can be harmful to your body, which is the temple of God (1 Cor. 3:16–17). Second, by taking drugs, you allow the drug to control your mind. Christians are commanded to let the Holy Spirit control their minds (Eph. 5:18). Finally, God often brings problems into the lives of Christians to increase their reliance on Him. Relying on drugs short-circuits the reason God allowed the difficulty. God wants Christians to commit their problems to Him (1 Pet. 5:7) and to rely on the strength He has promised (Ps. 46:1–3; 55:22).

For Christians, the only source of comfort in life and in death is found in God alone and what He has accomplished for those who trust Him. Though friendships fail, life becomes almost unbearable, or ruin seems certain, He provides more than enough love, mercy, and forgiveness.

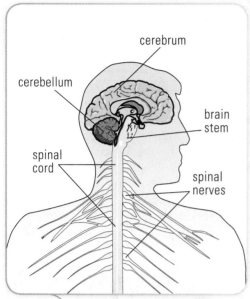

27A-6 Your spinal cord and spinal nerves relay impulses between your brain and body.

27A.4 *The Cerebellum, Brain Stem, and Spinal Cord*

The **cerebellum** is the second largest part of the brain. It monitors and controls bodily movements without your knowing about it. For example, in your cerebrum you make the decision to turn off the light. The cerebrum then sends this information to the cerebellum. The cerebellum works out which muscles will need to be stimulated and how much each muscle needs to contract in order for you to reach out and move the light switch. Your actions are smooth and accurate because of the cerebellum. Your cerebellum also helps to maintain posture and balance and sends impulses to your cerebrum regarding your body's position. This is why you know what your hands are doing even though you may not see them.

The **brain stem** is below and between the cerebrum and the cerebellum. The brain stem helps to control breathing, heartbeat, blood pressure, coughing, sneezing, and swallowing. It helps coordinate involuntary activities such as posture and balance.

The **spinal cord** is continuous with the brain stem and extends down your back. In an adult the spinal cord is about 42 to 45 cm (16.5 to 18 in.) long. It is protected by the vertebral column (backbone), which forms a bony tube that surrounds the spinal cord. Between the vertebrae are *spinal nerves* that branch off the spinal cord. These nerves go to the various parts of the body.

Section Review 27A

1. What two main body systems coordinate your body's activities?

2. List the two parts of the central nervous system.

3. How do an axon and a dendrite differ?

4. List three types of neurons. Which type would you expect to find connected to a muscle?

5. Which part of your brain is the largest?

27B The Sense Organs

The human body is equipped to receive many different kinds of stimuli. Scientists are not sure how many senses the human body has. The common list of five senses (sight, smell, taste, touch, and hearing) is far too short. You also can sense temperature, balance, motion, position, and pain, to name a few of the more familiar sensations. There are also some people who appear to sense things such as barometric pressure changes (changes in the pressure of the atmosphere). Just as some people cannot see as well as others, some people may not sense these other stimuli as well.

For the major senses, the body has **sense organs** with special neurons that are sensitive to certain stimuli. For example, your eyes respond to light, your ears to sound waves, your nose to odors, and your tongue to taste. The special neurons in these sense organs send

Objectives 27B

- Describe the structure of the eye and indicate the functions of its various parts.
- Differentiate between rods and cones in the retina.
- Describe the structure of the ear and indicate the functions of its various parts.

impulses to the central nervous system. You become aware of the stimuli only when the impulses reach your cerebrum.

There are, however, many things that the human body does not have the ability to sense. X-rays pass through your body without your being aware of them. Right now radio waves are all around you, but because you do not have receptors for them, you cannot receive their messages. Before you can become aware of the radio waves, you must have a device, such as a radio, that can convert the radio waves into sound.

In the spiritual realm there are things that only Christians can "sense." Christians are able to understand spiritual things, while those who are unsaved cannot. Christians can also receive the promptings of the Holy Spirit, which help them to live lives pleasing to God (Gal. 5:16–18). In a way, Christians have "spiritual receptors" that unsaved people do not have. The Holy Spirit deals with the unsaved only to convict them of their sin so that they might trust Christ as Savior (John 16:8–9). The unsaved are insensitive to spiritual things because they are spiritually dead (Eph. 2:1). Because the unsaved do not receive the promptings of the Holy Spirit, many spiritual things seem foolish to them (1 Cor. 2:14).

27B.1 *The Eye*

The eye is marvelously designed to receive and focus light, sending exact and continuous impulses to the brain. To do this in a space about the size of a Ping-Pong ball, the parts of the eye must work together accurately. The eyeball has three main layers: the sclera (SKLIHR uh), the choroid (KOR oyd), and the retina (RET n uh).

The **sclera** is the tough outside tissue that forms the "white of the eye." Most of the sclera does not let light into the eye. At the front of the sclera, however, is the clear **cornea**. Light passes into the eye through the cornea.

The **choroid** is the middle layer of the eye. The colored part of the eye, called the **iris**, is the front portion of the choroid layer. The black spot in the center of the iris is the **pupil**. The pupil is actually the opening of the choroid layer where light enters the eyeball. The size of the pupil opening is controlled by muscles in the iris.

The **retina** is the inner layer of the eye that begins along the sides of the lens and continues around to the back of the eye. In the retina are neurons that are sensitive to light.

There are two chambers in the eye. The chamber between the cornea and the lens is filled with a clear fluid called the *aqueous* (AY kwee us) *humor*. Nutrients in the aqueous humor provide energy for the cells of the cornea. Aqueous humor is constantly being made and then absorbed by the blood. The chamber behind the lens is filled with clear, jelly-like *vitreous* (VIT ree us) *humor*, which helps to keep the eyeball round. This substance forms in the eye before you are born and normally remains the same all your life.

Tracing the path of light through the eye is a simple way to understand how the eye works. Light first passes through the cornea and the aqueous humor. As the light reaches the pupil, the eye makes quick adjustments. If you are in bright light, reflexes cause the iris to make the pupil smaller because the sensitive retina may be damaged by too much light. In dim light the pupil opens wide to allow as much light as possible to enter the eye.

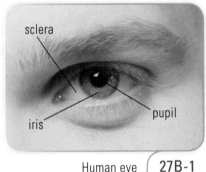

Human eye 27B-1

aqueous humor: aqueous (L. AQUA, water) + humor (L. UMOR, fluid)

vitreous: (L. VITRUM, glass)

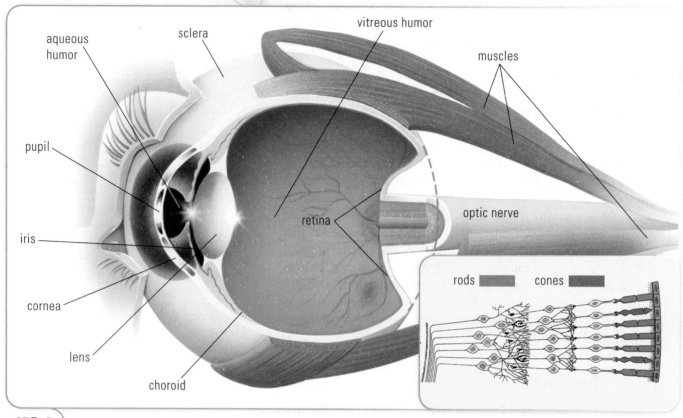

aqueous humor

sclera

vitreous humor

muscles

pupil

retina

optic nerve

iris

cornea

lens

choroid

rods   cones

27B-2 Cross section of the human eye (inset showing rods and cones in the retina)

Facets of **The Human Body:** *Shh! Your Eyes Are "Saying" Something*

Quiet! Your eyes are "talking"! If you "listen," they can give you some important information.

When you lose a staredown by blinking, your eyes are telling you that they are drying out. Light passing through the eye's cornea is normally bent inward. But the cornea bends light properly only if it is covered with a thin film of tear fluid. Each time you blink, tear fluid is spread over the surface of the cornea. When you try not to blink, sensor receptors in your eye detect that the cornea needs moisture, and soon you feel the urge to blink.

Why do your eyes sometimes produce so much fluid that it spills out of your eyes? At times your eyes must wash themselves. Ammonia, onions, and certain other substances give off airborne molecules that ir-

ritate the tissue of the eye. To wash the particles out of the eyes, the tear glands produce more fluid. Your eyes also produce more fluid when you feel strong emotion.

What happens when you leave the bright sunlight, enter a dim room, and suddenly cannot see anything? This inability to see is your eyes' signal that they are switching from their bright light system to their dim light system. During this switch, the pupils quickly enlarge, allowing more light to

pass through to each retina. In bright light the cones of the retina are used, but in dim light the rods accomplish most of your vision.

When you suddenly change from bright to dim light, the rods take a short time to react to the change and begin functioning. During the change neither the rods nor the cones are fully active, and for a minute or two it is hard to see.

If the rods do not begin functioning and you cannot see in dim light,

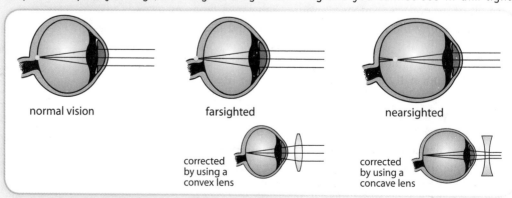

normal vision

farsighted

nearsighted

corrected by using a convex lens

corrected by using a concave lens

you have *night blindness*. If this happens, your eyes are telling you that your diet is probably short of vitamin A. The rods need this vitamin to function properly.

When you go to a baseball game, do you have problems seeing whether the outfielder caught the ball? If you cannot clearly see past the second baseman while you are sitting in the stands, your eyes are telling you that you are *nearsighted*.

When light enters the eye, the lens focuses it on the retina. However, if you are nearsighted, your eyeballs are too long from front to back. The light entering your eyes focuses somewhere in front of the retina. After the light focuses at this point, it begins to fan out in all directions. By the time the light reaches your retina, the images are out of focus.

Perhaps you can see the outfielder easily, but these words appear fuzzy when your head is near the page. In that case your eyeballs are probably too short from front to back, making you *farsighted*. Since your retina is farther forward than it should be, the light that enters your eyes is not yet focused when it reaches the retina.

This results in blurry images of nearby objects.

Special lenses can correct both nearsightedness and farsightedness. A concave lens placed in front of a nearsighted eye bends light outward before it reaches the cornea. This lens makes the light reaching the eye spread farther apart than it normally would. This increased spreading of the light rays causes the light not to be focused until it reaches the "too-far-back" retina. A convex lens placed in front of a farsighted eye bends light inward before it reaches the cornea, allowing the eye to properly focus the light on the "too-far-forward" retina.

If you see spots or cloudy patches in front of your eyes, your eyes could be warning you that they are developing *cataracts*. A cataract (KAT uh RAKT) is anything that stops light from passing through the lens of the eye. During old age, substances often accumulate in the lens of the eye, making it cloudy. But you do not have to be old to develop cataracts. Young people can develop cataracts if they receive a blow to the eye or swallow certain poisons.

Most cataracts can be cured. Sometimes the clouded area is on the surface of the lens and can be removed. In the past, cataracts have been corrected by the removal of the lens and the fitting of the eye with a contact lens. Most of the time, the clouded lens is replaced with an implanted plastic lens.

Cataract surgery is so advanced today that it takes only about thirty to sixty minutes. Only a mere eighth-inch (3 mm) incision is needed. Most patients are awake during the proce-

dure and return home within a few hours after the procedure.

The cornea also can become cloudy and prevent vision. Like the lens, it can be removed and replaced. In fact, the easiest and most successful type of transplant operation is the corneal transplant. This success is partly due to the cornea's location and its ability to heal without form-

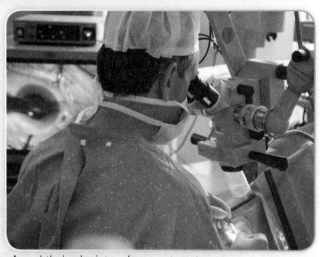

An ophthalmologist performs cataract surgery.

ing scar tissue. Another reason for the success of the transplant is that the antibodies in the blood that often cause *tissue rejection* (see p. 450) do not reach the cornea.

Some of the eye's messages are hard to interpret. A red, teary, and painful eye is often the result of an allergy, a cold, or a lack of sleep. However, an eye in this condition also can indicate a more serious problem called glaucoma (glaw KO muh). *Glaucoma* is caused by a build-up of too much fluid in the eye. As the fluid's pressure increases, it damages the retina. Glaucoma can often be controlled if it is detected early.

Your eyes normally tell you if something is wrong with them. Since vision is one of your most valuable senses, it is important to pay attention to what your eyes are saying. To protect your vision, have regular eye examinations by trained medical personnel.

Light passing through the pupil enters the *lens*. The lens bends the light waves to focus them on the retina. The light then passes through the vitreous humor to the retina. (Refer to Fig. 27B-2 on p. 486.)

In the retina are two special types of neurons called rods and cones. The **rods** are responsible for vision in dim light. They are stimulated by visible light, regardless of its color. Therefore, when you are looking at something in dim light, it appears only black and white. The **cones** are sensitive to the various colors of visible light. Light must be much brighter to stimulate a cone than to stimulate a rod. Thus, we see colors most clearly in well-lit areas.

Scientists believe that different cones are sensitive to different colors of light. In some people certain types of cones do not work properly. These people are partially *colorblind*. They usually cannot tell the difference between two colors. One of the most common types is red-green colorblindness. A person with this condition cannot tell the difference between red and green.

27B.2 *The Ear*

The ear is composed of three basic regions: the outer ear, the middle ear, and the inner ear. The outer ear consists of a flap of tissue that collects sound waves, the *ear canal* through which sound waves travel farther into the ear, and the eardrum. The **eardrum** is a membrane that stretches over the opening to the middle ear. Sound waves hit the eardrum, causing it to vibrate.

27B-3 Cross section of the human ear

The middle ear is an air-filled space with three tiny ear bones. These bones are named for their shapes—the *hammer* (malleus [MAL ee us]), *anvil* (incus [ING kus]), and *stirrup* (stapes [STAY peez]). The hammer is attached to the inner surface of the eardrum. As the eardrum vibrates, the hammer moves with it. The hammer moves the anvil, and the anvil moves the stirrup. In this way, the ear bones pass the vibrations of the eardrum to the inner ear.

The **eustachian** (yoo STAY shun) **tube** leads from the middle ear to the *pharynx*. Normally the eustachian tube remains closed, but when there is a significant change in air pressure, it opens up. (You might experience a change in air pressure when you climb a mountain or fly in an airplane.) When the eustachian tube opens, it allows air to enter the middle ear, making the pressure on both sides of the eardrum equal. Equalizing the pressure causes the eardrum to snap back into position, making a popping sound.

The inner ear consists of the cochlea (KOHK lee uh) and the semicircular canals. The **cochlea** is a coiled tubular structure containing

cochlea: (L. ᴋᴏᴋʜʟᴏꜱ, snail shell)

fluid. At the base of the cochlea is a small, membrane-covered opening for the stirrup. When vibrations from the eardrum pass through the ear bones, the stirrup vibrates the membrane-covered opening, which pushes against the liquid in the cochlea. These vibrations form waves in the cochlea fluid that cause hairlike neurons inside the cochlea to bend. When these neurons bend, they start nerve impulses that travel to the brain. The brain interprets the impulses as sound.

The **semicircular canals** in the inner ear provide a sense of the body's balance and position. Fluid inside the semicircular canals moves as you move your head, sending nerve impulses to the brain. The brain interprets the impulses and helps you know that you are moving even when your eyes are closed.

27B.3 *The Nose, Tongue, and Skin*

Your nose allows you to sense odors in the air. There are many special nerve endings in the mucous membrane along the inner surface of the nose. When you inhale molecules floating in the air, they land on the mucosa and stimulate these neurons to start impulses to the brain.

In addition to being used for chewing, speaking, and swallowing, the tongue has many microscopic **taste buds**. Each taste bud is a cluster of cells. Most of these cells serve to protect the neurons, which are located inside a tiny hole. When a fluid containing a dissolved substance enters the hole and stimulates the neurons, you taste something. Since only fluids can enter the hole of the taste bud, solid foods must be chewed and mixed with saliva before you can taste them.

Many scientists believe there are only four basic tastes: sweet, sour, salty, and bitter. Most flavors are a combination of these basic tastes. Some scientists believe that humans also can sense a few other distinct tastes. Most of the flavor of the food we eat is a combination of taste and smell. This is why food does not taste as good when you have a cold and cannot smell it.

The human skin has several different types of neurons, each able to respond to different factors. Some neurons respond to *cold*, while others respond to *heat*. Near the surface of the skin are neurons for *touch*. Deep

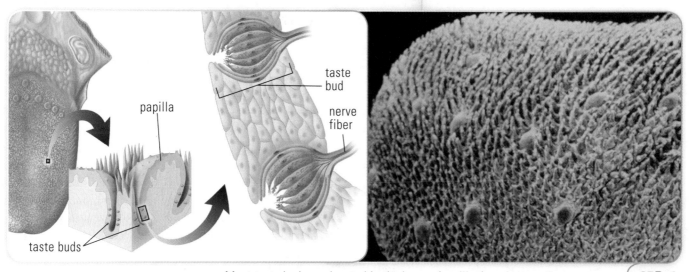

taste bud

nerve fiber

papilla

taste buds

Most taste buds are located in the bumps (papillae) on the top of your tongue.

in the skin are neurons that sense *pressure*. Similar pressure-sensing neurons are located elsewhere in the body (such as in the joints and the stomach area). Neurons that sense *pain* are located not only in the skin but also in almost every other tissue of the body. Not all areas of skin have the same number of sensory receptors. In more sensitive areas, such as your fingertips, there may be many. In other areas, such as the skin of your back, there are fewer.

Section Review 27B

1. The clear covering over the sclera of the eye is the _____.

2. What do the muscles in your iris do?

3. What is the function of your eustachian tubes?

4. In what part of the eye do cataracts occur?

5. List the four basic tastes.

27C The Endocrine System

The nervous system specializes in the quick transfer of impulses and short, rapid reactions. To continue the same reaction, the body sends many impulses over and over. Sometimes these reactions may involve only one muscle; other reactions use more of the body's systems.

The other system of control is the endocrine system. This system often responds slower than the nervous system, but its reactions usually last for a longer period of time. The **endocrine system** is a collection of glands that produce hormones. The glands of the endocrine system are sometimes called *ductless* (without tubes) *glands*. Many glands in your body have ducts for transferring their products. For example, sweat gland ducts carry sweat to the surface of the skin, and salivary gland ducts transport saliva from the gland to the mouth. The endocrine glands, however, lack ducts. They release their products directly into the blood.

27C.1 *Hormones*

A **hormone** is a chemical messenger made in an endocrine gland and carried by the blood. Each hormone causes a specific tissue or tissues to react. Hormones cause the starting or stopping of growth, the production or use of certain chemicals, and various other reactions. Just a small amount of a hormone can cause a tissue to react.

Hormones are highly specific. This means that a hormone usually affects tissue in a particular way. Once the hormone is in the blood, it will continue to function until it is either used up or filtered out of the blood by the kidneys. If the effect is to continue, the endocrine glands must make and release more of the hormone.

Because hormones travel in the blood, they have a slower effect on the body than the nervous system does. When a hormone is released into the blood, all of the tissues that respond to that hormone will be affected. In the nervous system, control is more independent.

Objectives 27C

- Describe the endocrine system and define *hormone*.
- Identify several endocrine glands and state the functions of the hormones they produce.
- Define *vestigial organ*.
- Discuss vestigial organs as an evolutionary concept and give arguments against the presence of vestigial structures in the human body.
- List several effects of epinephrine.

Facets of *The Human Body:* *Growing Up*

Puberty begins during a person's pre-teen or early teenage years. It is the time when a person matures physically. With this physical growth comes mental and emotional growth and, for the Christian, hopefully spiritual growth.

During puberty the body is under a great deal of strain. It must do all the complex growing needed to change a child's body into an adult's body. As boys become young men, they begin to lose their "baby fat," and their muscular growth increases. This change gives the male body the trimmer, angular lines of an adult.

Young ladies keep much of their "baby fat," and their muscles do not grow as much as do young men's. Because fat deposits fill the spaces between their muscles, women have a smoother look to their bodies.

During puberty there is also a growth of body hair. Not only do young men need to start shaving, but also both sexes notice a change in the hair on their heads. The soft, fine child's hair is replaced by coarser hair that may be a different color. Sometimes a person's hair changes from curly to straight or from straight to curly.

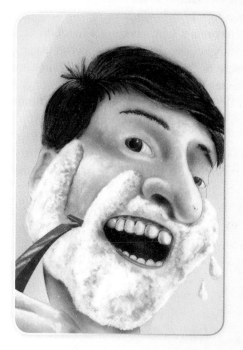

As the body grows, the vocal cords also grow, causing the voices of both sexes to deepen. Young men experience a greater amount of growth. Sometimes they have difficulty adjusting to the change. Stress and other factors can cause a young man to lose control of his vocal cords for an instant, often causing his voice to crack.

Other physical changes during puberty include growth in height, enlargement and development of the reproductive organs, changes in facial features, and a thickening and toughening of the skin.

As the skin changes during puberty, it often produces large amounts of the oil that normally keeps the skin soft and flexible. This excess oil often causes acne (AK nee). One of the best things to do for acne is to keep the face clean. Severe acne may require treatment by a physician.

Not everyone begins puberty at the same age. In fact, two people the same age could start puberty five years apart, and both would still be considered normal. Puberty also has no set order in which physical changes will occur. For this reason people of the same age going through puberty may appear quite different physically.

The best advice for a young person going through puberty is not to worry about his physical development. In time, the body will finish its maturing process.

For most people, growing up mentally and emotionally is much harder than growing up physically. A child is too immature to see the value of many things that are important to an adult. A child is mainly concerned with having fun right now. Since preparing

himself for the future is usually not fun, he often has to be forced to do his homework.

For a young child, homework can be made into "fun" or "play" to keep his interest. As a person grows up, however, he needs to learn self-discipline. Some things that will help him in the future may not be fun, but he must learn to do them without being forced.

Mental and emotional maturing is the ability to first determine something's value (even though it is not obvious at the time) and then to adjust one's actions accordingly.

For example, a child seeing two candy bars on the kitchen counter might think, "I'll eat *both* of these candy bars right now." Someone with a little more maturity might think, "Mom will be upset with me if I eat

both of these candy bars. I'll eat just one." A person who is even more mature might think, "I'll ask Mom if I can have these candy bars; then I'll give one to David. I have been trying to become his friend so that I can witness to him." Using a candy bar as an opportunity to witness is more worthwhile than eating two candy bars.

Growing up in the Lord is learning to make decisions based on God's Word. Christians please God by living according to the principles taught in

Growing Up (cont.)

the Bible (James 1:22–25). An immature Christian, however, may choose to ignore these principles. He may try to use arguments such as "Everyone else is doing it" or "What's so bad about this?" to try to justify his immature spiritual choices.

Being a mature Christian does not depend upon your physical age. You can be a grandparent and still be a baby spiritually. Nor does being a mature Christian depend on how long you have been saved (1 Tim. 4:12). Some teenagers who have been saved only a couple of years can make better spiritual decisions than some adults who have been saved a long time but are not living close to the Lord.

The teenage years are a time of growing up. It is not easy to mature physically, emotionally, and spiritually all at the same time. But God has promised His guidance concerning what is right and what is wrong (John 16:13). He also promises to give His children strength to do what is right (1 Cor. 10:13; Phil. 4:13). The Christian's responsibility is to claim those promises so that he can conquer the desire for sinful or childish things. As Christians do this, their desire to live for the Lord will increase (James 4:7-8, 10).

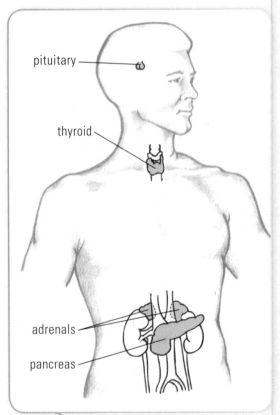

27C-1 Some of the endocrine glands

- pituitary
- thyroid
- adrenals
- pancreas

Different neurons connect with different areas of the body, allowing individual parts to react differently but at the same time. For example, the nervous system can cause some muscles in your arm to be relaxed while others are tense. If a gland releases a hormone that relaxes muscles, all muscles would react the same way.

27C.2 *The Endocrine Glands*

When the various endocrine glands were first discovered, scientists did not know that they produced hormones. At that time almost every endocrine gland in the body was considered a vestigial (veh STIJ ee ul) organ. A **vestigial organ** is one that no longer functions and, according to evolutionists, is evolving away. Endocrine glands, however, produce hormones that are essential to the normal functioning of the body and thus are not vestigial.

Evolutionists often point to organs with no known function and claim that they are vestigial. They believe that these organs were supposedly useful when humans were "a lower form of life" (such as an ape-like creature). They believe that the organ is now no longer useful and is disappearing little by little over long periods of time. Evolutionists often claim that the presence of vestigial organs supports evolutionary theory.

Just because the function of something is not known, scientists should not assume that it does not have a function. Years ago the list of supposedly vestigial organs in the human body was quite long. Yet, as scientists studied the body more closely, they found functions for every part. Although your body has structures that you can get along without (such as tonsils, appendix, fingers, or toes), each structure still has a purpose. That you can live without these structures does not make them vestigial.

The number of recognized human endocrine glands is increasing. This does not mean that humans are evolving new glands, nor does it mean that by looking more carefully scientists are finding new ones tucked away in hidden places. Rather, scientists keep discovering more hormones and hormone-like substances in the blood. Sometimes scientists learn that known endocrine glands produce these newly discovered hormones. Sometimes, however, scientists discover that a gland not known to be an endocrine gland produces these hormones. When this happens, that gland is added to the list of endocrine glands.

The *pancreas* is a good example of a gland that functions in the endocrine system as well as in another system. The pancreas produces several digestive enzymes. A duct carries the enzymes from the pancreas to the small intestine. The pancreas also releases hormones directly into the bloodstream. Because of these two distinct functions, the pancreas is an organ of both the digestive system and the endocrine system.

27C.3 *The Pituitary Gland*

The **pituitary** (pih TOO uh TEHR ee) **gland** is about the size of a small marble and is located under the brain. Although small, it secretes a greater number of hormones than any other endocrine gland. Many of the hormones that it secretes stimulate other endocrine glands to produce their hormones. Because of its influence on other glands, the pituitary gland is sometimes called the *master gland* of the body.

One of the hormones produced by the pituitary gland is *growth hormone*. This hormone stimulates bones, muscles, and various other tissues to grow. About half the people who enter teenage years have a growth spurt that causes them to grow more than 15 cm (6 in.) in a single year. This growth spurt happens, in part, because the pituitary gland releases large amounts of growth hormone. The other 50% of young people grow at a steadier rate. This slower growth rate occurs when the pituitary gland releases smaller amounts of growth hormone. Both of these growth rates are normal.

Sometimes a person's pituitary gland does not produce enough growth hormone, and the person does not grow. Some people are dwarfs because of a lack of growth hormone. On the other hand, sometimes a person's pituitary produces too much growth hormone, and the person grows very tall. Some people become giants because of too much growth hormone.

Physicians can measure the amount of growth hormone in a person's blood. If there is too much or too little of this hormone, the amount can be corrected. However, the correction must be started while the person is still young. Once the person is mature and his bones have either grown too much or lost their ability to grow, correcting the amount of hormone will not change his height.

27C.4 *The Pancreas and Insulin*

Inside the pancreas are tiny clumps of tissue that make insulin. *Insulin* is a hormone that helps regulate the amount of sugar in the blood.

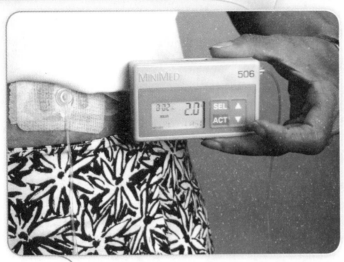

27B-3 An insulin pump automatically measures blood sugar and gives the proper amount of insulin—without multiple injections.

When you eat, sugar from your food enters your blood and stimulates the pancreas to release insulin. Insulin causes the body to take sugar from the blood and store it. Without insulin, the amount of sugar in your blood would become too high. If there is too much sugar in the blood, a person may begin to feel dizzy and weak and may even go into a coma and eventually die. If a person's pancreas does not make enough insulin, he has a condition called diabetes mellitus. Diabetes mellitus is often treated by injections of insulin.

If a person's pancreas produces too much insulin, his body takes too much sugar out of his blood and stores it. Without sufficient sugar in the blood for the cells to use, the person begins to feel extremely sleepy and later may go into a coma and die. The same thing can happen if a person with diabetes mellitus takes too much insulin. If this happens, the person must quickly eat some sugar. Eating extra sugar will not stop the overstoring. However, it will keep the blood-sugar level from dropping too low.

27C.5 *The Adrenal Glands and Epinephrine*

The **adrenal** (uh DREE nul) **glands** sit on top of the kidneys like tiny caps. These glands are known as the *glands of emergency*. They produce the hormone *epinephrine* (EP uh NEF rin), which is also called *adrenaline* (uh DREN ul in). Epinephrine is called the "fight or flight" hormone because it prepares the body for emergency situations. One way it prepares the body for action is by supplying the blood with more food and oxygen. Epinephrine supplies more oxygen to the blood by increasing a person's rate of breathing and widening his air passages. It supplies more food by triggering the liver to release large amounts of sugar into the blood stream. This highly oxygenated, sugar-rich blood is then quickly circulated through the body as the heart beats faster and harder.

Facets of *The Human Body:* *Epinephrine—The "Fight or Flight" Hormone*

Mrs. Morgan and her four-year-old son Jimmy were returning home from the grocery store. Running behind schedule, Mrs. Morgan quickly shifted the car into park, got out of the car, and headed toward the front door. As little Jimmy got out of the car, he dropped his ball, and it rolled down the driveway. Jimmy chased the ball, but as he ran behind the car, it suddenly slipped out of gear and went backward. When she heard Jimmy scream, Mrs. Morgan turned and saw her son pinned underneath the car. Moments later Jimmy was in her arms. Mrs. Morgan had lifted the rear end of the 3000 lb car by herself and rescued her son.

You may have read a story like this in a magazine and wondered how it could be true. Mrs. Morgan's reaction was possible because of a hormone called *epinephrine*. Epinephrine redirects the body's resources of energy and oxygen and chemically stimulates various structures.

Tiny amounts of epinephrine are normally released in your body. However, when under stress caused by sudden shock, a major emergency, fear, or great pain, the body may release large amounts of this hormone. When this happens, the body often appears to have superhuman strength. The epinephrine has prepared the body for "fight or flight."

Small problems such as worry or anger also can cause the body to release epinephrine. The physical effects of stage fright, for example, are caused primarily by epinephrine. Have you noticed when it is your turn to speak before a group that you feel cold and look "as pale as a sheet"? Epinephrine triggers your body to direct warm blood away from the skin and toward your muscles, preparing them for action. With less blood the skin becomes pale and cold.

As you begin your speech, perhaps your mouth feels dry and you have difficulty swallowing. This happens because epinephrine has "turned off" your mucous membranes.

Epinephrine also temporarily stops digestion, making your lunch feel like a lump in your stomach. These changes are a result of epinephrine's preparing the body for an emergency. The blood that would normally go to help produce saliva or to complete digestion is being redirected to supply the muscles, brain, and other structures with extra blood.

Though epinephrine works quickly to influence your body, its effects can last a long time. Hours after your speech, when you should be sleeping,

you may still be wide awake from the epinephrine in your system.

As you become more accustomed to performing on stage, the experience will become less frightening, and less epinephrine will be released. Some people, however, are constantly in situations that cause them to experience a great deal of pressure or worry. Others are continuously afraid or nervous. These people may be constantly releasing considerable amounts of epinephrine within their bodies. After long periods of this kind of treatment, body parts may wear out prematurely.

Everyone has problems. Trials and tribulations are part of the Christian life (Rom. 5:3; 1 Pet. 1:7). But Christians should not worry or be anxious about things (John 14:27). Instead they should take their burdens to the Lord in prayer, trusting Him to do what only He can do (Matt. 11:28-30).

Epinephrine also prepares the body for action by increasing muscular strength. Blood that normally goes to the skin, stomach, intestines, and a few other structures is redirected by epinephrine to go to the muscles. This additional blood supplies the muscles with even more food and oxygen for greater strength.

The brain also receives more blood, and the person becomes more alert. The pupils become larger, permitting more light into the eyes. The sweat glands work harder to help remove any extra heat your body may produce as it prepares for action. Epinephrine even helps to protect the person if he is injured; the hormone causes the blood to clot quickly and triggers the spleen to release its blood reserves.

27C.6 *Other Endocrine Glands*

The **thyroid** (THY ROYD) **gland** is located in the neck. It produces *thyroxine* (thy ROK sin), which controls the body's metabolic rate. Remember that the metabolic rate is the **body's rate of activity**. If a person lacks thyroxine, his metabolism will be low, and he will be sluggish. Thyroxine contains iodine. If a person does not get enough iodine in his diet, his body will not be able to produce thyroxine. Trying to make the needed thyroxine, his thyroid gland grows. Sometimes this causes the person's neck to have a large swelling called a *goiter* (GOY tur).

A person's ovaries or testes not only produce *gametes* (ova or sperm) but also make the male and female *reproductive hormones*. These hormones cause the body to mature and prepare it to function in producing children. In young children these organs do not make reproductive hormones. Normally during the preteen or early teen years, a person's pituitary gland produces a hormone which stimulates the reproductive organs to begin producing the reproductive hormones. These hormones start the maturing process. The period of life in which the reproductive hormones cause the body to mature is called *puberty* (PYOO bur tee).

Section Review 27C

1. What type of chemicals do endocrine glands produce?

2. What transports the endocrine chemicals?

3. In what two systems does the pancreas function?

4. What endocrine gland produces insulin?

5. Why is iodine important in your diet?

Chapter Review

1. What kind of cell has axons and dendrites?

2. Do you have to think about performing a reflex reaction in order for it to happen? Why?

3. How does an impulse pass from one neuron to another?

4. Name the four lobes of the cerebrum and describe the functions of each lobe.

5. What is the function of the cerebellum?

6. What is the function of the brain stem?

7. What is the black "hole" in your eye called? What does it do?

8. Which part of your eye contains the cells that are sensitive to light?

9. How are the two types of light receptors in your eyes different?

10. Which of the three bones in the middle ear attaches directly to the eardrum?

11. Name three endocrine glands.

12. What endocrine gland is sometimes called the master gland?

13. What would happen if your pancreas stopped producing insulin? What is this disease called?

14. Where are the adrenal glands located? What do they produce?

What Did You Learn?

1. Draw and label the parts of a neuron and explain which direction an impulse moves through it.

2. Describe how a reflex works when you touch a hot object.

3. How would your hearing be different if you had no outer ear?

4. How do sensory receptors make it possible to read Braille?

5. Why do you think you can see and hear things in your dreams even when your eyes are closed and your room is quiet?

Scientifically Speaking

central nervous system
peripheral nervous system
neurons
dendrites
axons
nerves
synapse
reflex
reflex arcs
sensory neuron
interneuron
motor neuron
cerebrum
cerebral cortex
cerebellum
brain stem
spinal cord
sense organs
sclera
cornea
choroid
iris
pupil
retina
rods
cones
eardrum
eustachian tube
cochlea
semicircular canals
taste buds
endocrine system
hormone
vestigial organ
pituitary gland
adrenal glands
thyroid gland

Self Quiz 27

1. The two major control systems of the body are the _____ system and the _____ system.

2. Dendrites carry nerve impulse away/toward the nerve cell body. (Circle the correct response.)

____ 3. The junction between two neurons is called a(n)
   A. synapse.
   B. interneuron.
   C. reflex arc.
   D. impulse.

____ 4. The central nervous system includes the
   A. spinal nerves.
   B. spinal cord.
   C. ears.
   D. brain.
   E. B and D
   F. A and C

5. The _____ is the largest portion of the brain.

____ 6. The portion of the brain that controls actions such as breathing and swallowing is the
   A. brain stem.
   B. cerebrum.
   C. cerebellum.
   D. temporal lobe.

____ 7. Which lobes are responsible for interpreting visual sensations?
   A. frontal lobes
   B. parietal lobes
   C. temporal lobes
   D. occipital lobes

____ 8. Which structure allows light to enter the eye?
   A. retina
   B. lens
   C. pupil
   D. choroid

9. The rods/cones are responsible for vision in dim light. (Circle the correct response.)

____ 10. Which structure works to equalize pressure in the middle ear?
   A. cochlea
   B. eustachian tube
   C. malleus
   D. eardrum

____ 11. Taste buds are located only on the tongue. (True/False)

____ 12. Which statement about hormones is *not* true?
   A. They are carried by the blood stream.
   B. They affect specific cells or tissues.
   C. They are very short acting.
   D. They are produced by ductless glands.

13. According to evolutionists, a _____ _____ is a left-over structure that no longer has any function.

____ 14. Which is considered the master gland?
   A. pancreas
   B. adrenal gland
   C. thyroid gland
   D. pituitary gland

15. Why is the gland you selected in the previous question called the master gland?

Match the following responses with the proper hormone.
   A. blood sugar
   B. fight or flight
   C. growth
   D. metabolism

____ 16. adrenal glands

____ 17. pancreas

____ 18. pituitary gland

____ 19. thyroid gland

Self Quiz Answer Key

15

1. T **2.** F **3.** A **4.** C **5.** C **6.** B **7.** D **8.** A
9. aortic arches **10.** E, A, B, D, C

16

1. C **2.** F **3.** A **4.** D **5.** T **6.** B **7.** C **8.** D **9.** C
10. D

17

1. E, B, D, A, C **2.** T **3.** B **4.** D **5.** A **6.** C **7.** F
8. B **9.** C **10.** T **11.** A **12.** D

18

1. F **2.** D **3.** A **4.** air sacs **5.** C **6.** T **7.** C **8.** D
9. B **10.** A

19

1. F **2.** T **3.** A **4.** D **5.** monarch butterfly **6.** C
7. C **8.** D **9.** C **10.** B

20

1. A **2.** D **3.** B **4.** C **5.** spawning **6.** B **7.** T **8.** C
9. A **10.** D

21

1. F **2.** A **3.** B **4.** C **5.** C **6.** producers **7.** D
8. A **9.** C **10.** B

22

1. D **2.** A **3.** T **4.** B **5.** F **6.** C **7.** A **8.** B **9.** D
10. C

23

1. B **2.** A **3.** D **4.** T **5.** C **6.** A **7.** Conservation
8. B **9.** F **10.** D

24

1. A **2.** subcutaneous layer **3.** epidermis **4.** hair
follicle **5.** sweat gland **6.** F **7.** Any three: framework for support and movement, protection of
internal organs, storage of minerals, or production
of blood cells **8.** F **9.** osteon **10.** joint **11.** F **12.** C

25

1. A **2.** F **3.** D **4.** Atrioventricular (AV) valves
5. Red blood cells (erythrocytes) **6.** B **7.** Platelets **8.** Antigens **9.** B **10.** Antibodies **11.** nephron **12.** to remove wastes from the blood and
eliminate them from the body

26

1. metabolism **2.** C **3.** A **4.** Alveoli **5.** contracts
or moves down **6.** E **7.** T **8.** B **9.** D **10.** liver
11. C **12.** A

27

1. nervous, endocrine **2.** toward **3.** A **4.** E
5. cerebrum **6.** A **7.** D **8.** C **9.** rods **10.** B
11. F **12.** C **13.** vestigial organ **14.** D **15.** Answers may vary but should make this point: The
pituitary gland is called the master gland because
it influences the function of many of the other
endocrine glands. **16.** B **17.** A **18.** C **19.** D

THE METRIC SYSTEM

	Metric unit	Approximate English system equivalent	Metric conversion	Handy comparisons
Length	kilometer (km) meter (m) centimeter (cm) millimeter (mm) micrometer (µm) nanometer (nm) Angstrom (Å)	0.62 mi; 1090 yd 1 yd 3 in.; 39 in. 0.4 in. 0.04 in. 0.00004 in. 0.00000004 in. 0.000000004 in.	1000 m 0.001 km 0.01 m; 10 mm 0.1 cm 0.001 mm 0.001 µm 0.1 nm	11 football fields a yardstick and 3 in. about half the diameter of a nickel the thickness of a penny a red blood cell is 7.5 µm a polio virus is 25 nm half the size of a hydrogen atom
Weight	kilogram (kg) gram (g) milligram (mg)	2.2 lb; 35 oz 0.035 oz 0.000035 oz	1000 g 0.001 kg 0.001 g	half of a sack of sugar the weight of 24 drops of water, or one paper clip the weight of 0.2 of a drop of water
Volume	liter (L) milliliter (mL) microliter (µL) liter dry (L)	1 qt and ¼ cup 0.004 cup 0.000004 cup 0.03 bu	1000 mL 0.001 L; 1000 µL 0.001 mL 1000 mL	¼ gal the volume of 24 drops of water, about 1/5 tsp the volume of 0.024 of a drop of water the volume of about 1 qt

Temperature

On the Celsius (centigrade) scale, water at sea level has a freezing point of 0°C and a boiling point of 100°C. On the Fahrenheit scale, water at sea level has a freezing point of 32°F and a boiling point of 212°F. Normal body temperature is 37°C or 98.6°F. The following formulas can be used to convert a measurement from one scale to the other:

  °F to °C—subtract 32, multiply by 5, divide by 9;
  °C to °F—multiply by 9, divide by 5, add 32.

Unit Abbreviations

Å	angstrom(s)	**L**	liter(s)	**sq mi**	square mile(s)
AD	anno Domini (in the year of our Lord)	**lb**	pound(s)	**sq yd**	square yard(s)
		m	meter(s)	**tn**	ton(s)
BC	before the birth of Christ	**m²**	square meter(s)	**w**	week(s)
bpm	beat(s) per minute	**mg**	milligram(s)	**×**	times larger, power (enlargement)
bu	bushel(s)	**mi**	mile(s)		
°C	degree(s) Celsius	**mL**	milliliter(s)	**y**	year(s)
Cal	kilocalorie(s)	**mm**	millimeter(s)	**yd**	yard(s)
cm	centimeter(s)	**mm Hg**	millimeters of mercury		
°F	degree(s) Fahrenheit	**mph**	mile(s) per hour		
ft	foot (feet)	**µL**	microliter(s)		
g	gram(s)	**µm**	micrometer(s)		
gal	gallon(s)	**nm**	nanometer(s)		
in.	inch(es)	**oz**	ounce(s)		
kcal	kilocalorie(s)	**pH**	measure of acidity		
kg	kilogram(s)	**pt**	pint(s)		
km	kilometer(s)	**qt**	quart(s)		
km/h	kilometer(s) per hour	**sec**	second(s)		

PERIODIC TABLE OF THE ELEMENTS

Legend (key box):

- Radioactive
- Atomic number
- Name
- Symbol
- Atomic mass
  - rounded to four significant digits
  - mass number of isotope with longest known half-life indicated by ( )
- Electron structure by energy level

86 — Radon — **Rn** — (222) — 2, 8, 18, 32, 18, 8

The names given to elements 112–116 represent the Latin names for their Arabic numbers.

Color key:
- Alkali metals
- Alkaline-earth metals
- Transition metals
- Post-transition metals
- Metalloids
- Nonmetals
- Halogens (also nonmetals)
- Noble gases
- Radioactive isotopes

IA	IIA	IIIB	IVB	VB	VIB	VIIB	VIIIB	VIIIB	VIIIB	IB	IIB	IIIA	IVA	VA	VIA	VIIA	VIIIA
1 Hydrogen **H** 1.008 — 1																	2 Helium **He** 4.003 — 2
3 Lithium **Li** 6.939 — 2,1	4 Beryllium **Be** 9.012 — 2,2											5 Boron **B** 10.81 — 2,3	6 Carbon **C** 12.01 — 2,4	7 Nitrogen **N** 14.01 — 2,5	8 Oxygen **O** 16.00 — 2,6	9 Fluorine **F** 19.00 — 2,7	10 Neon **Ne** 20.18 — 2,8
11 Sodium **Na** 22.99 — 2,8,1	12 Magnesium **Mg** 24.31 — 2,8,2											13 Aluminum **Al** 26.98 — 2,8,3	14 Silicon **Si** 28.09 — 2,8,4	15 Phosphorus **P** 30.97 — 2,8,5	16 Sulfur **S** 32.06 — 2,8,6	17 Chlorine **Cl** 35.45 — 2,8,7	18 Argon **Ar** 39.95 — 2,8,8
19 Potassium **K** 39.10 — 2,8,8,1	20 Calcium **Ca** 40.08 — 2,8,8,2	21 Scandium **Sc** 44.96 — 2,8,9,2	22 Titanium **Ti** 47.90 — 2,8,10,2	23 Vanadium **V** 50.94 — 2,8,11,2	24 Chromium **Cr** 52.00 — 2,8,13,1	25 Manganese **Mn** 54.94 — 2,8,13,2	26 Iron **Fe** 55.85 — 2,8,14,2	27 Cobalt **Co** 58.93 — 2,8,15,2	28 Nickel **Ni** 58.71 — 2,8,16,2	29 Copper **Cu** 63.55 — 2,8,18,1	30 Zinc **Zn** 65.38 — 2,8,18,2	31 Gallium **Ga** 69.72 — 2,8,18,3	32 Germanium **Ge** 72.59 — 2,8,18,4	33 Arsenic **As** 74.92 — 2,8,18,5	34 Selenium **Se** 78.96 — 2,8,18,6	35 Bromine **Br** 79.90 — 2,8,18,7	36 Krypton **Kr** 83.80 — 2,8,18,8
37 Rubidium **Rb** 85.47 — 2,8,18,8,1	38 Strontium **Sr** 87.62 — 2,8,18,8,2	39 Yttrium **Y** 88.91 — 2,8,18,9,2	40 Zirconium **Zr** 91.22 — 2,8,18,10,2	41 Niobium **Nb** 92.91 — 2,8,18,12,1	42 Molybdenum **Mo** 95.94 — 2,8,18,13,1	43 Technetium **Tc** (98) — 2,8,18,14,1	44 Ruthenium **Ru** 101.1 — 2,8,18,15,1	45 Rhodium **Rh** 102.9 — 2,8,18,16,1	46 Palladium **Pd** 106.4 — 2,8,18,18	47 Silver **Ag** 107.9 — 2,8,18,18,1	48 Cadmium **Cd** 112.4 — 2,8,18,18,2	49 Indium **In** 114.8 — 2,8,18,18,3	50 Tin **Sn** 118.7 — 2,8,18,18,4	51 Antimony **Sb** 121.8 — 2,8,18,18,5	52 Tellurium **Te** 127.6 — 2,8,18,18,6	53 Iodine **I** 126.9 — 2,8,18,18,7	54 Xenon **Xe** 131.3 — 2,8,18,18,8
55 Cesium **Cs** 132.9 — 2,8,18,18,8,1	56 Barium **Ba** 137.3 — 2,8,18,18,8,2	57 Lanthanum **La** 138.9 — 2,8,18,18,9,2	72 Hafnium **Hf** 178.5 — 2,8,18,32,10,2	73 Tantalum **Ta** 180.9 — 2,8,18,32,11,2	74 Tungsten **W** 183.9 — 2,8,18,32,12,2	75 Rhenium **Re** 186.2 — 2,8,18,32,13,2	76 Osmium **Os** 190.2 — 2,8,18,32,14,2	77 Iridium **Ir** 192.2 — 2,8,18,32,15,2	78 Platinum **Pt** 195.1 — 2,8,18,32,17,1	79 Gold **Au** 197.0 — 2,8,18,32,18,1	80 Mercury **Hg** 200.6 — 2,8,18,32,18,2	81 Thallium **Tl** 204.4 — 2,8,18,32,18,3	82 Lead **Pb** 207.2 — 2,8,18,32,18,4	83 Bismuth **Bi** 209.0 — 2,8,18,32,18,5	84 Polonium **Po** (209) — 2,8,18,32,18,6	85 Astatine **At** (210) — 2,8,18,32,18,7	86 Radon **Rn** (222) — 2,8,18,32,18,8
87 Francium **Fr** (223) — 2,8,18,32,18,8,1	88 Radium **Ra** (226) — 2,8,18,32,18,8,2	89 Actinium **Ac** (227) — 2,8,18,32,18,9,2	104 Rutherfordium **Rf** (261)	105 Dubnium **Db** (262)	106 Seaborgium **Sg** (266)	107 Bohrium **Bh** (264)	108 Hassium **Hs** (269)	109 Meitnerium **Mt** (268)	110 Darmstadtium **Ds** (271)	111 Roentgenium **Rg** (272)	112 Ununbium **Uub** (285)	113 Ununtrium **Uut** (284)	114 Ununquadium **Uuq** (289)	115 Ununpentium **Uup** (288)	116 Ununhexium **Uuh** (292)		

Lanthanide series

58 Cerium **Ce** 140.1 — 2,8,18,20,8,2	59 Praseodymium **Pr** 140.9 — 2,8,18,21,8,2	60 Neodymium **Nd** 144.2 — 2,8,18,22,8,2	61 Promethium **Pm** (145) — 2,8,18,23,8,2	62 Samarium **Sm** 150.4 — 2,8,18,24,8,2	63 Europium **Eu** 152.0 — 2,8,18,25,8,2	64 Gadolinium **Gd** 157.3 — 2,8,18,25,9,2	65 Terbium **Tb** 158.9 — 2,8,18,27,8,2	66 Dysprosium **Dy** 162.5 — 2,8,18,28,8,2	67 Holmium **Ho** 164.9 — 2,8,18,29,8,2	68 Erbium **Er** 167.3 — 2,8,18,30,8,2	69 Thulium **Tm** 168.9 — 2,8,18,31,8,2	70 Ytterbium **Yb** 173.0 — 2,8,18,32,8,2	71 Lutetium **Lu** 175.0 — 2,8,18,32,9,2

Actinide series

90 Thorium **Th** 232.0 — 2,8,18,32,18,10,2	91 Protactinium **Pa** 231.0 — 2,8,18,32,20,9,2	92 Uranium **U** 238.0 — 2,8,18,32,21,9,2	93 Neptunium **Np** (237) — 2,8,18,32,22,9,2	94 Plutonium **Pu** (244) — 2,8,18,32,24,8,2	95 Americium **Am** (243) — 2,8,18,32,25,8,2	96 Curium **Cm** (247) — 2,8,18,32,25,9,2	97 Berkelium **Bk** (247) — 2,8,18,32,26,9,2	98 Californium **Cf** (251) — 2,8,18,32,28,8,2	99 Einsteinium **Es** (252) — 2,8,18,32,29,8,2	100 Fermium **Fm** (257) — 2,8,18,32,30,8,2	101 Mendelevium **Md** (258) — 2,8,18,32,31,8,2	102 Nobelium **No** (259) — 2,8,18,32,32,8,2	103 Lawrencium **Lr** (262) — 2,8,18,32,32,9,2

THE LIVING KINGDOMS

This section lists some of the more familiar groups and examples of living things. Although the term *division* is sometimes used in place of *phylum* for the nonanimal kingdoms, the term *phylum* is kept here for consistency. The numbers in parentheses that follow many of the headings indicate the chapter section where that group is discussed.

Kingdom Archaebacteria (11A)
(AR kee bak TEER ee uh)

Kingdom Archaebacteria contains tiny unicellular organisms that live in some of the most extreme environments on earth. While some live in the hot springs near geysers, others thrive around undersea volcanic vents. Like eubacteria, archaebacteria lack membrane-bound internal structures. One key difference of archaebacteria is that they lack certain compounds found in the cell walls of all eubacteria.

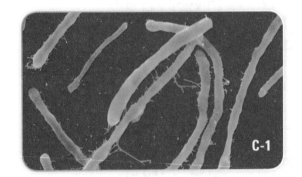

C-1 These bacteria can live in water that is nine times saltier than the ocean. They will even survive dehydration. A pigment molecule in these organisms causes them to appear red, sometimes coloring entire saltwater lakes.

Kingdom Eubacteria (11A)
(YOO bak TEER ee uh)

Kingdom Eubacteria contains thousands of different organisms, but only a few of them can be seen without the aid of a powerful microscope. All of them are either unicellular or colonial. The cells of these organisms lack some cellular parts, such as membranes around their nuclei, that other cells have.

Phylum Firmicutes (11A)
(fur mih CUE teez)

Bacteria that have cell walls and stain "gram positive"

C-2 *Streptococcus pneumoniae* is a type of bacterium that can cause pneumonia if present in sufficient numbers in your body. These bacteria usually form small colonies of two cells each, one of which is usually pointed (see arrow). Other members of this genus of bacteria are responsible for various other infections of the nose, throat, and lungs. This picture was taken by a scanning electron microscope and shows the bacteria 10,000 times their normal size.

C-3 Each colony of *Staphylococcus aureus* looks like a cluster of grapes. Each of the spheres is an individual cell. This genus of bacteria is associated with pimples and boils on the skin, with food poisoning, and with other infections. It is also present in the nose and on the skin of healthy individuals. This picture was taken by a scanning electron microscope and shows the bacteria 10,000 times their normal size.

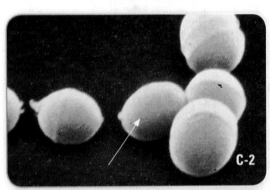

Phylum Cyanobacteria (11A)

(SY uh noh bak TEER ee uh)

Blue-green bacteria

C-4 The blue-green bacteria *Nostoc* forms slimy green balls that grow near the edges of ponds and lakes. Its cells release waste products that produce a bad odor and give the water a bad taste. This photograph shows *Nostoc* filaments as seen through a microscope.

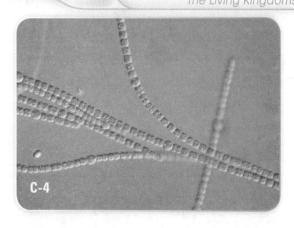

Kingdom Protista (11B)

(pro TIS tuh)

All the organisms in kingdom Protista are either unicellular or colonial; none of them produce true tissues. Kingdom Protista contains about 125,000 different organisms. These are often divided into two main groups—the algae and the protozoans. All the algae in kingdom Protista contain chlorophyll and are able to produce their own food. Most protozoans, however, obtain their food from other sources.

Phylum Ciliophora (11B)

(SIL ee AWF uh ruh)

Ciliates *(SIL ee its)*

Short hairlike extensions from a cell that are used in movement are called *cilia*. All the protozoans in phylum Ciliophora are called ciliates because they have cilia.

C-5 The paramecium is a ciliate that has cilia over its entire surface. A single paramecium has 10,000–14,000 cilia.

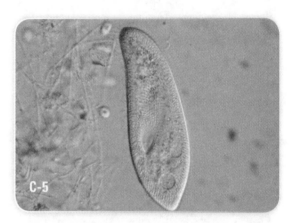

Phylum Sarcodina (11B)

(sar koh DYE nuh)

Amoebas, sarcodines

These types of protozoans move by sliding pseudopodia, extensions of their cytoplasm. Pseudopodia are also used to surround food, engulf it, and make a food vacuole inside the cell.

C-6 The flowing pseudopodia of an amoeba give it a constantly changing shape. Here, one amoeba extends its pseudopodia to engulf and digest another amoeba.

Phylum Euglenophyta (11B)

(YOO gluh NAWF uh tuh)

Euglenas

Exhibiting characteristics of both plants and animals, a euglena carries on photosynthesis to make its own food and uses two flagella for movement.

C-7 A euglena pulls itself through the water by twirling a pair of flagella. The eyespot (indicated by the arrow) is sensitive to light.

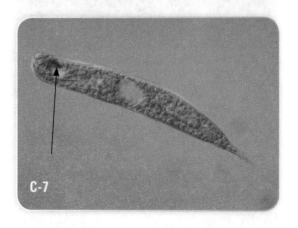

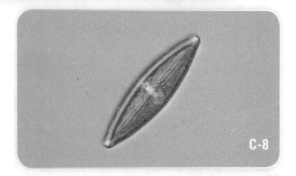

Phylum Chrysophyta (11B)
(kruh SAWF uh tuh)

Diatoms, golden-brown algae, yellow-green algae
Diatoms, the most familiar members of this phylum, have beautiful cell walls made of silica, which looks like glass. They make up a significant percentage of ocean plankton.

C-8 Diatoms have interesting geometric shapes. A single diatom has two nearly identical cell walls, or shells.

Phylum Chlorophyta (11B)
(kloh RAWF uh tuh)

Green algae
Though some green algae are unicellular, others form filaments. Colonies of some species of green algae can grow to be several meters long.

C-9 Organisms in the genus *Oedogonium* are characterized by long unbranched filaments. The chloroplasts within each cell give the filaments their green color.

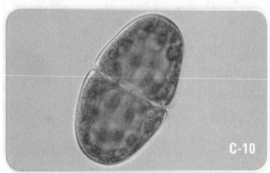

C-10 Desmids are free-floating green algae. Usually they are unicellular, but some are joined end to end, forming filaments. Some desmids are pinched in the middle, forming two symmetrical halves. Often desmids' cell walls have unusual patterns.

Phylum Phaeophyta (11B)
(fee AWF uh tuh)

Brown algae
Most brown algae live in the ocean. These algae are often made of filaments that intertwine to form large structures, many of which look like plants.

C-11 Fucus (FYOO kus) is a brown alga that is found growing along rocky ocean shores. This alga is under water during high tide and is swept back and forth by breakers during low tide.

Phylum Rhodophyta (11B)
(roh DAHF uh tuh)

Red algae
Red algae usually live in the ocean. Many red algae cells form filaments that intertwine with one another to form large structures.

C-12 Red algae are used as a source of chemicals, food, and food additives. One such food additive from the algae known as Irish moss (*Chondrus crispus*) is commonly used as a thickener in ice cream, candy, and pudding.

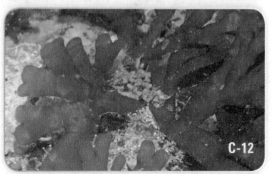

Phylum Myxomycota (11B)
(MIK suh mye KOH tuh)

Slime molds

Slime molds often appear as brightly colored networks of slimy threads on rotting logs and other decaying matter. This phylum has some characteristics so unique that it could be classified in kingdom Protista, kingdom Fungi, or even by itself.

C-13 This slime mold has glided across bark mulch, some of which it ate by secreting enzymes. The mold shown here is forming a less slimy structure, which will produce spores.

Kingdom Fungi (11C)
(FUN jye)

Some members of the kingdom Fungi are unicellular, but many are colonial. Some colonies of fungi are long filaments that are twisted together to form complex structures such as mushrooms and puffballs. Such fungi may look like plants, but they do not have true stems, roots, or leaves as plants do. Fungi lack chlorophyll, so they cannot make their own food. They obtain their food by secreting enzymes to digest substances, which they then absorb. Many fungi live on dead plants and animals and decompose them. Other fungi live as parasites on living things.

Phylum Basidiomycota (11C)
(buh SID ee oh mye KOH tuh)

Mushrooms, puffballs, rusts, shelf fungi

C-14 This poisonous mushroom can be found in lawns and meadows over most of the United States. Mushrooms have an underground network of filaments that absorb food substances. When a mushroom is fully developed, it releases millions of spores from the gills of the underside of its cap. After they are carried away by wind and water, spores may produce new mushrooms if they land in a place that has the proper conditions.

C-15 The spots on these leaves are wheat rust. This fungus lives on both wheat and barberry plants. It absorbs nutrients from wheat, weakening it so that it produces less grain. Each year wheat rust fungus destroys millions of dollars' worth of wheat around the world.

Phylum Zygomycota (11C)
(ZYE goh mye KOH tuh)

Black bread mold, other molds

C-16 This slice of bread has black bread mold growing on it. Thousands of dark-colored spores form on tiny stalks during asexual reproduction, producing a fuzzy appearance. Another type of spore, called a zygospore, is produced during sexual reproduction.

Other important phyla in kingdom Fungi are Ascomycota and Deuteromycota.

C-17

C-18

C-19

Kingdom Plantae (12C)
(PLAN tee)

The members of kingdom Plantae have tissues, but not all have tissues that conduct water. Most members of this kingdom use the green pigment chlorophyll to manufacture food. Plant cells are surrounded by cell walls, which contain cellulose. Cell walls help give plants the stiff crispness characteristic of fresh leaves. The wood of trees and shrubs is made of cells with very thick cell walls. Some plants reproduce using spores, some flower and produce seeds, and many from either group can also reproduce asexually.

Phylum Bryophyta (12C)
(brye AWF uh tuh)

Mosses

Many plants that do not have tissues for conducting water belong to phylum Bryophyta. Water gets to the cells of these plants by seeping through the spaces between cells. Bryophytes are usually less than two inches high and do not produce flowers.

C-17 This forest moss produces spores in the tiny capsules on top of its slender stalks (inset). These spores will be released and can grow into new moss plants if they fall in moist, shady places.

Phylum Pteridophyta (12C)
(TEHR uh DAWF uh tuh)

Ferns

Ferns have tissues that conduct water and other materials efficiently, so they are not limited in height as the bryophytes are. Ferns are often found in moist places, because liquid water is necessary for sexual reproduction to occur.

C-18 Ferns usually grow in moist, shady spots. Ferns do not produce flowers or seeds. Instead, they produce reproductive structures called *sori* (inset) on the underside of the fronds. The sori contain spores that are distributed near and far to grow into new ferns.

Phylum Coniferophyta (12C)
(kuh NIF uh RAWF uh tuh)

Cedars, junipers, pines, redwoods, yews

The name of this phylum literally means "cone-bearing plant." This is an accurate description of its unique characteristic: seed- and pollen-bearing cones. Coniferophyta includes some of the oldest, largest, and economically most important plants in the world. Many are evergreens.

C-19 The sequoia redwood trees of California are large conifers. Ironically, these huge trees produce relatively small cones about the size of a golf ball. No conifer produces flowers; instead, they have some form of cones that produce seeds.

Phylum Anthophyta (12C)
(an THAWF uh tuh)

Flowering plants

Plants that reproduce by means of flowers are called *angiosperms*. Although some of their flowers are tiny and many lack showy petals, all angiosperms produce flowers. Certain flower parts develop into fruit, which contains seeds. The fruit may be large or small, juicy or hard. There are only two classes in the phylum Anthophyta: Monocotyledoneae (MAHN uh KAHT uh LEE duh NEE ee) and Dicotyledoneae (dye KAHT uh LEE duh NEE ee). However, there are more than 460 families in the phylum and perhaps as many as 400,000 species. Each photo below shows an example of the family listed. The first three are in class Monocotyledoneae. All the others represent class Dicoyledoneae.

Liliaceae	Orchidaceae	Iridaceae	Cornaceae	Violaceae
tulip	tricolor bandana orchid	iris	flowering dogwood	pansy

Rosaceae	Fagaceae	Cactaceae	Asteraceae
rose	red oak	prickly pear cactus	daisy

Kingdom Animalia (15B)
(AN ih MAY lee uh)

The members of the kingdom Animalia have tissues but do not contain chlorophyll and thus cannot manufacture their own food. Most animals move about in search of their food. Animal cells are not surrounded by cell walls.

Phylum Porifera (15B)
(puh RIF uh ruh)

Sponges

Adult sponges do not move around in their environment. Instead, they pump water into and out of their bodies through tiny pores. Some sponges are supported by tough, flexible spongin fibers.

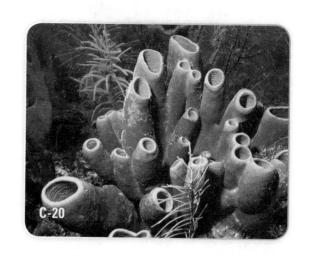

C-20 This sponge is sometimes called the bread crumb sponge. Water is pulled in through tiny pores on its surface and is forced out through larger openings on the top of the sponge.

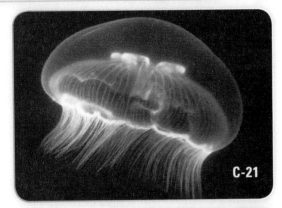

C-21

C-22

C-23

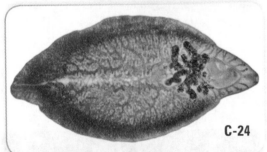

C-24

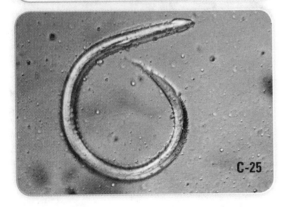

C-25

Phylum Cnidaria (15C)
(nye DAIR ee uh)

Corals, jellyfish, sea anemones

The organisms in phylum Cnidaria all live in water, and most of them live in the ocean. They use stinging cells, called nematocysts, to paralyze their food as they capture it. Cnidarians' bodies are made up of two thin tissue layers separated by a jellylike material. Many cnidarians exhibit radial symmetry.

C-21 The jellyfish is one large cnidarian that floats in the ocean. Its tentacles contain many nematocysts. Some cause painful stings if they come in contact with human skin, but many are harmless.

C-22 Not all coral polyps build up reef material. These corals grow slowly because they do not contain the algal food source found in the reef-building corals.

Phylum Platyhelminthes (15D)
(PLAT ee hel MIN theez)

Flatworms, flukes, planarians, tapeworms

Worms in the phylum Platyhelminthes look like they have been flattened. Flatworms have three tissue layers in their body walls and exhibit bilateral symmetry.

C-23 Some of the most colorful worms are the nonparasitic marine flatworms found in the warm oceans of the world. This species is from Hawaii.

C-24 The sheep liver fluke is a parasite that damages the liver of sheep and, less commonly, humans. Its life cycle involves a period of development inside a snail.

Phylum Nematoda (15E)
(neem uh TOH duh)

Roundworms: hookworms, nematodes, pinworms, trichina worms

The worms in phylum Nematoda have rounded bodies and do not have segments. Most nematodes have a *cuticle*, a tough outer wall that protects them from harmful substances. This is especially important to nematodes that live as parasites inside other organisms.

C-25 This common hookworm leaves the soil to penetrate a human's skin and travels through the circulatory system to the lungs, where it is coughed up and swallowed. When it reaches the intestines, it attaches to the inner wall and feeds on blood.

Phylum Annelida (15F)
(uh NEL ih duh)

Segmented worms: earthworms, featherworms, leeches

The worms in phylum Annelida have rings around their bodies, dividing them into segments. These segments usually look alike and contain many similar structures. Most are free-living, but some are parasites.

C-26 The leech is a segmented worm that sucks blood from other organisms. Some leeches can live for several months on a single meal of blood. Leeches have suckers at both ends of their bodies. One is used to hold on to rocks and organisms; the other is used for both holding on and feeding.

Phylum Mollusca (16A)
(muh LUS kuh)

Phylum Mollusca contains animals with soft bodies that are not divided into segments. Many of these creatures have hard shells. Most shells on the seashore are those of mollusks that have died and left their homes vacant.

Class Cephalopoda (SEF uh LAHP uh duh)

Nautiluses, octopuses, squids

C-27 Octopuses are able to rapidly change the color and pattern of their skin to blend in with their environment. Their suction cups are muscular, not air or water powered.

Class Bivalvia (bye VAL vee uh)

Clams, mussels, oysters, scallops

C-28 Bivalves have shells made of two halves that are joined by a hinge, as represented by this clam. As the soft-bodied clam grows, its hard mineral shell also grows by having new shell material added to its outer edge. A clam gets its nourishment by filtering tiny food particles from the water it pumps through its body.

Class Gastropoda (ga STRAHP uh duh)

Slugs, snails, whelks

C-29 Like many gastropods, the snail has a spiral shell. A snail crawls along on a broad, flat foot. Its head, at the front of its foot, has two eyes, each on the tip of a tentacle. When the snail senses danger, it pulls its soft foot and head entirely into its spiral shell.

C-30

C-31

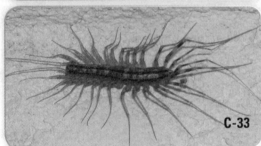

C-32

C-33

C-34

C-35

Phylum Arthropoda (16B)

(ar THRAHP uh duh)

Phylum Arthropoda contains more animals than any other phylum. All arthropods have a hard outer covering called an exoskeleton. In order to grow, arthropods periodically shed their exoskeletons as they form new ones. Arthropods have appendages (legs, antennae, wings, etc.) with joints that enable them to move. The word arthropod means "jointed leg."

Class Crustacea *(kruh STAY shuh)*

Barnacles, crabs, crayfish, lobsters, shrimp

C-30 Most crustaceans, such as this blue crab, live in the water and breathe with gills. If one of a crab's pincers or legs is lost, another one will grow in its place.

Class Insecta *(in SEK tuh)*

Aphids, ants, beetles, butterflies, cockroaches, dragonflies, fleas, flies, grasshoppers, lice, termites

Insects are arthropods that have three pairs of jointed legs when they are adults. Class Insecta is the largest class of animals.

C-31 Some insects are brightly colored, like this peacock butterfly. The eye spots might function to scare away birds.

C-32 Beetles account for forty percent of all insects, making them the largest order in class Insecta. This male stag beetle uses its mandibles in battling other males at mating time.

Class Chilopoda *(KYE LAHP uh duh)*

Centipedes

The centipede's long, flat body is made of many segments, and almost every segment has a single pair of jointed legs.

C-33 This house centipede should be a welcome guest since it eats spiders and small insects, but most homeowners would rather not see them.

Class Diplopoda *(duh PLAH puh duh)*

Millipedes

C-34 Millipedes have two pairs of legs per body segment, giving them even more legs than centipedes have. Because millipedes are primarily scavengers of decaying plant material, they do not kill prey with poison.

Class Arachnida *(uh RAK nud uh)*

Mites, scorpions, spiders, ticks

C-35 Like this golden orb spider, members of class Arachnida all have four pairs of legs and can form silk, though not all spin webs. When an insect is captured, the spider bites it with its poisonous fangs to paralyze it. While most spiders and all scorpions are poisonous, only a few species are potentially deadly to humans.

Phylum Echinodermata (16C)
(ih KYE nuh dur MAH tuh)

Sand dollars, sea urchins, starfish
Echinoderms move along by using tiny *tube feet*. Tube feet work like suction cups on stalks. Members of this phylum are supported by a layer of small, hard plates that have spines extending through the animals' skins. All echinoderms live in the ocean.

C-36 The spines of a sea urchin are moveable and, in some species, poisonous. With all this armor, few organisms attack them. One notable exception, however, is the starfish, which feeds on them.

C-36

Phylum Chordata (17)
(kohr DAH tuh)
Phylum Chordata contains several subphyla. Most of the animals in phylum Chordata belong in subphylum Vertebrata. Subphylum Vertebrata includes the animals that have a backbone to support them. A backbone is a column of vertebrae, usually made of bone. Vertebrates' (VUR tuh brits) bodies are supported by an internal skeleton attached to their vertebral column.

Class Agnatha (AG nuh THUH) (17B)

Hagfish, lampreys

C-37 The hagfish is a jawless fish that lives on the sea floor and scavenges for dead or dying animals.

C-37

Class Chondrichthyes (kahn DRIK thih EEZ) (17B)

Rays, sharks, skates
Class Chondrichthyes contains fish that have skeletons made of a flexible material called cartilage.

C-38 Like this shark, animals in class Chondrichthyes can also be distinguished from other fish by their mouths, which are located on the underside of their bodies.

C-38

Class Osteichthyes (ah stee IK thih EEZ) (17B)

Bass, eels, flounders, piranhas, salmon, sea horses, trout

C-39 The barracuda, like other members of class Osteichthyes, has a bony skeleton and scales. All bony fish have fins and get oxygen from water with gills.

C-39

Class Amphibia (am FIB ee uh) (17C)

Frogs, salamanders, toads
Most amphibians have gills and live in water when they hatch. When they become adults, they breathe air and can live on land.

C-40 Adult frogs live near water all their lives since they must keep their skin moist. In addition to breathing air through their lungs, frogs also obtain oxygen through their thin, moist skin.

C-40

C-41

Class Reptilia (rep TIL ee uh) (17D)

Alligators, crocodiles, lizards, snakes, turtles
Reptiles are animals that have scales and spend their entire lives breathing air. Most reptiles shed their scales periodically as they grow.

C-41 This bearded dragon is native to Australia, where it is one of the most common lizards. It feeds on insects, mice, and smaller lizards. When disturbed, it will inflate a spiny fold of skin under its chin (its "beard") in a threat display.

Class Aves (AY veez) (18B)

Birds

C-42 The hawk uses its long hooked bill and powerful curved claws to capture birds and small mammals. It has light, hollow bones (as all birds do) that enable it to fly. The design of its wings allows the hawk to soar in the air as it searches for food. Hawks live on every continent of the world except Antarctica. No matter what climate a hawk lives in, however, its body temperature remains constant because hawks, like all birds, are endothermic.

Class Mammalia (muh MAYL yuh) (18C)

Bats, beavers, buffalo, camels, cats, elephants, deer, horses, mice, moles, monkeys, opossums, rabbits, rats, seals, whales

C-43 Lions are mammals that eat meat. Their sharp hooked claws, their long canine teeth, and their great strength enable them to spend only two to three hours per day hunting. They spend the rest of their time sleeping and resting.

C-44 Kangaroos are among the most recognizable marsupials. Though they have hair and produce milk like other mammals, they give birth to very underdeveloped offspring and then nourish the offspring in a pouch for an extended period.

C-42

C-43

C-44

MAJOR BIOMES OF THE WORLD

God has designed various areas of the earth to provide different conditions for living things. Thus, one type of organism may thrive in one area but be unable to survive in another area. A biome (BYE ohm) is a large geographical area that contains a particular group of plants and animals and has a specific abiotic environment. An important characteristic of a biome's abiotic environment is the consistency of each of its factors. For example, throughout a biome there will be the same basic temperature, land shape, and soil, as well as the same basic amounts of sunlight and rainfall. Because of the consistency of the environmental factors, the same types of organisms usually exist throughout the biome. Biomes are terrestrial (tuh RES tree ul). This means they are on land. Aquatic ecosystems are usually discussed along with terrestrial biomes but are far more diverse. In fact, because aquatic areas contain such a diverse blend of ecosystems, there are no typical examples.

Terrestrial Biomes

Normally terrestrial biomes spread over large areas of the earth. Ecologists have divided the earth into terrestrial biomes based on climax vegetation. Climax vegetation is the community of plants that grow in an area at the end of succession. (See Facet, pp. 362–63.) In each terrestrial biome these plants are the producer organisms. The kinds of producer organisms in a biome also help to determine which consumer organisms can live in that area.

Although other environmental factors must be considered, a terrestrial biome is usually determined by the interaction of two factors: the amount of rain and the prevailing temperatures. The seasonal temperatures and distribution of rain greatly affect the climax vegetation of an area. Winter rain and summer drought will result in one kind of biotic community, while summer rain and winter drought will result in another.

Aquatic Ecosystems

There are two major types of aquatic ecosystems: freshwater ecosystems and marine (saltwater) ecosystems. Aquatic ecosystems are further divided by depth, current, salinity (salt concentration), and temperature. With the exception of certain marine ecosystems, many common aquatic ecosystems, such as lakes, tidal pools, coral reefs, and swamps, are relatively small. Although they are small, freshwater and marine ecosystems exist abundantly in many different areas of the world.

Many ecologists would agree that the biomes and ecosystems listed on the following pages are correctly classified. However, do not become confused if you see different biomes and ecosystems listed in other books. Some ecologists subdivide the major biomes and ecosystems to include biomes and ecosystems not mentioned in this book.

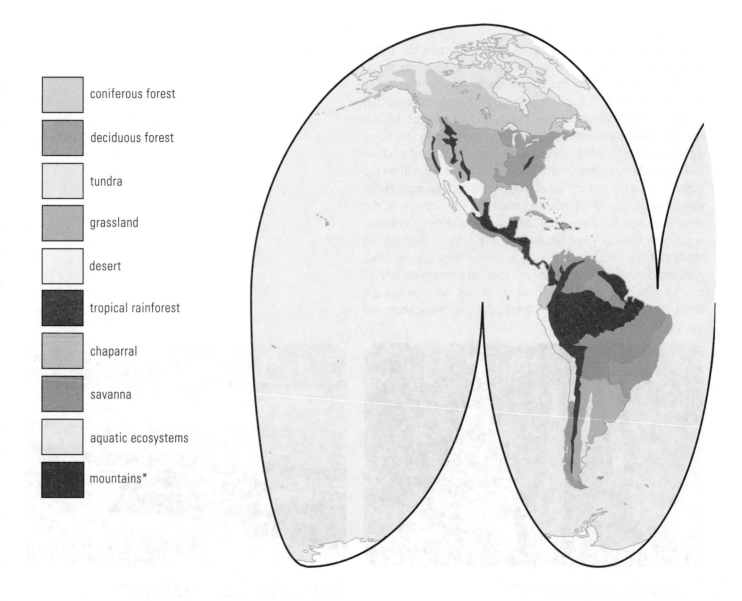

coniferous forest

deciduous forest

tundra

grassland

desert

tropical rainforest

chaparral

savanna

aquatic ecosystems

mountains*

MAJOR BIOMES OF THE WORLD

This map displays the biome locations commonly recognized by ecologists. Of course, the changes in vegetation are rarely as abrupt as the map seems to indicate. The biome regions shown on the map are a synthesis of many sources and reflect that areas sharing a common color have many of the same physical characteristics.

*Several biomes can be represented on one mountain. As you climb a mountain, seasonal temperatures decrease. Thus a mountain often has one type of biome at its base and different biomes as you progress toward the summit.

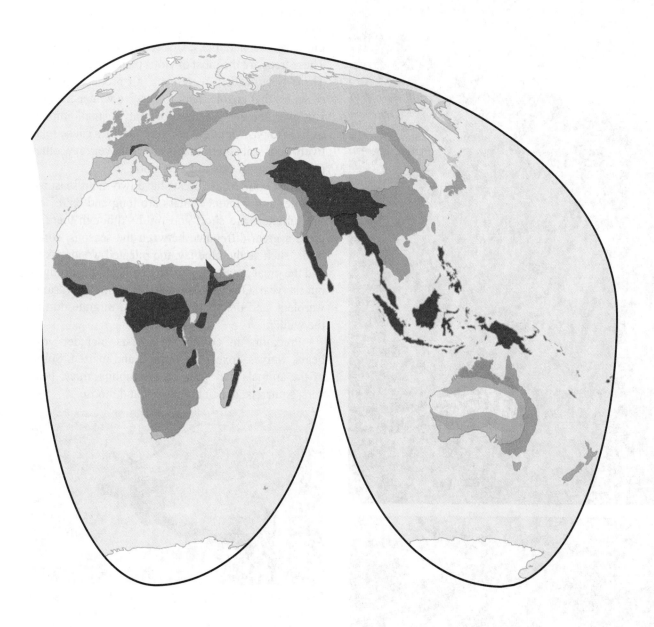

The cougar is common in many coniferous forests of the northern United States, Canada, and Alaska. A very adaptable predator, the cougar also thrives in grasslands, deserts, tropical rainforests, and deciduous forests ranging from the Alaskan tundra to the southern tip of South America.

CONIFEROUS FOREST

Coniferous (ko NIF ur us) forests grow in large areas of North America, Europe, and Asia. *Coniferous* refers to the cone-bearing gymnosperm trees such as pines, cedars, hemlocks, firs, redwoods, and spruces. These trees are the most obvious plants in this biome. These trees, called evergreens, all produce needles or scales that enable them to survive winter freezes. However, the evergreens allow only a small amount of light to pass through, and their needles cause relatively poor soil conditions. As a result, very few other plants can grow on the forest floor.

Most coniferous forests have two main seasons: summer and winter. Winters are long and cold, and the summers are short and mild. Although there is often a great difference between the seasons, some birds, such as the blue jay, the pileated woodpecker, and the great gray owl, remain in this biome throughout the year. Other birds, such as the merlin, various warblers, and the short-tailed hawk, migrate during the winter.

Predators in coniferous forests include lynx, bears, wolves, foxes, wolverines, and marten. Some of the animals they prey on are rabbits, mice, beavers, squirrels, deer, chipmunks, and moose.

The elk is one of the largest herbivores living in coniferous forests. A full-grown bull (male) elk, for example, may weigh 500 kg (1100 lb) and be 1.5 m (5 ft) tall at the shoulders.

Certain mushrooms are more likely to be found in coniferous forests than in other habitats. These decomposers recycle dead organic matter, such as pine needles, into soil components.

DECIDUOUS FOREST

Deciduous (dih SIJ oo us) trees are those that lose their leaves during the nongrowing season. Oaks, elms, maples, sycamores, poplars, willows, cottonwoods, and hickories are all deciduous trees, which are the major plants of the climax vegetation in areas known as deciduous forests. These areas have growing seasons longer than six months, a yearly rainfall of about 100 cm (39 in.) of rain, and summers without long droughts.

Often an area's soil will determine what kind of deciduous trees will grow best. Those trees best suited for the environment will increase in number and eventually determine the kind of deciduous forest in the area.

The leaves of these trees decay to form a rich soil. Good soil with abundant rain during the growing season permits the growth of many ferns, mosses, orchids, lilies, shrubs, and vines on the forest floor.

Some of the common birds in this biome are wood thrushes, woodpeckers, and tufted titmice. Other common animals include deer, which are herbivores, as well as raccoons, bears, and skunks, which are all omnivores. Some of the predators in deciduous forests are bobcats, owls, gray foxes, and wolves.

Some showy orchids grow in the rich soils of deciduous forests.

During autumn the leaves of many deciduous trees turn beautiful colors before they drop from the branches.

Many deciduous trees produce fruits and nuts, which are food sources for squirrels and other animals. Gray squirrels are one kind of tree-dwelling rodent found in deciduous forests.

Most tundra plants, such as this purple saxifrage, grow close to the ground where the temperature is more moderate. Colorful leaves also help them to absorb more heat. The period for flowering is short, but blossoms are abundant.

TUNDRA

Although the tundra remains frozen during most of the year, for about two months the first few centimeters of ground thaw out. Below this surface layer is a layer called the *permafrost*, which never thaws. Because water cannot penetrate the permafrost, the melting snow forms many bogs, lakes, and streams during the short, warm season. Mosses, lichens, grasses, and dwarf woody plants make up most of the climax vegetation of the tundra. Trees are not found there because the permafrost and limited precipitation limit root growth.

There are two main types of tundra: arctic tundra and alpine tundra. The arctic tundra is found in the extreme north. The alpine tundra is found on or near the tops of high mountains.

During the warm season many insects live in the tundra. Most of these insects lay eggs that are resistant to the freezing winter temperatures. Then when the ground thaws the following year, the eggs hatch. Also during the warm season, many birds migrate to the tundra and build nests. The tundra provides a good environment for the birds since there are few predators and the abundance of insects makes it easy for them to obtain food. Most birds leave the tundra before the snow returns. Some common tundra mammals are musk oxen, caribou, arctic foxes, and small rodents.

The ptarmigan is a permanent resident of the tundra. In the snowy winter, its feathers are usually all white. During its short breeding period, it molts the white feathers to put on better camouflage for the rocky, exposed ground where it nests.

With their dense, shaggy coats, musk oxen are ideally suited for the winter extremes on the tundra.

GRASSLAND

Grasslands usually occur in areas where there is not enough rainfall to support a forest. Although some grassland areas may receive enough rain to become a forest, fires during the dry season prevent this from happening. Many grasslands receive 25–75 cm (10–30 in.) of rain each year. The amount of rain in an area determines which grasses will grow. Less rain usually permits only the shorter species of grasses to grow.

Because of their deep, fertile soils, grasslands serve man as natural pastures or as areas for growing grain crops. Since the interiors of several continents contain grasslands, much farming takes place in these areas.

Herds of large herbivores often live on grasslands. In North America the bison (buffalo) once formed large herds that extended as far as the eye could see. Antelope, wild horses, and donkeys inhabit grasslands in other areas of the world.

Burrowing rodents such as prairie dogs, gophers, and ground squirrels often form large colonies on grasslands. Predators such as coyotes, kit foxes, badgers, ferrets, and hawks help to control the size of these rodent populations. Some of the birds that live on grasslands include prairie chickens, meadowlarks, and horned larks. Snakes and lizards prey on the abundant rodents and insects.

The American badger is a predatory "digging machine" that feeds on prairie dogs, ground squirrels, and other rodents of the plains.

Guanacos, the wild ancestors of llamas, are native to the grasslands of South America.

Some grasslands have large swift-running birds, such as this emu found in Australia. The rhea of South America and the ostrich of Africa also live in grasslands.

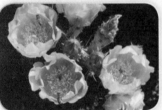

Cactus flowers bloom for a short time compared to other plants. This short blooming period keeps the cactus from losing too much water through its flowers.

DESERT

Water is the limiting factor in deserts. A desert receives a scant 25 cm (10 in.) or less of rainfall per year. The lack of rainfall decreases the number of organisms that can survive in this biome. Some desert areas, such as the middle of the Sahara Desert, receive no rain and therefore have almost no biotic community. Not all deserts are hot, though. Asia, North America, South America, and Africa all have cold deserts that receive most of their precipitation in the form of snow.

The ability to survive long periods of time with little water is the outstanding characteristic of most desert organisms. Many of the plants that can survive the harsh desert environment are succulents such as cacti. *Succulents* store water in thick stems or leaves. Their thick, tough coverings and spines help to protect the plants from water loss and from damage caused by browsing animals.

During the morning, late afternoon, and night, the desert is cooler, and most desert animals are active. However, during the heat of the day, the animals become inactive as they rest in their burrows or under rocks. The bodies of desert animals are specially designed to deal with extremes in temperature.

In the desert there are many reptiles, insects, and spiders. Those organisms can survive on the fluid they get from the plants or animals they eat. Only a few mammals, such as the kangaroo rat and the jerboa, can survive on the moisture they receive from the food they eat. Most desert birds, such as vultures and screech owls, fly to other areas for water.

Sand dunes, hills formed of wind-deposited sand, usually occur in groups called dune fields. Though dunes may appear lifeless, certain organisms burrow beneath the surface, emerging at night. Dunes usually form in deserts but may also be found in other places, such as near seashores.

In the hot summer months, the western diamondback rattlesnake, an effective predator of rodents and birds, is active during the cooler night-time hours.

TROPICAL RAINFOREST

Most tropical rainforests are near the equator and thus are quite warm year-round. Rainforests often have a greater difference between their nighttime and daytime temperatures than between their seasonal temperatures.

The average annual rainfall in a tropical rainforest exceeds 230 cm (90 in.), but some rainforests receive twice this amount. During the rainy season the forest usually receives some rain every day. However, during the dry season rain may fall only once a week or, in some areas, only once a month.

There are four basic layers of plant growth in most tropical rainforests. The first layer is made up of tall trees that grow far above the rest of the forest. These trees form the *emergent layer*. The next layer is made up of trees about 24–30 m (79–98 ft) tall. The leaves on these trees form a dense *canopy layer* high above the ground. The branches of the canopy trees are often covered with epiphytes, plants that attach to other plants. The next level is the *understory*, which includes small trees, bushes, and large-leafed plants that can survive in the shady conditions beneath the canopy. The *forest floor* is the bottom level. Though very few plants are considered to be part of this level, fungi and bacteria are abundant as they help to decompose the fallen plant and animal material.

In some tropical rainforests, the understory exists only in areas in which there are breaks in the canopy and sunlight can reach the forest floor. Because of the scarce sunlight, rainforests often have vines that have their roots in the soil but have their leaves in the canopy.

Most animals in tropical rainforests live in trees. For example, primates (monkeys, lemurs, and apes) are tree-dwelling mammals. Other common rainforest mammals include sloths, bats, and jaguars. Tree snakes, geckos, iguanas, and chameleons are common tropical rainforest reptiles that also live in trees. Some of the birds that live in this biome are toucans, hornbills, and parrots. Besides these organisms, the rainforest also contains a large number of different kinds of insects.

The toucan lives in dense tropical forests of America. Although its large beak makes the toucan appear top-heavy, the beak is actually very light because it contains air spaces.

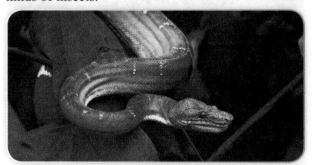

The green tree python of Asia, a nonpoisonous snake, suffocates its prey by coiling its body tightly around its victim.

Although epiphytes commonly grow in rainforests, these plants are actually designed to conserve water since their location is comparatively dry when it is not raining.

CHAPARRAL

Chaparrals (SHAP uh RALZ) usually have mild year-round temperatures, dry summers, and wet winters. Some chaparrals never have frosts and are therefore excellent areas for orchards. Farmers use much of America's western chaparral to grow citrus fruits.

The chaparral's climax vegetation consists of a few trees and many shrubs with hard, thick evergreen leaves. An important environmental factor to all the vegetation in a chaparral is fire. Often, during the dry summers, fire destroys much of the lower plant growth, clearing the ground for new plants. The trees in the area receive only minor damage from the fire.

There are several strategies that animals use to respond to the seasonal changes in a chaparral. One way many birds and larger mammals respond is by migration. During the winter, when food is more abundant, these animals live in the chaparral. Then later during the summer when food is scarce, the animals leave. Some amphibians and smaller mammals (rodents and rabbits) do not migrate but become less active during the dry season. Most reptiles, being less affected by the changes in moisture and food availability, can remain active all year long.

Much of the area around the Mediterranean Sea is chaparral. Since this region is the geographical setting of much of the Bible, many of the plants and animals referred to in Scripture normally live in a chaparral. The psalmist, for example, speaks in Psalm 1:3 of the abundant growth of a "tree planted by the rivers of water." Usually the largest trees on a chaparral are those that live by a river. The river provides a year-round supply of water, allowing the trees to grow even during the dry summer months.

The horned lizard is named for the spines on its head. It dines on insects, especially ants, which are abundant in the chaparral.

Jackrabbits spend the hot daylight hours beneath bushes, coming out to feed only at night. Coyotes, a common predator of jackrabbits, are also nocturnal.

The mule deer is one of the American chaparral's winter residents. During the hot dry summers, the mule deer migrates north to higher, cooler areas. It is named for its large ears, which resemble a mule's.

SAVANNA

Widely spaced trees with grasses and shrubs between typify a savanna (suh VAN uh). A savanna receives 100–150 cm (39–59 in.) of rainfall per year, but most of the rain comes during a wet season. During the wet season, the grasses and scattered trees thrive. In the prolonged dry season, however, the tops of the grasses often dry out and die and the trees and shrubs shed their leaves.

Occasionally some of the dry grass and dead leaves catch fire. The fire usually does not damage the mature trees or the grass roots deep in the ground, but it does destroy the shrubs. The fire also affects the savanna's animal population. Most of the large animals can escape the fire, but it usually traps many of the small animals and insects and kills them.

Although fire is an important factor on the savanna, climate is also important. The climate sometimes affects the types of animals that can live on the savanna. For instance, insects are more abundant during the wet season, but reptiles are more abundant during the dry season.

The climate also affects the living habits of the animals. During the dry season, the smaller streams and pools on the savanna dry up. To obtain water, large grazing animals such as antelope, wildebeests, and giraffes must stay near lakes or large water holes. Lions, leopards, and other predators also stay near water, where they watch and wait for easy prey.

The cape buffalo may look like a long-horned cow, but it is one of Africa's deadliest creatures. It is aggressive and not afraid to charge if it feels threatened.

Even though they are the top predators of the African savanna, lions do not necessarily have a safe or easy life. Males frequently battle each other for control of a pride, hyenas will attack lions, and large prey can injure them as well.

Although they can fly, hornbills spend most of their time walking and running along the ground where they feed on insects, amphibians, reptiles, and even small mammals.

The American alligator is an example of a transient aquatic animal. Although able to live on land, the alligator spends much of its time in the water and normally catches and eats its prey there.

Whirligig beetles are nekton organisms that usually swim in small groups on the surface of ponds and slow streams. The beetle beats its back legs sixty times a second to propel itself across or through the water.

FRESHWATER ECOSYSTEMS

Ecologists separate the many different freshwater ecosystems into two main categories—those ecosystems that have *standing water* (lakes, ponds, swamps, and bogs) and those ecosystems that have *running water* (streams and rivers). The differences between the two types of ecosystems are so great that many organisms living in one could not survive in the other.

There are four environmental factors that further separate one freshwater ecosystem from another. The water's temperature, transparency, concentration of dissolved gases such as oxygen and carbon dioxide, and concentration of minerals determine which organisms can live in each ecosystem.

There are several different types of populations in a freshwater ecosystem. Frequently, these populations are grouped as follows:

- *Benthos* (BEN THAHS) *organisms* rest on or attach to the bottom of a pond or lake. Worms, clams, and snails are common benthos organisms.

- *Plankton* (PLANGK tun) *organisms* float more or less with the current. Common plankton organisms include tiny algae, protozoans, larval stages of many insects, and other organisms.

- *Nekton* (NEK tun) *organisms* are able to swim and navigate at will. Fish, large swimming insects, newts, and some turtles are nekton organisms.

- *Transient animals* are animals that spend only a part of their time in an aquatic ecosystem but are in some way dependent on it. Aquatic birds, such as ducks and cranes, and many amphibians, such as frogs and toads, are transient animals.

Water lilies are anchored in the mud beneath standing or slow-moving bodies of water by thick underground stems called *rhizomes*. New plants come from seeds or from the spreading of these rhizomes.

MARINE ECOSYSTEMS

About 70% of the earth's surface is covered with marine (saltwater) ecosystems. In the ocean, living things can be found from the shoreline to the extreme depths of its trenches (over 7 mi beneath the surface).

Different areas of the ocean have their own abiotic environments and biotic communities. The *intertidal zone* is covered with water during high tide and is exposed to the air during low tide. The algae, plants, and animals of intertidal zones have characteristics that suit them to this alternating environment.

Surrounding each continent is a *continental shelf.* Along these shelves the ocean is only about 1000 m (0.6 mi) deep. This area is often called the *coastal ocean.* The waters along the continental shelves usually have an abundance of organisms. Most commercial fishing for lobster, shrimp, flounder, cod, herring, and other marine products is done along the continental shelves in the coastal ocean.

Light penetrates only a short distance into ocean water. Photosynthetic plankton (mostly algae), which live near the surface, serve as the producers in most marine food chains. Even large marine predators, such as sharks and whales, are dependent on photosynthetic plankton as their primary energy source.

In the great depths of the *open ocean*, the area beyond the continental shelf, live various kinds of detritus feeders and predators. Many organisms, such as sponges, fan worms, and crinoids, live on the bottom of the ocean and filter microscopic debris from the ocean water. Others, such as the brittle stars, are detritus feeders that eat the dead organisms that fall from the upper ocean.

The Nassau grouper is one of the largest predatory reef fish in the Caribbean, sometimes reaching a length of 1.2 m (4 ft). It is a camouflage artist, quickly changing its color and patterns to disguise itself as it watches for prey.

The banded coral shrimp waves its long antennae to attract the attention of fish. The fish do not eat it but rather will wait their turn to be cleaned of parasites by this cleaner shrimp.

Sea turtles, such as this loggerhead, spend their entire lives in the water, coming ashore only to bury their eggs in the sand. Many will migrate thousands of miles in the course of a year.

GLOSSARY

Note: The number in parentheses indicates the chapter where the term is introduced.

A

abiotic environment (21) The non-living parts of an ecosystem.

abortion (7) The killing of an unborn baby.

absorption (26) The movement of digested food from the digestive tract into the body (usually into the bloodstream) of an organism.

accessory organ (26) An organ that secretes substances that are carried through ducts into the alimentary canal.

acne (27) A disease of the skin that is marked by excessive pimples.

active transport (4) The passage of particles through a membrane, requiring the use of cellular energy.

adrenal gland (27) An endocrine gland located on each kidney; secretes epinephrine (adrenaline) and other hormones.

adrenaline (27) See **epinephrine**.

aerobic (5) Refers to processes requiring oxygen.

aerobic cellular respiration (5) The process by which cells use oxygen to obtain usable energy from an energy source.

agriculture (23) The growing of crops and livestock.

air pollution (23) A combination of liquids, gases, and small particles that are released into the atmosphere, resulting in harm to the environment.

albinism (8) A condition in which an organism is unable to produce certain pigments, especially noticeable in the cells of the skin, hair, and iris of the eyes.

albumen (20) The white of an egg.

alcoholic fermentation (5) Anaerobic cellular respiration that produces alcohol and carbon dioxide from glucose.

algae (11) The more plantlike organisms in kingdom Protista; usually can perform photosynthesis and are unable to move themselves.

alimentary canal (26) The digestive tract.

allergy (25) The overreaction of the immune system to a foreign substance that is normally not a pathogen.

alveoli (sing., **alveolus**) (26) The microscopic sacs in which the exchange of gases takes place in the lungs.

amino acid (3) A type of organic compound that combines to form proteins.

amnion (7) A membranous sac around an embryo.

amniotic fluid (7) The fluid that fills the amnion; cushions the developing embryo and protects it from harmful chemicals.

amoeboid movement (11) Movement of a cell by the formation of pseudopodia.

anaerobic cellular respiration (5) The process by which cells obtain energy from an energy source without using oxygen.

analyze (7) To determine whether a set of data supports a hypothesis.

anaphase (6) The third phase of mitosis; during this phase the daughter chromosomes move to opposite ends of the spindle.

anatomy (12) The bodily structure of an organism.

anemia (25) A condition in which the blood does not carry enough oxygen.

angiosperm (12) A plant that produces flowers (and thus fruit and seed), e.g., a nectarine tree, rice, or a violet.

animal society (22) A group of animals of the same species that live together.

annual growth ring (12) The layer of springwood and summerwood produced each year in the stem of a woody plant.

annual plant (21) A plant species that survives the dormant season as seeds; mature plants live for less than a year.

anther (14) The saclike structure that forms part of the stamen and produces pollen.

antibody (25) A protein the body produces to attack or mark for attack invading materials such as bacteria and viruses.

antigen (25) The molecules that the macrophages recognize as not belonging in the body, triggering the immune system.

anus (17) The opening at the end of the alimentary canal through which undigested food and wastes are expelled from the body.

aorta (25) The largest artery in the body; carries blood from the heart to smaller arteries.

aortic arches (15) Organs that help to control blood pressure in earthworms.

aquatic ecosystem (21) An ecosystem that has large amounts of water in it; a lake, river, or swamp.

aqueous humor (27) A clear fluid that fills the chamber between the cornea and the lens of the eye.

arrhythmia (25) An irregular heartbeat.

artery (16) A blood vessel that carries blood away from the heart.

asexual reproduction (6) The production of a new organism without the joining of gametes; reproduction that takes place by mitotic cell division.

assimilation (26) The process by which living cells convert nutrients into cellular structures.

atrioventricular valve (**AV valve**) (25) A one-way valve that separates the atrium from the ventricle in the heart and prevents a backflow of blood into the atrium.

atrium (25) An upper heart chamber that receives blood from the lungs or body.

autoimmune disease (25) A disease in which a person's immune system attacks and destroys his own cells.

autotransfusion (25) When a person receives his own blood during surgery; the blood may be donated and stored prior to surgery or collected, filtered, cleaned, and replaced into the patient's own bloodstream during surgery.

auxin (13) A plant hormone that stimulates cell elongation, among other effects.

axon (27) A part of a neuron that carries impulses away from the cell body.

B

background research (1) Finding out what is already known about a topic; part of the scientific method; used when establishing a problem for study.

ball-and-socket joint (24) The type of joint that allows movement in several directions.

bark (12) The outer covering of woody plant parts.

basal metabolic rate (26) The rate at which an organism uses energy while inactive.

biblical Creationism (9) The belief in the account of Creation in the Bible.

biblical kind (2) The grouping of organisms, established by God, that are able to breed among themselves and produce offspring (Gen. 1:11, 21, 24).

bilateral symmetry (15) A type of symmetry in which there are two equal sides to an animal; only one plane can divide it into equal halves.

bile (26) A substance secreted by the liver; helps to separate lipids into small droplets to aid digestion.

biodegradable pollutant (23) A pollutant that is capable of being broken down by the environment.

biological evolution (**organic evolution**) (10) The supposed gradual change of one kind of organism into another kind of organism; occurs over many generations.

biomass (22) The mass of living material produced by a given area.

biotic community (21) All the living organisms in an ecosystem.

birthrate (23) The rate at which members are born into a population.

bivalve (16) A mollusk having two shells that are hinged together, e.g., a clam or scallop.

blade (12) The typically flat, green portion of a leaf.

blister (24) A water-filled swelling of the epidermis of the skin.

blood (16) The fluid tissue that moves through the bodies of certain organisms, carrying substances to and from cells.

blood clot (25) A collection of blood cells and fibers normally formed to prevent bleeding.

blood plasma (25) The fluid portion of the blood.

blood pressure (25) The pressure of the blood against the walls of the arteries.

bone (17) The strong supporting structure of vertebrates.

bone marrow (24) A soft tissue that produces blood cells; located in the marrow cavity of long bones and in the spaces of spongy bones.

brain (17) An organ that coordinates the bodily functions; made of nerve tissue.

brain stem (27) A part of the brain that controls involuntary actions.

breathing (26) Moving air into and out of the lungs.

breed (8) A group of organisms that is purebred for certain characteristics.

bronchi (sing., **bronchus**) (26) The two branches of the trachea; function in carrying air to and from the lungs.

bronchiole (26) One of many tiny branches from the bronchi; carries air to and from alveoli within the lung.

bryophyte (12) One group of nonvascular plants that live on land, e.g., mosses.

budding (6) Asexual reproduction in which a portion of the parent separates to form a new organism.

C

callus (24) An area of skin with a thickened epidermis.

calorie (26) A unit used to indicate the amount of energy released from food during cellular respiration.

camouflage (22) A coloration or pattern that blends with the surroundings.

canine (18) A pointed tooth generally used for tearing.

capillary (15) One of many small blood vessels that have walls that are one cell thick; materials are exchanged between the blood and other body tissues in the capillaries.

carbohydrate (3) A substance that contains only carbon, hydrogen, and oxygen, e.g., sugar or starch.

carbon cycle (21) The exchange of carbon between organisms carrying on photosynthesis and those carrying on cellular respiration; functions in relationship with the oxygen cycle.

cardiac muscle (24) A kind of striated involuntary muscle that is found in the heart.

carnivore (22) An organism that eats only animals.

carotene (24) A yellow or orange pigment.

carrier (7) An individual that possesses a gene for a specific trait, even if he does not exhibit that trait.

cartilage (17) A flexible supporting tissue that makes up part or all of some animals' skeletons.

castings (15) An earthworm's digestive wastes, which are sometimes piled outside the earthworm's tunnel.

catalyst (5) A substance that affects the rate of a reaction but is not changed in the reaction.

cataract (27) A condition in which the lens of the eye does not allow light to pass through it clearly; often due to accumulated substances in the lens.

caterpillar (16) The larva of a moth or butterfly.

cell (3) The tiny, living, structural, and functional unit of all living things; the smallest unit that can be alive.

cell body (27) Part of a neuron; contains cytoplasm, organelles, and the nucleus.

cell division (6) The division of one cell into two cells; includes mitosis and cytokinesis.

cell membrane (4) The membrane that surrounds all the cytoplasm of a cell.

cell theory (3) The theory that all living things are made up of microscopic units called cells and that cells carry on the functions of living things.

cellular respiration (5) The process by which cells obtain usable energy from energy sources.

cellulose (3) A long molecule made up of many sugar molecules bonded end to end; a key component in the cell walls of plants.

cell wall (4) A rigid structure manufactured by certain organisms and secreted to the exterior of the cell membrane; plants, fungi, and bacteria have cell walls.

central nervous system (17) The part of the nervous system consisting of the brain and spinal cord.

central vacuole (5) The large vacuole located in the middle of a plant cell and certain other cells; collects and holds water.

cerebellum (27) The part of the brain that monitors and adjusts body activity involving muscle tone, body posture, and balance.

cerebral cortex (27) The outer layer of the cerebrum; has many wrinkles and folds in its surface.

cerebrum (27) The part of the brain containing the major motor and sensory centers; controls voluntary muscle activity and is the area of conscious thought.

chemical digestion (26) Chemically breaking down food into substances that the body can use.

chlorophyll (5) The green pigment that aids in capturing light energy necessary for photosynthesis.

chloroplast (4) A cellular organelle that contains chlorophyll and other pigments; the organelle in which photosynthesis occurs.

choroid (27) The middle layer of the eyeball.

Christian worldview (1) A Christian perspective of the world, based on the Bible; usually organized in terms of Creation, Fall, and Redemption.

chromosomal change (8) A change involving the number of chromosomes or the number or location of genes in a chromosome.

chromosome (4) A strand of DNA with associated proteins; usually found in the nucleus of a cell; the basis of heredity.

chromosome number (7) The number of chromosomes normally found in each cell of an organism.

chrysalis (16) The pupa stage of a butterfly.

chyme (26) The semiliquid mixture of digestive juices and partly digested food in the stomach and small intestine.

cilia (4) Short hairlike extensions from a cell membrane; aid in movement.

circadian rhythm (21) A regular fluctuation in a living organism that repeats on a 24-hour cycle.

circulatory system (15) In vertebrates, it is a system composed of the heart, blood vessels, and blood; transports substances to and from cells.

class (2) In the modern classification system, a subdivision of a phylum; includes one or more orders of organisms.

classify (1) To arrange experimental data so that relationships can be seen; (2) to assign or arrange organisms in a particular group.

climax community (21) The final, relatively stable community in the succession of organisms in an area.

clone (8) A population of organisms with identical genes and produced by the asexual reproduction of an individual; the process of producing such organisms.

closed circulatory system (15) A type of circulation in which the blood remains in vessels.

cochlea (27) A coiled, tubular structure in the inner ear; contains fluid and the neurons that sense sound waves.

cocoon (16) The pupa stage of a moth; the covering spun by a moth caterpillar.

codominance (7) A type of inheritance pattern where the dominant and recessive traits are both expressed.

codon (6) A sequence of three nucleotides in a DNA molecule; each codon identifies an amino acid to be used in the protein coded by the DNA.

colonial organism (3) A living thing that is composed of a group of similar cells living together; each cell is capable of living individually.

colony (11) See **colonial organism**; (22) a group of social animals, such as insects, living together.

colorblindness (27) A vision defect in which one cannot tell the difference between colors; caused by certain types of cones in the retina not working properly.

commensalism (22) A relationship in which one organism benefits and the other one is not helped or harmed.

common ancestor (10) An organism from which evolutionists claim different groups of organisms have evolved or descended.

competition (22) The struggle among organisms for an essential factor that is in short supply in the environment.

complete metamorphosis (16) Insect metamorphosis that consists of four stages: egg, larva, pupa, and adult.

compound eye (16) Eye having many small lenses; provides a mosaic of images rather than a single image; found in insects.

compound leaf (12) A leaf in which the blade is divided into two or more smaller leaflets.

compound light microscope (4) A microscope with two sets of lenses to magnify the light from a specimen.

cone (27) A type of neuron in the retina that is sensitive to colors of light.

conjugation (11) The union of two organisms or cells for the purpose of exchanging portions of their genetic material; occurs in many unicellular and colonial organisms.

conservation (23) The preservation and wise use of natural resources.

consumer organism (consumer) (21) An organism that uses food manufactured by other organisms.

contour feather (18) The longer type of bird feathers; covers and helps insulate the bird, gives it a stream-lined shape, and repels water.

contractile vacuole (4) A structure that collects water from the cytoplasm and passes it to the outside of the cell; found in unicellular organisms.

control group (1) The group in an experiment that is not exposed to the experimental variable.

cork (12) Tough, thick-walled, waterproof cells forming the outer layer of bark in woody plant stems.

cork cambium (12) A layer of living cells just under the dead cork; constantly divides, producing new cork cells.

cornea (27) The clear front portion of the sclera of the eye.

coronary artery (25) A blood vessel that supplies blood to the heart muscle.

cotyledon (14) The source of food in a seed that aids growth; sometimes called a seed leaf.

cranial nerves (17) Nerves that branch from the brain to various structures of the head, neck, and internal organs.

Creation week (9) The seven days described in the first chapter of Genesis.

crop (15) An enlarged section of the digestive tract of some animals; temporarily stores food.

crop rotation (23) Periodically changing the crops grown in a field to prevent the depletion of soil minerals.

crosier (12) A coiled young fern frond.

cross (7) The process of mating organisms to test how they inherit traits; the offspring produced by such a mating.

crossbreeding (8) Breeding animals from different varieties to produce a breed with traits of both parents.

cuticle (12) In plants, a noncellular protective covering of leaves and young stems; (15) in certain animals, a noncellular protective covering.

cytokinesis (6) The division of the cytoplasm during the process of cell division.

cytoplasm (3) All the material, except the nucleus, inside a cell.

cytoplasmic organelle (4) A structure in the cytoplasm; organelles perform various cellular functions.

D

data (1) Recorded information from an experiment or survey.

day-age theory (9) See **long-day theory**.

day-neutral plants (13) Plants that bloom whenever conditions such as moisture and temperature are acceptable, regardless of the length of light or dark periods.

death rate (23) The rate at which members of a population die.

decomposer organism (decomposer) (22) An organism that breaks down dead organisms and returns this material to the soil.

degeneration (8) The principle that all things tend to become disordered or are running down.

dendrite (27) The part of the neuron that carries nerve impulses toward the cell body.

deoxygenated blood (17) Blood that contains little oxygen.

deoxyribonucleic acid (6) See **DNA**.

dermis (24) The thick inner layer of the skin.

detritus food chain (11) A food chain beginning with dead organisms being eaten by consumer organisms instead of being decomposed by decomposer organisms.

diabetes mellitus (5) A disease caused by a lack of insulin in the blood; causes excess sugars to be excreted in the urine.

dialysis machine (25) An artificial kidney.

diaphragm (4) The microscope part that regulates the amount of light that passes through the specimen; (17) the muscle that separates the thorax from the abdomen in mammals and humans; aids breathing.

diffusion (4) The movement of molecules from an area of higher concentration to an area of lower concentration; a form of passive transport.

digestion (26) The breaking of food into smaller substances that the body's cells can use.

digestive system (26) A group of tissues and organs that work together to digest an organism's food.

dinosaur (9) An extinct reptile of the order Saurischia or Ornithischia.

diploid (8) Having one pair of each type of chromosome in an organism.

diurnal (21) Active during the day.

division (2) In the modern classification system, a subdivision of any of the nonplant kingdoms; includes one or more classes of organisms.

division of labor (5) The condition in which certain organs and tissues of multicellular organisms perform specialized functions that are not being performed by other tissues and organs.

DNA (deoxyribonucleic acid) (6) The nucleic acid that carries genetic information; usually found in the nucleus.

domesticated organism (23) A living thing that man raises primarily for his own use.

dominant (7) Refers to the characteristic that is expressed, even when a recessive gene is present.

Dominion Mandate (1) The charge that God gave to humans in Genesis 1:28 to exercise dominion, or stewardship, over the earth.

dormant bud (21) The tissues of a new stem and leaves or flower that are covered by scales during a period when there is no growth.

down feather (18) A short fluffy feather next to a bird's skin that insulates the bird by holding warm air close to its body.

drone (16) A male bee, whose only function in life is to fertilize the queen.

duct (26) A tube through which a substance passes; a tube connecting accessory organs to the alimentary canal.

E

eardrum (27) A membrane over the opening to the middle ear; vibrates when sound waves enter the ear.

echinoderm (16) A spiny-skinned invertebrate that lives in the ocean, e.g., a starfish, sea urchin, or sand dollar.

ecological pyramid (22) An illustration shaped like a pyramid and divided into layers to show the energy relationships between organisms in an ecosystem.

ecologist (21) A scientist who studies organisms and the relationships between organisms and their physical environments.

ecology (21) The study of the relationships between organisms and their physical environments.

ecosystem (21) A limited area in which living and nonliving things interact.

ectothermic (17) Refers to animals that cannot control their body temperatures by internal means; cold-blooded.

egg (20) A zygote surrounded by a protective shell; the gamete formed by a female, usually unable to move by itself and larger than the male gametes of the same species.

embryo (12) In plants, the immature plant within a seed; (20) in animals, the young before hatching or birth; the stage during which organs and systems are developing.

endangered species (23) A species that may soon become extinct.

endocrine system (27) A system of hormone-producing glands.

endoplasmic reticulum (4) A cellular organelle consisting of a network of membranes; enables substances to be transported throughout the cell.

endoskeleton (17) An internal skeleton; usually made of cartilage and bone.

endothermic (18) Refers to animals that can control their body temperatures by internal means; warm-blooded.

energy (3) The ability to do work.

energy pollutant (23) Any energy that pollutes an ecosystem.

enzyme (3) A protein that serves as a catalyst for a cellular reaction.

epidermis (12) A tissue that serves as a protective covering layer in plants; (24) the outer layer of tissue in humans and many animals.

epiglottis (26) A thin flexible flap in front of the larynx; folds over and blocks the glottis during swallowing.

epinephrine (27) A hormone secreted by the adrenal glands; stimulates the body to prepare for an emergency; sometimes called *adrenaline*.

epiphyte (22) A plant that grows on the outside of another plant but does not take nourishment from the plant on which it grows.

erythrocyte (25) A red blood cell; functions primarily to transport oxygen.

esophagus (26) A part of the digestive tract; connects the pharynx and stomach in humans.

estivation (17) A dormant state involving a slowing of life processes that permits certain animals to survive during hot, dry weather.

eukaryote (4) A unicellular or multicellular organism whose cell or cells have a nucleus and other membrane-bound organelles.

eustachian tube (27) A tube leading from the pharynx to the middle ear; equalizes air pressure in the ear.

euthanasia (23) The killing of a person who is old or very sick.

evaporation (21) The movement of water into the atmosphere by changing from a liquid into a vapor.

evolution (10) A process in which gradual changes cause something to improve or to become more complex. (See also **theory of evolution**.)

evolutionary family tree (10) A diagram demonstrating the supposed stages of biological evolution.

evolutionism (9) The belief that the physical universe, including life, was not created but happened by chance.

excretory system (17) The structures or organs that filter wastes out of the body.

excretory tubule (16) A threadlike tube that extracts wastes from an insect's blood and empties them into the intestine.

exhale (26) To force air out of the lungs; to breathe out.

exoskeleton (16) An external skeleton composed of tough plates that protect and support an animal.

experiment (1) A situation or process designed and controlled by a person for the purpose of gaining data about a particular problem; tests a particular hypothesis.

experimental group (1) The group that receives the experimental variable; sometimes called the experimental factor.

experimental variable (1) The factor or condition being tested in an experiment.

external fertilization (20) The uniting of a sperm and ovum outside the parent organisms' bodies.

external parasite (22) An organism that obtains nourishment from and lives on the outer surface of another organism.

extinct (23) Refers to species that are no longer existing.

eyepiece (4) The part of a light microscope that contains the lenses that are closest to the viewer; the ocular.

F

factor (7) The term Mendel used for what is now known as a **gene**.

family (2) A subdivision of an order; includes one or more genera of organisms.

farming (23) The growing of organisms to supply human needs.

farsightedness (27) A vision defect in which only distant objects can be focused clearly; usually caused by an eyeball that is too short from front to back.

feces (26) The solid waste material of an organism.

fertilization (20) The formation of a zygote from the union of two gametes.

fertilizer (23) A substance containing minerals needed by plants.

fiber (12) Long thick-walled cells that function to support a plant.

fibrillation (25) An arrhythmia in which the heart quivers vigorously but does not pump blood.

fibrous root system (12) A type of root system having a cluster of roots that are about equal in size.

fiddlehead (12) See **crosier**.

filament (14) The stalk of the stamen.

filter feeder (15) An organism that obtains food from water circulating through its body.

final answer (1) An answer that is absolutely true and therefore never needs to be rejected, revised, or corrected.

flagella (sing., **flagellum**) (4) Long hairlike extensions from a cell membrane; aid in movement.

flame cell (15) A part of a planarian's excretory system.

flower (14) The sexual reproductive organ of angiosperm plants; contains structures that make the male and female gametes.

fluid mosaic model (4) A model of cell membranes in which the lipid membrane consists of a flexible (fluid) two-layer film where proteins float and move about, making different patterns (mosaics).

food chain (22) The passing of materials and energy from one organism to another.

food vacuole (11) A membrane-bound sac that contains food within a cell; formed as the cell membrane invaginates toward the inside of the cell and pinches off.

food web (22) A method of illustrating the interrelationships between food chains in an ecosystem.

fossil (9) Any evidence or remains of an organism preserved by natural means.

fossil fuel (23) An energy source that is the product of plants and animals that once lived on the earth.

fossil record (10) Historical evidence supplied by fossils.

fracture (24) A break in a bone.

fragmentation (11) Asexual reproduction caused by the breaking of a colonial organism by a physical disturbance.

fraternal twins (8) Twins that are the result of two sperm and two ova uniting separately; they do not have the same genetic makeup.

free living (15) Refers to organisms that are neither parasitic nor symbiotic.

frond (12) A fern leaf.

fruit (14) The ripened ovary of a flower.

fungus (11) An organism that produces spores, lacks chlorophyll, has cell walls, and obtains nourishment by absorption.

fur (18) A thick coat of hair; found on some mammals.

fused joint (24) The type of joint that does not allow any movement.

G

gallbladder (17) The sac underneath the liver; stores bile.

game laws (23) Laws that regulate hunting, fishing, and trapping activities by imposing seasons, limits, weapon restrictions, and similar controls.

gamete (7) A haploid cell that contains only one of each type of chromosome found in an organism; an egg or sperm.

ganglion (15) A mass of nerve tissue; sometimes called a simple brain.

gap theory (9) The belief that there was a long period of time between the events of Genesis 1:1 and 1:2.

gastrovascular cavity (15) In certain animals, the internal cavity in which digestion and food circulation take place.

gene (6) A segment of DNA in which the sequence of nucleotides codes for a specific protein (or part of a protein), which in turn contributes to a specific characteristic.

genealogy (9) A list of an individual's ancestors.

gene mutation (8) A change in the sequence of the nucleotides in a gene.

genetic engineering (8) The use of special techniques to control the genetic makeup of an organism.

genetics (7) The study of heredity.

genetic variation (14) The normal genetic differences between organisms of the same species.

genome (8) A complete set of an organism's genes.

genotype (7) The specific factors (genes) an organism contains in its genetic makeup.

genus (pl., **genera**) (2) In the modern classification system, a subdivision of a family; includes one or more species of organisms.

genus-species name (2) See **scientific name**.

germ mutation (8) A mutation in a gamete or gamete-forming cell.

gestation (20) The period of pregnancy.

gill (17) A respiratory structure in fish and other aquatic organisms; exchanges oxygen and carbon dioxide in the water.

gizzard (15) A muscular organ that grinds food.

glaucoma (27) A disease of the eye caused by too much fluid pressure in the eye, damaging the retina.

gliding joint (24) The type of joint that allows adjacent bones to slide and twist, e.g., the joint between two vertebrae.

global flood (9) The worldwide Flood of Noah's day (Gen. 6–8).

glottis (26) The space between the vocal folds.

Golgi apparatus (4) A cellular organelle that collects chemicals from the cytoplasm, processes them, and secretes them.

gravitropism (13) The growth of a plant part in a certain direction in response to gravity.

gray matter (27) See **cerebral cortex**.

groundwater (21) Precipitation that enters the soil.

grow (3) To increase in size by the addition or enlargement of cells.

growth hormone (27) One of the hormones produced by the pituitary gland; stimulates bones, muscles, and various other tissues to grow.

grub (16) The larva of a beetle.

guard cell (13) One of the cells that surround a stoma and control the opening and closing of the stoma.

guard hair (18) The longer, stiffer hair of a mammal's fur; contains the pigments that produce the colors of fur.

gymnosperm (12) A plant that produces seeds that are not fully covered or shielded from the environment, e.g., a pine, spruce, cycad, or ginkgo tree.

H

habitat (21) The place where an organism lives.

hair (18) The filamentous structures made mostly of keratin that grow from the epidermis of mammals; the characteristic covering of mammals.

hair follicle (18) The structure in the skin where hair is produced.

haploid (14) Having only one of each type of chromosome normally found in the cells of an organism.

hazardous substance (23) Chemicals that can harm living things.

hazardous waste (23) A hazardous substance that is discarded.

heart (16) A muscular organ that pumps blood.

heart murmur (25) An abnormal sound usually caused by defective heart valves.

heartwood (12) Dead xylem cells that contain tars or resins.

hemoglobin (25) The red pigment found in red blood cells; transports oxygen and some carbon dioxide.

herbaceous stem (12) Softer, more flexible, and often green plant stems.

herbivore (22) An organism that eats only plants.

hereditary (8) Refers to traits that are capable of being transmitted genetically from parent to offspring.

hibernation (21) A dormant state involving a slowing of life processes; permits certain animals to survive winter conditions.

hinge joint (24) The type of joint that allows movement in only one direction, back and forth in one plane.

homeostasis (25) The internal balance an organism must maintain.

homologous structures (10) Similar structures found in different species that are attributed to common ancestry.

hormone (13) A chemical produced by living cells and transported to other body tissues where it causes a specific effect.

host (22) An organism that provides nourishment for and is harmed (but usually not killed) by another organism (parasite).

human population (23) The number of people living on the earth at one time.

humus (21) Decaying plant material in the soil.

hybrid (7) An offspring of two genetically unrelated individuals.

hybrid vigor (8) A greater strength, productivity, or health that sometimes occurs in offspring produced by crossbreeding.

hydrostatic skeleton (15) A type of skeleton in which confined fluid provides support.

hyphae (sing., **hypha**) (11) The slender filaments of a fungus; secrete enzymes that function in external digestion.

hypothesis (1) An educated guess at the solution to a problem.

I

identical twins (8) Twins that are the result of a zygote formed by the uniting of a single sperm and ovum, which then divides and develops into two separate individuals; they have the same genetic makeup.

immune system (25) The body system that gives resistance to disease.

immunity (25) The ability of an organism to recognize and attack a pathogen to which it has been previously exposed; dependent on the formation of antibodies.

inbreeding (8) The mating of closely related organisms.

incisor (18) A flat, thin tooth used in gnawing, biting, and cutting.

incomplete dominance (7) A type of inheritance in which the genes expressing a particular characteristic are neither dominant nor recessive; both genes influence the characteristic of an organism.

incomplete metamorphosis (16) Insect metamorphosis that includes three stages: egg, nymph, and adult.

incubation (20) The maintaining of the conditions necessary to hatch an egg.

independent organism (22) An organism that exists without the aid of other members of the same species.

infer (1) To make a decision based on the available evidence.

inferior vena cava (25) A large vein that returns blood from the lower body regions to the heart.

inflammation (25) A local response to a foreign substance in a body; may be characterized by swelling, redness, and increased temperature.

inhale (26) To draw air into the lungs; to breathe in.

inherited disorder (7) An abnormal characteristic passed on through genes.

innate behavior (19) An action or reaction that an animal is born with, e.g., a reflex or instinct.

inner ear (27) The part of the ear consisting of the cochlea and the semicircular canals.

insecticide (16) A chemical that kills insects.

instinct (19) A complex innate behavior.

insulin (27) A hormone produced by the pancreas; affects the amount of sugar in the blood.

intelligent behavior (19) An action or reaction marked by thought, emotion, analysis, and the use of tools or symbols.

intelligent design (**ID**) (9) A theory that states that nature shows evidence of design that could not have been the result of biological evolution alone, i.e., there must have been a designer at some point along the way.

interferon (11) A chemical produced by cells when a virus attacks; interferes with the reproduction of viruses.

internal fertilization (20) The union of a sperm and ovum within the female parent's body.

internal parasite (22) An organism that obtains nourishment from and lives inside another organism.

interneuron (27) A neuron of a reflex arc; located in the central nervous system; transmits impulses from a sensory neuron to other neurons.

interphase (6) The phase of a cell's life cycle before cell division; genes are copied during this period.

intestine (17) A section of the digestive tract where chemical digestion and the absorption of foods usually occur.

invertebrate (15) An animal that lacks a backbone.

involuntary muscle (24) A muscle controlled automatically by the brain; controlled without conscious effort.

iris (27) The colored (pigmented) portion of the eye; regulates the size of the pupil.

J

joint (24) The place where two or more bones meet.

K

keratin (18) The protein that makes up scales, feathers, hair, fingernails, claws, and hooves.

kidney (17) An organ that filters wastes from the blood.

kingdom (2) In the modern classification system, the largest group of living organisms.

L

lactic acid (5) An acid produced in lactic acid fermentation; might be the cause of soreness in overused muscles.

lactic acid fermentation (5) A type of anaerobic cellular respiration that produces lactic acid from sugar.

large intestine (17) The part of the digestive tract that extends from the end of the small intestine to the anus; absorbs water and minerals.

larva (16) An immature stage in the life cycle of many animals.

larynx (voice box) (26) The short passageway that leads from the pharynx to the trachea; the sound-producing organ.

lateral line (17) A sensory organ on each side of a fish; used to detect vibrations and pressure.

lateral root (12) A smaller root that branches off a main root in a taproot system.

leaf (12) A plant organ that does not have a node but is connected to a stem at a node.

leaflet (12) One of the sections of the blade of a compound leaf.

learned behavior (19) An action or reaction that is learned by experience and is often motivated by reward or punishment.

lens (4) A curved piece of glass or other material that magnifies images by bending light rays; used in instruments such as microscopes; (27) the part of the eye that bends light waves to focus them on the retina.

lenticel (13) One of the small openings in the cork layer of woody roots and stems through which gases enter and exit.

lethal mutation (8) A mutation that causes death.

leukocyte (25) A white blood cell; functions primarily in the body's immune system.

lichen (11) A fungus and an algae living together for mutual benefit and appearing to be a single organism; the fungus obtains energy from the algal cells, and the algae receive protection, water, and perhaps some minerals from the fungus.

life cycle (3) The sequence of stages during an organism's life; usually includes birth, growth, reproduction, and death.

life science (1) Human observations of and decisions about living things.

ligament (24) A band of connective tissue that holds the bones of a joint in place.

limiting factor (21) A factor in a habitat that limits the growth or existence of a species.

lipid (3) A substance such as fat or oil; not soluble in water; an important component of membranes.

literal view (ordinary-day view) (9) The belief that the Creation week was six consecutive twenty-four-hour periods.

liver (17) The organ that produces bile, helps to regulate substances in the blood, and stores minerals and vitamins.

long-day plant (13) A plant that requires long periods of light and short periods of darkness in order to bloom.

long-day theory (9) The belief that each day of the Creation week was actually a long period of time (millions or billions of years).

longitudinal nerve (15) A nerve that extends the length of an organism's body; found in some invertebrates.

lung (17) An organ that exchanges gases between the atmosphere and the blood.

lysosome (4) An organelle that contains digestive enzymes.

M

maggot (16) The larva of a fly.

mammary gland (18) An organ that produces milk to nourish young offspring; found in mammals.

marsupial (18) A mammal that rears its young in a pouch.

mating ritual (19) An instinctive sequence of actions exhibited by some animals while selecting a mate.

maxillary teeth (17) The teeth that form a tiny ridge around the rim of a frog's upper jaw.

mechanical digestion (26) The process of breaking food into smaller pieces and mixing it with the digestive juices.

meiosis (6) The process whereby one diploid cell forms haploid cells (gametes).

melanin (24) A dark brown or black pigment.

membrane (4) A thin structure that surrounds a cell and structures inside a cell. (See also **fluid mosaic model**.)

messenger RNA (mRNA) (6) The RNA molecule that transports a coded message from the nucleus to the cytoplasm.

metabolic rate (26) The rate at which an organism uses energy.

metabolism (26) The total of all reactions occurring in a living organism.

metamorphosis (16) A changing of an animal's shape or form as the animal develops from an egg to an adult.

metaphase (6) The second phase of mitosis; the chromosomes align by their centromeres across the middle of the spindle.

middle ear (27) An air-filled space behind the eardrum; contains the ear bones.

migration (19) The long-distance seasonal movement of animals from one area to another.

milk (18) A liquid substance produced in mammary glands of mother mammals; fed to newborn offspring; provides the fat, protein, carbohydrates, minerals, and water that an infant mammal needs.

milt (20) The sperm released into the water by aquatic animals during external fertilization.

mimicry (22) A relationship between organisms in which one organism looks like another, usually providing some survival benefit.

mineral (26) A naturally occurring, inorganic substance not usually made by living organisms; used by the body to build certain materials.

missing link (10) An "in-between" organism that must have existed if one type of organism evolved into another; also called a transitional form.

mitochondria (4) The cellular organelles in which aerobic respiration occurs to release usable energy from food.

mitosis (6) The duplication and separation of a cell's chromosomes; usually followed by cytokinesis.

mitotic cell division (6) Cell division that involves both mitosis and cytokinesis.

molar (18) A large broad-topped tooth used for crushing and grinding food; located directly behind the premolars.

molecule (3) The smallest unit existing as a particular substance.

molt (16) To shed scales, feathers, fur, or an exoskeleton.

monotreme (18) A mammal that lays eggs.

morphology (12) The exterior shape or form of an organism.

motor neuron (27) A neuron that receives impulses from the central nervous system and stimulates muscles or glands.

mouth (15) An opening through which food enters the digestive system of an organism.

movement (3) One of the life processes of organisms; requires energy and involves the moving of an organism from place to place or the moving of substances within an organism.

mucus (17) A slimy protective substance on the exterior of many fish and some amphibians; (26) a thick sticky substance secreted by the mucous membranes in the human body.

multicellular organism (3) A living thing that is composed of more than one cell and whose individual cells are not normally able to live singly apart from the organism.

multiple gene inheritance (7) Two or more gene pairs producing a single trait.

mutation (8) A change in the genetic material of a cell.

mutation-selection theory (**Neo-Darwinism**) (10) An evolutionary theory that states that mutations produce variations and that natural selection determines which variations will survive in order to produce biological evolution.

mutation theory of evolution (10) The belief that mutations provide the source of change for the evolution of species.

mutualism (22) A relationship that is beneficial to both organisms involved.

mycelia (sing., **mycelium**) (11) Densely packed fungal hyphae.

mycorrhizae (11) Fungi that form a symbiotic association with the roots of plants.

N

nastic movements (13) Reversible, repeatable plant movements.

natural resource (23) A naturally occurring material that is valuable to and used by humans.

nearsightedness (27) A vision defect in which only nearby objects are focused clearly; usually caused by an eyeball that is too long from front to back.

nectar (14) A sugary liquid produced by glands in some flowers; functions as an attractant to certain pollinators.

nematocyst (15) A type of stinging cell possessed by cnidarians; used for defense or for capturing food.

Neo-Darwinism (10) See **mutation-selection theory**.

nephron (25) A microscopic unit that filters blood in the kidney.

nerve (15) A number of neurons arranged side by side and wrapped in a protective covering.

nerve cord (15) A bundle of neurons for the conduction of impulses.

nervous system (27) The group of organs that regulate the internal body functions and responses to external stimuli.

neuron (15) A long thin nerve cell that carries impulses between various parts of the body.

niche (21) The role or function of an organism in its environment.

night blindness (27) A vision defect in which one cannot see in dim light; caused by rods that do not function.

nitrogen cycle (21) The process by which nitrogen moves, in various compounds, through biotic and abiotic communities as it is used and reused.

nocturnal (21) Active at night.

node (12) A region on a stem where a leaf is or was attached.

nonbiodegradable pollutant (23) A pollutant that cannot be broken down by living organisms.

nonrenewable (23) Cannot be replaced.

nonvascular plant (12) A plant that lacks tissues that conduct water and other materials.

no-till agriculture (23) A type of farming in which the soil is not cultivated; results in crop residue and reduced erosion, improving the soil.

nucleic acid (3) A molecule that contains the genetic information of a cell; DNA and RNA are the main types.

nucleotide (6) The basic structural unit of DNA and RNA; contains a sugar, a phosphate, and a base.

nucleus (pl., **nuclei**) (4) The cellular organelle that contains the chromosomes; control center of the cell.

nymph (16) The immature stage of an insect with incomplete metamorphosis.

O

objective (4) The microscope part that contains the lenses nearest the specimen.

observation (1) The information gathered from the environment by one's senses; the gathering of such information.

old-earth theory (9) The belief that the earth is millions or billions of years old.

omnivore (22) An organism that eats plants and animals.

open circulatory system (16) The type of circulation in which the blood passes from blood vessels into body spaces around organs and tissues before returning to the heart.

order (2) A subdivision of a class; includes one or more families of organisms.

organ (5) Two or more tissues that work together to perform a specific function.

organic compound (3) A substance that contains carbon; normally made by living organisms.

organic evolution (10) See **biological evolution**.

organism (3) A complete living thing.

osmosis (4) The diffusion of water through a selectively permeable membrane.

osteon (24) A microscopic unit of a bone consisting of a blood vessel and layers of hard nonliving material around it.

outer ear (27) The external structure of the ear; consists of the ear canal and the flap of tissue that collects sound waves.

ovary (14) In plants, the part of the pistil containing the ovules and eventually maturing into the fruit surrounding the seeds; (20) in animals and humans, the female reproductive organ that produces eggs.

ovule (14) The structure that contains the egg of a plant.

oxygenated blood (17) Blood that carries an abundant amount of oxygen.

oxygen cycle (21) The exchange of oxygen between organisms carrying on photosynthesis and those carrying on cellular respiration; functions in relationship with the carbon cycle.

P

palisade layer (13) The leaf tissue that consists of closely packed, tall, thin cells that carry on the majority of the photosynthesis.

palmate venation (12) An arrangement of veins in a leaf in which the larger veins branch away from the base of the leaf.

pancreas (17) An organ that secretes enzymes into the small intestine to help perform digestion; also secretes the hormone insulin into the bloodstream.

papillae (24) Ridges of the dermis that push up into the epidermis; produce fingerprints.

parallel venation (12) An arrangement of veins in a leaf in which the larger veins are all parallel to each other.

parasite (22) An organism that obtains nourishment from and harms (but usually does not kill) another organism.

passive transport (4) The passage of substances across a membrane without the use of cellular energy.

peptic ulcer (26) An internal open sore that usually occurs in the linings of the esophagus, the stomach, or the first part of the small intestine.

perennial plant (21) A plant species that lives for more than two years, usually many years.

pericardium (25) The fluid-filled sac that surrounds the heart.

periosteum (24) A layer of fibrous tissue covering the surface of a bone.

peripheral nervous system (17) The part of the nervous system consisting of sensory receptors, sensory organs, and nerves that connect to the central nervous system.

peristalsis (26) A series of muscular contractions that moves food along the alimentary canal.

permanent resident bird (21) A bird that lives in a certain area all year.

perspiration (24) A liquid (mostly water) secreted on the surface of the epidermis; cools the skin when it evaporates; also called sweat.

petal (14) One of the appendages of a flower; usually colorful; often functions to attract pollinators.

petiole (12) The part of a leaf between the node and the blade.

pharynx (26) The passageway between the mouth and the nose, esophagus, and larynx; also called the throat.

phenotype (7) The way an organism looks (its physical characteristics).

pheromone (19) A chemical released by animals that affects other animals of the same species.

phloem (12) A plant tissue that conducts dissolved food in a plant.

photoperiodism (13) The response of a plant to changes in the length of daylight and night.

photosynthesis (5) The process that forms simple sugars from carbon dioxide and water, using light energy in the presence of chlorophyll.

phototropism (13) The growth of a plant part in a certain direction in response to light.

phylum (2) In the modern classification system, a subdivision of a kingdom; includes one or more classes of organisms.

physical life (3) A characteristic produced when organized systems of nonliving substances use energy and maintain the characteristics of living things.

phytochrome (13) A pigment that is affected by day length and initiates a plant's response to day length.

pigment (5) A colored substance in plants that absorbs light energy; a chemical that produces coloration.

pinnate venation (12) An arrangement of veins in a leaf in which one main vein extends the length of the leaf and smaller veins branch away from it along its entire length.

pioneer species (21) The organisms that live in an area in the early stages of succession.

pistil (14) The female reproductive part of a flower; includes the stigma, style, and ovary.

pituitary gland (27) An endocrine gland attached to the lower part of the brain; secretes several hormones.

pivot joint (24) The type of joint that allows circular movement between bones.

placenta (18) The structure in which the mother's and the embryo's blood vessels pass near each other and exchange nutrients and wastes; attached to the wall of the uterus.

placental mammal (18) A mammal in which the developing young in the uterus exchange nutrients and wastes with the mother through a placenta.

plankton (11) Microscopic organisms that float or drift near the ocean surface; a key food source in the ocean's food chain.

plantlet (14) A small complete plant formed by asexual reproduction.

plastid (12) The organelle in which photosynthesis occurs.

platelet (25) A small structure found in the blood; involved in the formation of blood clots.

pollen (14) The structure that contains the male gamete of a plant; produced in the anther and covered by a protective coating.

pollen tube (14) The tube that grows from pollen on a stigma, down the style, and into the ovary of a flower.

pollination (14) The process of transferring pollen from the anther to a stigma.

pollinator (14) Anything that transfers pollen from an anther to a stigma, e.g., an insect, bat, bird, wind, or water.

pollution (23) The addition of impurities to an ecosystem.

population (21) All the members of one kind of organism living in a particular ecosystem.

portal vein (26) The blood vessel that carries blood from the digestive organs to the liver.

precipitation (21) The movement of water from the atmosphere to the ground.

predator (22) An animal that feeds on other animals.

predict (1) To make a statement about the expected future outcome of a certain action.

pregnant (20) Carrying a developing embryo in the uterus.

premolar (18) A broad-topped tooth used for crushing and grinding food; located directly behind the canines.

presupposition (1) Something a person assumes to be true without requiring convincing proof.

prey (11) Animals that a predator eats.

problem (1) A question that may be answered by the use of the scientific method.

producer organism (producer) (21) An organism that manufactures its own food.

progressive Creationism (9) The belief that God created life in stages over a long period of time and that evolution and extinction occurred in the intervals between the creative acts.

prokaryote (4) A unicellular organism that lacks a nucleus and other membrane-bound organelles; classified in kingdoms Archaebacteria and Eubacteria.

prophase (6) The first phase of mitosis; when chromosomes coil and sister chromatids become obvious.

protein (3) A substance made of long chains of amino acids; may serve as an enzyme or as a cellular building block; found in certain foods.

protein synthesis (6) The manufacturing of protein inside a cell.

protoplasm (3) All the living material of a cell.

protozoa (11) The more animal-like organisms in kingdom Protista; usually can move and capture prey.

pseudopod (pl., **pseudopodia**) (21) An extension of the cell membrane and cytoplasm of a cell; used for locomotion or feeding.

puberty (27) The period of life in which the reproductive hormones cause the body to mature; begins during a person's preteen or early teenage years.

pulmonary artery (25) The artery that transports deoxygenated blood from the heart to the lungs.

pulmonary vein (25) The vein that returns oxygenated blood from the lungs to the heart.

pulse (25) The rhythmic expansion of the arteries caused by the pumping of the heart.

Punnett square (7) A diagram used to visualize genetic crosses.

pupa (16) A resting stage during the complete metamorphosis of certain insects.

puparium (16) The pupa stage of a fly.

pupil (27) The circular opening in the iris of the eye.

purebred (7) An organism that is the offspring of parents with similar genetic makeups; usually the result of many generations of such breeding.

R

radial symmetry (15) A type of symmetry in which several different planes could divide an animal into equal halves.

recessive (7) Refers to the characteristic that is masked when a dominant gene is present.

recycle (23) To use again.

red-green colorblindness (7) A vision defect in which a person is unable to tell the difference between red and green; a sex-linked trait.

red tide (11) The overpopulation of a section of ocean water by dinoflagellates (a type of protist), giving it a reddish color; deadly to fish; makes shellfish inedible.

reflex (19) A simple immediate response to a change in the environment; usually involuntary.

reflex arc (27) A series of neurons that receive a stimulus and cause the body to react to it without conscious effort.

regeneration (6) The ability to replace missing structures; in some organisms, serves as a method of asexual reproduction.

renewable (23) Can be replaced.

replication (6) The process of forming two DNA molecules from one original DNA molecule.

respiration (5) The release of energy from a food source; (26) the process of supplying oxygen to and removing carbon dioxide from the body of an organism.

respiratory system (26) The system of organs that obtain oxygen from the air and eliminate carbon dioxide from the body; in humans, the lungs, trachea, and other associated organs.

response (3) A living thing's reaction to its surroundings.

retina (27) The innermost layer of the eye; composed of light-sensitive neurons.

rhizoid (12) A thin rootlike structure.

rhizome (12) An underground stem that grows horizontally.

rhythm (21) A cyclic change that occurs in an ecosystem.

ribonucleic acid (6) See **RNA**.

ribosome (4) A cellular organelle that directs the assembling of proteins.

RNA (ribonucleic acid) (6) A nucleic acid made of a single chain of nucleotides; functions with ribosomes to form proteins.

rod (27) A neuron in the retina used for vision in dim light.

root (12) The primary plant organ that absorbs water and minerals; does not have nodes and is not connected to other organs at nodes.

root hair (13) A tubular outgrowth of epidermal cells of the roots of plants; aids in absorbing water.

root system (12) All the roots of a plant.

runner (14) A stem joining a plantlet to its parent plant.

S

saliva (26) The watery fluid secreted into the mouth by the salivary glands that moistens foods and begins starch digestion.

salivary gland (26) A digestive gland that secretes saliva into the mouth.

sanitary landfill (23) A trash dump over which a layer of dirt is spread periodically.

saprophyte (11) A fungus that absorbs food that is already dead.

sapwood (12) Xylem (wood) that still functions in transporting water; usually a lighter color than heartwood.

scavenger (22) An animal that eats dead or decaying matter.

science (1) The systematic investigation of the natural world based on observations; the body of knowledge that has resulted from this study.

scientific method (1) A logical problem-solving method that involves experimenting or surveying, observing, and choosing an answer.

scientific name (genus-species name) (2) The unique two-word name of a particular organism.

scientism (1) The belief that scientific observation is the only way to learn about the world and that science can yield answers in all fields of study.

sclera (27) The outer protective layer of the eye.

seasonal rhythm (21) A change that takes place annually in an ecosystem.

sedimentary fossil (9) A fossil formed by sedimentation.

sedimentation (9) The process whereby matter settles out as a moving substance slows down.

seed (14) A mature ovule consisting of an embryo and stored food enclosed by a seed coat.

seedless vascular plant (12) A plant that has tissues that conduct water and other materials but does not reproduce by forming seeds, e.g., a fern, club moss, or horsetail.

seed plant (12) A vascular plant that produces seeds through sexual reproduction.

selective breeding (8) Choosing certain organisms with desirable traits to breed in the hope that their offspring also will have the desired traits.

selectively permeable (4) Allowing only certain molecules to pass through.

semicircular canals (27) A set of three structures, located in the inner ear; responsible for sensing balance.

semilunar valve (25) A structure that allows the blood to leave the ventricles but prevents it from returning.

sensory neuron (27) A neuron that receives stimuli and carries impulses toward the spinal cord or brain.

sensory organ (sense organ) (17) An organ that consists of many sensory receptors and various tissues needed to keep the receptors functioning, e.g., the eye or the ear.

sensory receptor (15) A structure capable of receiving a stimulus from the environment and sending an impulse along a neuron.

sepal (14) The outermost appendage of a flower; often small, green, and leaflike.

septum (25) A muscular wall dividing the right side of the heart from the left side.

sewage (23) A substance consisting primarily of biodegradable wastes and water; often a chief source of water pollution.

sex-linked trait (7) A characteristic that has a gene on the X chromosome but no gene on the Y chromosome.

sexual reproduction (6) The joining of haploid gametes to form a diploid zygote, which develops into a new individual.

shell gland (20) A gland that secretes substances that form the shell of an egg.

short-day plant (13) A plant that requires short periods of light and long periods of darkness in order to bloom.

simple brain (15) See **ganglion**.

siphon (16) A tubelike structure used for drawing in or expelling water.

sister chromatid (6) One of two identical chromosomes formed from one original chromosome during mitosis.

skeletal muscle (24) Muscle tissue that attaches to and moves the skeleton.

skeleton (15) A structure in animals and humans that provides mechanical support for muscle attachment and maintaining body shape.

skull (17) The group of bones that cover and protect the brain.

small intestine (17) The digestive organ in which most of the digestion and absorption of food occurs.

smog (23) A combination of smoke, auto exhaust, and fog.

smooth muscle (24) Muscle tissue that lacks striations; forms the walls of many internal organs.

social insect (22) An insect that lives in a colony; the colony usually exhibits some division of labor.

somatic mutation (8) A mutation that occurs in the body cells (those cells that do not make gametes).

spawning (17) The laying of eggs in water by aquatic animals.

species (2) A group of similar organisms that interbreed and produce offspring capable of reproducing.

sperm (20) A gamete formed by a male; usually able to move by itself and smaller than the female gamete of the same species.

spicules (15) Sharp pointed structures in certain sponges that function as a skeleton; made of calcium carbonate or silica.

spinal cord (17) The cord of nerve tissue that conducts messages between the brain and the rest of the body.

spinal nerve (17) A nerve that carries impulses to and from the spinal cord.

spindle (6) A set of fibers that form during mitotic cell division.

spiracle (16) A pore that allows air to enter and exit an insect's body.

spiritual life (3) Man's relationship with God (John 17:3).

spongin (15) A fibrous protein that functions as a skeleton in certain sponges.

spongy bone (24) A type of bone with spongelike spaces inside it.

spongy layer (13) The leaf tissue consisting of loosely packed cells that carry on photosynthesis; has air spaces between the cells.

sporangia (11) A structure that produces spores; found in nonvascular plants, seedless vascular plants, and certain fungi.

spore (6) A cell with a hard protective covering; under favorable conditions it can produce a new organism.

springwood (12) The part of an annual growth ring of a woody plant that consists of larger cells produced during the spring.

stamen (14) The male reproductive structure of a flower; composed of an anther and a filament.

stem (13) The only plant organ that has nodes; supports leaves.

stethoscope (25) An instrument used to listen to the heart.

stigma (14) The expanded tip of the pistil; receives the pollen.

stimulus (pl., **stimuli**) (15) Anything that causes a response in an organism.

stomach (17) A saclike portion of the digestive tract; performs mechanical and chemical digestion.

stomata (sing., **stoma**) (13) Openings between guard cells of a leaf; permit water vapor and gases to pass into and out of the leaf.

striated muscle (24) Muscle tissue that displays a pattern of light and dark bands.

style (14) A portion of the pistil above the ovary and below the stigma.

subcutaneous layer (24) The layer of fat and connective tissues below the dermis of the skin.

substance pollutant (23) A solid, liquid, or gas that pollutes an ecosystem.

substrate (21) The substance below the soil or a body of water; supplies chemicals to the soil or water.

succession (21) A predictable series of changes that occur in biotic communities as they progress toward a climax community.

summer resident bird (21) A bird that lives in a certain environment only in the summer.

summerwood (12) The part of an annual growth ring of a woody plant that consists of small cells produced during the summer and autumn.

sunburn (24) Redness and soreness of the skin resulting from increased blood flow to the skin as the body replaces skin cells killed by ultraviolet light.

superior vena cava (25) The large vein that carries blood from the upper body regions to the heart.

survey (1) A method of data collection that determines how common or rare particular observations are; the data collected by this method.

swim bladder (17) An air-filled organ in certain fish that helps them to maintain buoyancy at a certain depth.

symbiotic (11) Refers to a relationship in which two organisms live together.

synapse (27) The space between an axon and a dendrite or between an axon and the body structure it affects.

T

taproot system (12) A type of root system having one or a few main roots that are thicker and longer than the other roots of the plant.

taste bud (27) A group of cells that sense taste.

telophase (6) The last phase of mitosis; when sister chromatids reach the ends of the spindle and the nucleus re-forms.

tendon (24) The connective tissue that attaches muscle to bone.

tentacle (15) A long flexible extension of an animal's body used for locomotion, sensation, or defense.

terrapin (17) A freshwater turtle that may venture onto land.

testis (pl., **testes**) (20) The male reproductive organ that produces sperm; usually paired in vertebrates.

theory of acquired characteristics (10) The theory that physical changes caused by an organism's environment can be passed on to offspring.

theory of evolution (10) The concept that the physical universe began without God and has changed by random processes, over a period of time, into what we observe today.

theory of mutations (10) See **mutation theory of evolution**.

theory of natural selection (10) The idea that only those organisms best suited for their environment will survive and reproduce, thus causing certain traits to become more common among a population.

thorax (16) A body region between the head and abdomen.

thyroid gland (27) An endocrine gland in the neck; secretes the hormone thyroxine.

tissue (3) A group of similar cells that together perform a specific function.

tortoise (17) A turtle that lives its entire life on land.

trachea (16) In insects, one of the tiny tubes that branch throughout the body, carrying air to the tissues; (26) in humans, the tube that carries air between the pharynx and the lungs.

transcription (6) The manufacture of a single mRNA strand from a DNA molecule.

transfer RNA (tRNA) (6) The RNA molecule that transfers amino acids to the messenger RNA.

transpiration (13) The release of water from leaves through stomata.

transverse nerve (15) A nerve that extends from one side of an organism's body to the other side.

trash (23) Solid waste material that is useless or unwanted.

tropism (13) The growth of plants in response to external stimuli such as light, gravity, or contact.

tube feet (16) Small tubular structures of echinoderms; used for locomotion and feeding.

turgor pressure (12) Water pressure inside a plant cell's central vacuole; causes the stiffness of the plant cell.

U

umbilical cord (18) The structure through which the embryo's blood vessels pass to the placenta.

underhair (18) The shorter, softer hair of a mammal's fur; provides insulation.

unicellular organism (3) A living thing composed entirely of one cell.

univalve (16) A mollusk having one shell, which is often coiled, e.g., a snail or conch.

universal negative (1) A statement that excludes everything; often uses words such as *all* or *none*.

urea (25) A waste product filtered from the blood by the kidneys.

ureter (17) The tube that carries the wastes and water filtered out of the blood to the urinary bladder.

urethra (25) The tube that carries wastes away from the urinary bladder.

urinary bladder (17) An organ that temporarily stores the fluid wastes from a kidney; a reservoir for urine.

urine (17) A fluid that is passed out of the body; contains wastes from the blood.

uterus (20) A special structure in which the zygote develops in a mother that gives live birth.

V

vaccinate (11) To intentionally expose to a weakened virus or part of a virus to cause immunity.

vaccine (25) Weakened virus or part of a virus that is used to cause antibody production in the body against these substances.

vacuole (4) A membrane-bound sac that contains various substances, including water and wastes, within a cell.

value judgment (1) A decision regarding the rightness, beauty, worth, or some other unmeasurable characteristic of an object or action.

vascular bundle (12) A strand of vascular tissue (xylem and phloem) in the leaves, young plants, and non-woody stems.

vascular cambium (12) A layer of living cells located between a plant's xylem and phloem that constantly divides, producing new xylem and phloem for the plant.

vascular plant (12) A plant that has tissues that conduct water and other materials.

vascular tissue (12) A plant tissue, such as xylem or phloem, that conducts water and other materials in some plants.

vein (12) In plants, the vascular tissues in leaf blades; (15) in animals, a blood vessel that carries blood toward the heart.

ventricle (25) A heart chamber that pushes blood into the arteries.

verify (1) To test many times and observe the same result each time.

vertebra (pl., **vertebrae**) (17) One of the bones that protect the spinal cord and support the body.

vertebral column (17) A series of similar bones that support the body; also called the backbone.

vertebrate (17) An animal that has a backbone.

vestigial organ (27) An organ that has no apparent function; evolutionists claim it had a function but has lost it over a long period of evolution.

villi (sing., **villus**) (26) Microscopic fingerlike structures that line the wall of the small intestine.

virus (11) A nonliving, tiny strand of DNA or RNA surrounded by a coat of protein.

vitamin (25) A substance that is not a protein, carbohydrate, or lipid but is needed in order for the body to function properly.

vitreous humor (27) A clear jellylike substance that fills the chamber behind the lens and keeps the eyeball round.

voice box (26) See **larynx**.

voluntary muscle (24) A muscle that can be controlled at will.

vomerine teeth (17) The two inconspicuous teeth in the roof of a frog's mouth.

W

warning coloration (22) The bright or contrasting coloration of certain animals that serves as a signal to other animals that the animal is dangerous or undesirable.

water (5) A substance composed of oxygen and hydrogen; necessary for the proper functioning of the human body and all living things.

water cycle (21) A continuous movement of water from the atmosphere to the earth and back to the atmosphere.

water pollution (23) Foreign substances that are added to water.

water table (21) A reservoir of water beneath the surface of the earth.

water-vascular system (16) A series of canals and tubules in echinoderms; used for movement and feeding.

winter resident bird (21) A bird that lives in a certain environment only in the winter.

wisdom teeth (26) The four molars at the back of a person's jaws.

wood (12) A collection of layers of xylem.

woody stem (12) A harder, nonflexible type of plant stem.

workable (1) Refers to things that are able to be used successfully in situations in life.

worldview (1) The perspective or collection of presuppositions from which one interprets all evidence in life. (See also **Christian worldview**.)

X

X chromosome (7) The female sex chromosome.

xylem (12) The plant tissue characterized by long hollow cells that carry water.

Y

Y chromosome (7) The male sex chromosome.

yolk (20) Food material stored in an egg to nourish the embryo.

young-earth theory (9) The belief that the earth is only a few thousand (about 6000) years old.

Z

zygote (7) A diploid cell formed by the union of two gametes.

INDEX

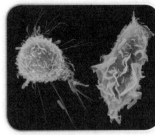

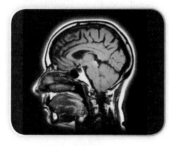

PHOTOGRAPH CREDITS

The following agencies and individuals have furnished materials to meet the photographic needs of this textbook. We wish to express our gratitude to them for their important contribution.

Agriculture Research Service (ARS)
Theo Alofs
Suzanne R. Altizer
Anderson Hill Farm
Stephanie Asher
R. F. Ashley
Associated Press (AP)
Max Azisov
L. Bassett
Brad Batdorf
Scott Bauer
John Bean
Bill Beatty
Beranger
Ronald F. Billings
Biodisc
Biophoto Associates
Graeme Black
Bob Jones University Collection
Joanna Bolick
Andrea Booher
Mark Boulton
Dan Brandenburg
Brand X Pictures
Charles T. Bryson
Bureau of Alcohol, Tobacco, Firearms and Explosives
Scott Camazine
Tony Campbell
Octavio Campos
Christy Cantrell
Patrice Ceisel
Kevin Chan
Libby Chapman
Peter Chen
David Clegg
Clemson University
CNRI
David Coder
Betty and Nathan Cohen
Brandon Cole
Ray Coleman
Corbis
COREL Corporation
Gerald and Buff Corsi
Jason Crabb
TA Crafts
Creation Science Foundation, Ltd., Australia

Jan Csernoch
Russ Curtis
Robert Dalton
Julie Deshaies
Aaron Dickey
Mike Donenfield
Wally Eberhart
Chris Evans
Richard Fagan
William Fawcett
Federal Emergency Management Agency (FEMA)
David Fleetham
Linda Fleuren
Flutterby Fotos
D. Follett
Forestry Images
João Freitas
Adrian Gabriel
Chris Gates
General Dynamics Electric Boat
General Motors
Barbara Gerlach
Ines Gesell
Getty Images
Global Exposure
Nathan Goodman
Daniel W. Gotshall
Joe Gough
Bill Grove
Guidant Corporation
Richard Gunion
Adam Hart-Davis
Mark Hayes
Dr. Terry Hazen
Hemera Technologies, Inc.
Gerald Herbert
Christine Herlin
Richard Herrmann
Michael Howell
Mark Huntington
Iowa State University
iStock Photo
Japan Society of Protozoology
Adam Jones
Jupiter Images
Dr. Randy Kardon
Randy Kayle
Breck Kent

Dr. Richard Kessel
Geoff Kuchera
Dr. Dennis Kunkel
George Lama
Joyce Landis
Laurent
C. K. Lorenz
Michael Lynch
Susan Mackenzie
Dr. P. Marazzi
Andrew J. Martinez
Steve Maslowski
Massachusetts Institute of Technology (MIT)
Jared Matson
Alan McCredie
Joe McDonald
Tom McHugh
Eamonn McNulty
Charles McRae
Steve McWilliam
Oliver Meckes
ChartChai MeeSangNin
Charles Melton
Gary Meszaros
Thomas Mounsey
Museum & Gallery Collection
National Oceanic and Atmospheric Administration (NOAA)
Natural Resources Conservation Services (NRCS)
Kyle Nelson
Dr. W. Ober
Old Haa Museum
Nicole Ottawa
Brian Palmer
Wendy Pandolfo
Susan Perry
David Philips
Dr. David Phillips
PhotoDisc
Photo Researchers, Inc.
Photos.com
Thomas Polen
Princess Margaret Rose Orthopaedic Hospital
Ashveen Rampeara
Paul Rapson
Ashok Rodrigues
Jeff Rotman

Dennis Sabo
Wang Sajun
Laurie-Ann Sarachie
Ian Scott
Paul Senyszyn
Chahine Shields
Dr. Gene Shih
Goh Siang
Arthur Siegelman
SIU
Skulls Unlimited
Marty Snyderman
Stem Labs, Inc
Sterling Industries, Inc.
Nicola Stratford
Sarah S. Strawhorn
Kori Sullivan
Lesa Sweat
Andrew Syred
Hung Meng Tan
Texas Forest Service
Andrzej Tokarski
Raymond Truelove
Dr. Yuuji Tsukii
Steven Tulissi
Uncle Milton Industries
Unusual Films
United States Department of Agriculture (USDA)
United States Fish and Wildlife Services (USFWS)
United States Navy (US Navy)
L' Univesita' di Roma La Sapienza
The University of Georgia
Gustav W. Verderber
Visuals Unlimited
William Walsh
Wieck Media Services
Gladden Willis, MD
Mark Wilson
Fred Winner
World Bank
Paul Wray
Wright State University
Zoe Yau
Yellowstone National Park
Dr. Paul A. Zahl

Student Activities

Chapter 16
Aaron Dickey SA163; © Bill Beatty/ Visuals Unlimited SA165; Charles T. Bryson, USDA, Agricultural Research Service, www.forestryimages.org SA166

Chapter 17
Unusual Films SA174

Chapter 18
Unusual Films SA185

Chapter 19
From the Bob Jones University Collection SA190; Ant Farm® Uncle Milton Industries SA193; www.istockphoto

.com/ Tony Campbell SA195 (bottom); Unusual Films SA195 (top)

Chapter 20
PhotoDisc/Getty Images SA198, SA200 (all); © Scott Camazine/ Photo Researchers, Inc. SA197

Chapter 21
© Joe McDonald/Visuals Unlimited SA205 (top); © Theo Alofs/Visuals Unlimited SA205 (bottom); USFWS SA210; Unusual Films SA217

Chapter 22
From the Bob Jones University Collection SA221; PhotoDisc/Getty Images SA227 (all); Brad Batdorf SA231 (left); www.istockphoto.com/Nicola Stratford SA231 (middle); www.istockphoto.com/

Susan Mackenzie SA231 (right); www .istockphoto.com/Linda Fleuren SA234

Chapter 23
Photo taken by Michael Howell, Southern Research Station, Knoxville, TN SA235; PhotoDisc/Getty Images SA240; www.istockphoto.com SA242; www .istockphoto.com/Steven Tulissi SA243

Chapter 24
Unusual Films SA261

Chapter 25
Susan Perry SA274 (both)

Chapter 27
Unusual Films SA299

STUDENT ACTIVITIES

Third Edition

15 INVERTEBRATES I: SPONGES, JELLYFISH, AND WORMS

ideas

15A Sponges and Jellyfish

name:

date: hour:

Directions

Read the following descriptions and decide whether a sponge or jellyfish is being described. In the space by each statement, write *S* if it describes a sponge, *J* if it describes a jellyfish, or *SJ* if it describes both.

_____ 1. Lacks a backbone

_____ 2. Has a body filled with pores

_____ 3. Has a hydrostatic skeleton

_____ 4. Has tentacles

_____ 5. Is a filter feeder

_____ 6. Lives mostly in oceans

_____ 7. Is classified in phylum Porifera

_____ 8. Digests food in a gastrovascular cavity

_____ 9. Can sting you with nematocysts

_____ 10. Has a skeleton made of spongin or spicules

_____ 11. Is classified in Kingdom Animalia

_____ 12. Has collar cells with flagella

ideas

15B The Planarian: A Type of Flatworm

Directions

In the spaces below, write the words that are described by the following statements.

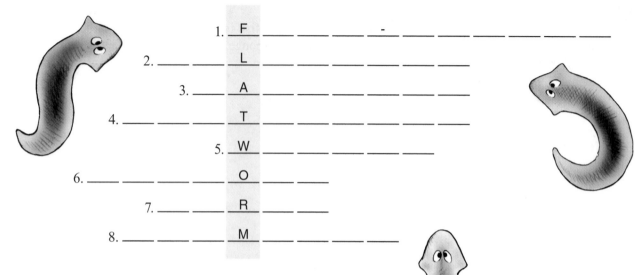

1. F ____ ____ ____ - ____ ____ ____ ____ ____ ____
2. ____ ____ L ____ ____ ____ ____ ____ ____
3. ____ A ____ ____ ____ ____ ____ ____
4. ____ ____ ____ T ____ ____ ____ ____ ____
5. ____ W ____ ____ ____ ____ ____
6. ____ ____ ____ O ____ ____
7. ____ ____ R ____ ____
8. ____ ____ ____ M ____ ____ ____

1. Not permanently attached to an object
2. Body symmetry in which one side mirrors the other side
3. A simple brain
4. Secretes digestive enzymes in the intestine
5. Removed by flame cells and excretory pores
6. Long, thin cells that run through the body and carry impulses from place to place
7. A collection of neurons wrapped in protective coverings
8. Something an organism can sense

ideas

15C The Planarian's Digestive System

Directions

The following sentences describe the normal process of planarian digestion. Put the sentences in order, from 1 to 6, by writing the correct numbers in the blanks provided.

_____ The gastroderm secretes enzymes.

_____ The cells of the gastroderm absorb the small pieces of food, and cellular digestion begins.

_____ The planarian attacks food and pulls it through its mouth and into its intestine.

_____ Nutrients are absorbed into the tissues of the planarian from the cells of the gastroderm.

_____ Indigestible material is pushed out through the mouth.

_____ Enzymes break down food into small pieces.

ideas
15D The Earthworm's Digestive System

name:

date: hour:

Directions

Label the following drawing by supplying the missing terms or definitions and then drawing a line from each term to the proper structure in the drawing.

1. intestine

   _____

2. _____
   (chamber where food is temporarily stored)

3. pharynx

   _____

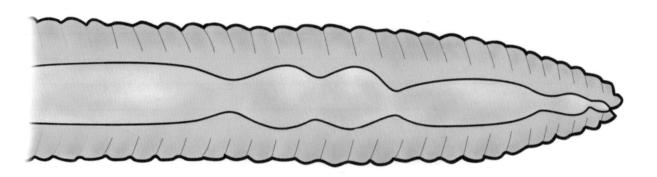

4. gizzard

   _____

5. esophagus

   _____

6. _____
   (opening where food enters the digestive tract)

ideas
15E The Earthworm and Other Segmented Worms

Directions

Below are several groups of words. In each group, three of the four words (or phrases) are related to one another. Draw a line through the unrelated word and then write a sentence using the remaining words. Your sentence should show how the words are related. (You may slightly change the form of the word in your sentence.)

1. bristles / flagella / muscles / earthworm _____

   _____

   _____

2. neurons / ganglia / impulses / cuticle _____

   _____

   _____

3. nephridia / capillaries / aortic arches / blood vessels _____

   _____

   _____

4. pharynx / esophagus / sensory receptor / crop _____

   _____

   _____

5. earthworm / leeches / segments / planaria _____

   _____

   _____

class investigation

15F Earthworm Dissection

name: _____

date: _____   hour: _____

Procedures and Observations

Examine the earthworm's exterior.

1. Find the clitellum, the smooth enlarged area on the earthworm's body. This structure is closest to the "head" end of the earthworm.

2. Notice that the earthworm has many segments. Count the number of segments from the tip of the "head" to the clitellum. How many

   are there? _____

3. Carefully feel for the earthworm's bristles. The bristles are located on the lower side of the earthworm. Determine which surface of the earthworm is the upper surface and which is the lower surface.

4. Place the earthworm in the dissection pan; the earthworm's lower surface should be facing down.

5. Often you can see a dark line extending down the middle of the earthworm's upper surface. This is the dorsal blood vessel. (See page 279 of your text.)

Open the earthworm's body.

1. With your scissors cut a small opening (1 mm long) in front of the clitellum.

2. Insert the point of your scissors into the slit and cut an opening along the middle of the earthworm's back. Cut just to the side of the dorsal blood vessel. You can see the dorsal blood vessel if you lift the cut edge of the body wall with your probes. Be sure you are cutting only the body wall.

3. Carefully pull apart the sections of the body wall. Note the partitions inside the body. These partitions separate the inside of the earthworm's body. Use a probe to break apart these partitions.

4. Pull the body walls back; insert pins through the body walls and into the wax of the dissection pan. Place the pins into segments 5, 10, 15, 20, and 25. The earthworm's reproductive structures are light-colored masses in segments 9–12. (Locations for the particular structures may vary somewhat. The segment numbers given tell the approximate locations.) The reproductive structures lie over the aortic arches. (See page 279 of your text.) Carefully remove the reproductive structures but do not destroy the aortic arches, the dorsal blood vessel, or the digestive system structures beneath.

5. Find all the aortic arches. They are located near segment 10. The aortic arches come in pairs, one on each

   side of the earthworm. How many pairs of aortic arches are there? _____

Goals

- Learn how to dissect.
- Learn about the structures of an earthworm.

Materials

- dissection pan
- dissection pins
- preserved earthworm
- probes
- scalpel or single-edged razor blade
- scissors

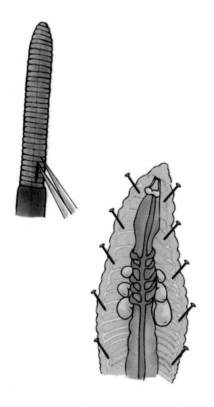

6. Locate the dorsal blood vessel in segments 20–25. Move the intestine carefully to one side and locate the ventral blood vessel. The dorsal blood vessel pumps blood in which direction? _____

   The ventral blood vessel pumps blood in which direction? _____

7. What type of circulatory system does the earthworm have?

   ☐ open   ☐ closed   Describe this type of circulatory system. _____

   _____

Procedures and Tools for Dissection

Never use the dissection equipment for anything other than dissection. Since this equipment can be very dangerous, do not play with it.

Do not carve in the wax or foam pad of the dissection pan.

Before you begin a dissection, read the entire investigation thoroughly. In your textbook, look up pictures of the organism you will be dissecting.

Reread the directions before you begin to cut.

Be sure that you have identified the proper structure(s) before you cut.

When you are told to cut something but are not told which tool to use, you must decide whether to use the scissors or the scalpel (razor blade).

When you are finished with your specimen, wrap it in a paper towel and place it in the trash can.

If you must keep your specimen overnight, wrap it in a wet paper towel and place it in a plastic bag. Gently remove most of the air from the bag and tightly close it.

Locate the following organs of the digestive system.

Tell which segments the following organs are located in and describe their functions.

1. pharynx _____

2. esophagus _____

3. crop _____

4. gizzard _____

5. intestine _____

Digging into the Word

Now that you have dissected an earthworm, look up and read each of the following verses: Genesis 3:19; Job 21:26; and Micah 7:17. Answer the following questions on a separate sheet of paper.

1. What do these passages teach us about the origin and destination of human bodies?

2. How is Micah 7:17 different? (Look at verses 16–20.) What does it teach us about the nations?

research investigation

15G **Other Sponges, Jellyfish, and Worms**

name:

date: hour:

Procedures and Observations

The table below lists some other examples of the invertebrates studied in Chapter 15. Use encyclopedias or other reference books to find the missing information needed to complete the table. Some of the more difficult answers have been provided.

Materials
- encyclopedia
- other reference books

Animal	Phylum	Symmetry (radial/bilateral)	Parasite? (yes/no)	Type of food
1. redbeard sponge				
2. Portuguese man-of-war		bilateral		
3. box jellyfish (sea wasp)				
4. anemone				
5. brain coral				
6. liver fluke		bilateral		
7. marine flatworm (turbellarian)				small marine organisms
8. hookworm				
9. vinegar eel		bilateral		
10. leech				
11. bearded fireworm				
12. lugworm				
13. fanworm ("feather duster")		bilateral		

16 INVERTEBRATES II: MOLLUSKS, ARTHROPODS, AND ECHINODERMS

ideas

16A **Mollusks**

name:

date: _____ hour: _____

Directions

Read the following descriptions and decide whether a clam, an octopus, or a snail is being described. In the space by each statement, write a *C* if it describes a clam, an *O* if it describes an octopus, and an *S* if it describes a snail. Some descriptions will have more than one answer.

_____ 1. Has an exceptionally soft body

_____ 2. Has suction discs

_____ 3. Has one or more shells

_____ 4. Filters food from water

_____ 5. Changes color with stimulation

_____ 6. Is a univalve

_____ 7. Uses a "smoke screen"

_____ 8. Is a bivalve

_____ 9. Has one or more siphons

_____ 10. Can be eaten by humans

_____ 11. Has a coiled shell

_____ 12. Can regenerate arms

_____ 13. May harbor human parasites

_____ 14. Is in the class Cephalopoda

_____ 15. Has a muscular foot

_____ 16. Is in the class Gastropoda

ideas
16B Insect Life Cycles

Directions

Below are diagrams of the two types of metamorphoses commonly found in insects. On the line below each diagram, indicate which type of metamorphosis is being illustrated. Add arrows to the curved lines to show the order in which metamorphosis occurs. Then label the stages of metamorphosis on the lines provided.

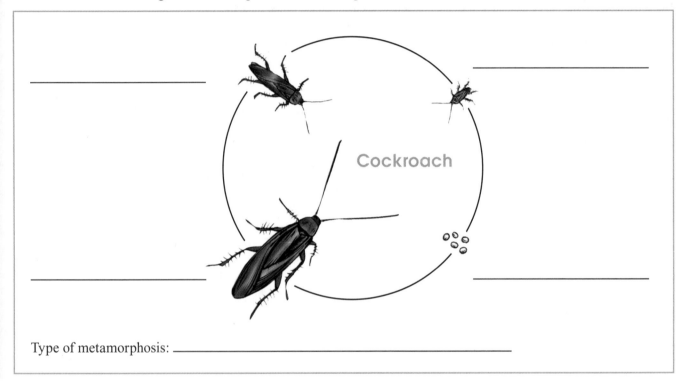

Type of metamorphosis: _____

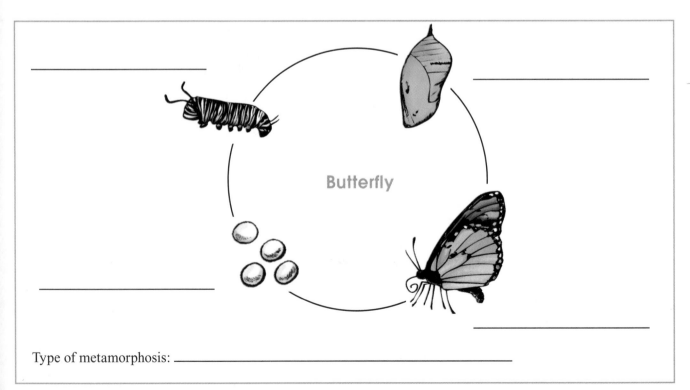

Type of metamorphosis: _____

name: _____

date: _____ hour: _____

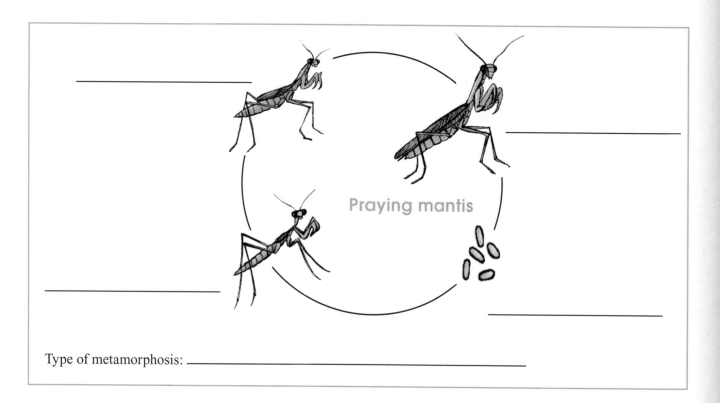

_____

_____

_____

Praying mantis

_____

Type of metamorphosis: _____

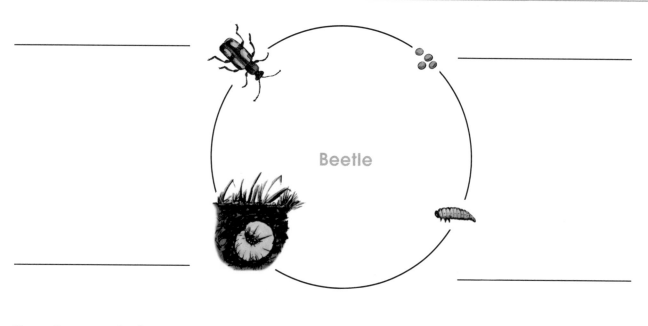

_____

_____

_____

Beetle

_____

Type of metamorphosis: _____

ideas

16C **Arthropods**

Directions

In each of the following statements, draw a circle around the correct choice in the parentheses.

1. Class (Insecta / Arthropoda) has the most species of any animal class.

2. Insects have (endoskeletons / exoskeletons).

3. Eyes with thousands of small sections are called (simple / compound) eyes.

4. Spiracles are openings in a grasshopper's respiratory system that lead into the (tracheae / excretory tubules).

5. Insects that molt repeatedly and become a little more mature with each molt exhibit (complete / incomplete) metamorphosis.

6. Barnacles and millipedes are (insects / arthropods).

7. Insects have (six / eight) legs.

8. In (closed / open) circulatory systems, the blood does not remain in blood vessels.

9. If an insect's life cycle includes a caterpillar, then the life cycle is described as (complete / incomplete) metamorphosis.

10. An arthropod's muscles are on the (inside / outside) of its skeleton.

11. An insect's body sections include the head, (trunk / thorax), and abdomen.

12. An insect's (antennae / arteries) are sensory structures.

13. Many insecticides target an insect's (respiratory / circulatory) system.

14. A butterfly chrysalis is an example of a (larva / pupa).

15. (Centipedes / Millipedes) have one pair of legs per body segment and are predators.

ideas

16D **Review**

name:

date: hour:

Directions

Below is a list of scrambled words. Unscramble the words and write them on the lines to the right of the words. Then match them to the clues given below by writing the proper letters in the blanks by the clues.

A. lettacens   _____

B. dilpelmie   _____

C. texosleonek   _____

D. bute tefe   _____

E. pohnis   _____

F. hidemoecrns   _____

G. creathae   _____

H. dopmucno   _____

I. livesvab   _____

J. aupp   _____

K. ltmo   _____

L. moelpect ratmmossihoep _____

_____ 1. Arthropod that usually has two pairs of legs per body segment

_____ 2. A hard outer covering that supports and protects

_____ 3. The long, flexible, armlike structures of an octopus

_____ 4. Structures that help starfish move and hold on to things

_____ 5. Breathing tubes in insects

_____ 6. Clams, scallops, and mussels, but not snails

_____ 7. Starfish and sea urchins

_____ 8. The life cycle that includes a cocoon, chrysalis, or puparium

_____ 9. The eyes of an insect

_____ 10. Part of the jet propulsion system of an octopus

_____ 11. To shed and replace an exoskeleton

_____ 12. The resting stage of metamorphosis

research investigation

16E Sea Monsters: Fact or Fiction?

name:

date:

hour:

The classic story *Twenty Thousand Leagues Under the Sea* follows the adventures of Captain Nemo as he travels the seas in his submarine, the *Nautilus*. Published in 1869, this story was futuristic science fiction. It incorporated the newest technology of the day, such as submarines and electricity. Jules Verne, the author, showed great insight into what modern technology would develop. But how would Jules Verne deal with the topic of sea monsters? In the late 1800s people believed that sea monsters existed. He took what was known and used his imagination to fill in what was unknown. Sometimes he guessed right, sometimes wrong.

Materials
- encyclopedia
- other reference books

Directions

Read the following excerpt from Chapter 18 of *Twenty Thousand Leagues Under the Sea*, which records a description of a giant cuttlefish they were about to battle. (A cuttlefish is a type of mollusk similar to a squid and an octopus.) Then, consult encyclopedias and other reference books to determine which parts of Verne's description of the cuttlefish could be true and which parts are false. Use the table on the next page as a guide.

I looked in my turn, and could not repress a gesture of disgust. Before my eyes was a horrible monster, worthy to figure in the legends of the marvellous. It was an immense cuttle-fish, being eight yards long. It swam crossways in the direction of the *Nautilus* with great speed, watching us with its enormous staring green eyes. Its eight arms, or rather feet, fixed to its head, that have given the name of cephalopod to these animals, were twice as long as its body, and were twisted like the furies' hair. One could see 250 airholes on the inner side of the tentacles. The monster's mouth, a horned beak like a parrot's, opened and shut vertically. Its tongue, a horned substance, furnished with several rows of pointed teeth, came out quivering from this veritable pair of shears. What a freak of nature, a bird's beak on a mollusc! Its spindle-like body formed a fleshy mass that might weigh 4000 to 5000 lbs; the varying colour changing with great rapidity, according to the irritation of the animal, passed successively from livid grey to reddish brown. What irritated this mollusc? No doubt the presence of the *Nautilus*, more formidable than itself, and on which its suckers or its jaws had no hold. Yet, what monsters these poulps are! what vitality the Creator has given them! what vigour in their movements! and they possess three hearts! Chance had brought us in presence of this cuttle-fish, and I did not wish to lose the opportunity of carefully studying this specimen of cephalopods. I overcame the horror that inspired me; and, taking a pencil, began to draw it.

Description	True/False	If False, Give Correct Description
8 yd long		
fast swimmer		
green eyes		
eight arms		
arms twice as long as body		
250 air holes on inner surface of tentacles		
beaked mouth		
horned or toothed tongue		
4000–5000 lb		
can change color		
suckers (on arms)		
three hearts		

class investigation

16F **Butterfly Metamorphosis**

name: _____

date: _____   hour: _____

Note: This investigation is written for use with the painted lady butterfly (*Vanessa cardui*), a small, common butterfly that is available from science supply companies. If you use another species of butterfly, you may need to alter the directions.

Procedures and Observations

Raise the larvae

1. Place several larvae in a container with a suitable food source. In the wild, these caterpillars would pull the edges of a leaf together, with themselves inside, and would then begin eating the leaf. If you have purchased your caterpillars, they probably have come with a food source. Thistles are a favorite food of painted lady butterfly caterpillars.

2. Place the container in a well-lit, warm area. The caterpillars should not be in direct sunlight, and the temperature should not go above 25°C (77°F).

3. Observe your caterpillars daily and record your observations on a separate sheet of paper. Note such things as changes in size, shape, and activity.

4. After a time of feeding and growing, the caterpillars will climb to the top of the container and will hang from it. They will then form a chrysalis.

Observe the chrysalises

1. How many days did you observe the caterpillars before the first one formed a chrysalis? _____

   _____

2. Describe the shape, size, color, and other characteristics of the chrysalises. _____

   _____

3. How many days did you observe the caterpillars before the last one formed a chrysalis? _____

   _____

4. Take the chrysalises and place them in a larger container.

5. How many days did you observe the chrysalises before any adults emerged? _____

   _____

Goals

- Observe the stages of complete metamorphosis.
- Learn about the life cycle of a butterfly.

Materials

- containers for growing larvae and hatching butterflies
- painted lady butterfly larvae
- suitable food source

6. Once an adult comes out, observe the other chrysalises carefully. Try to observe a butterfly emerging from a chrysalis. On a separate sheet of paper, describe the process. Tell what part of the butterfly came out first, how long the butterfly took to come out, and how long it was out before it tried to fly.

Raise the adults

1. The adults will feed on a weak sugar solution placed in a bottle with a wick of paper towel sticking out of it.

2. Place leaves, stems, or seedlings of mallow or hollyhock in with the butterflies. If these materials are supplied for them, the adults will mate and begin to lay eggs on the plant leaves within about a week.

3. The eggs are small, light green balls with lines on them. They will hatch in about a week.

Summing Up

1. What did you learn about butterfly metamorphosis that you did not know before? _____

_____

_____

_____

_____

_____

_____

_____

2. Which observation was the most fascinating to you? Why? _____

_____

_____

_____

_____

_____

_____

_____

17 VERTEBRATES I: FISH, AMPHIBIANS, AND REPTILES

ideas

17A **Vertebrate Digestive System**

name:

date: hour:

Directions

Label the following drawing by supplying each missing term or definition and then drawing a line from each term to the proper structure.

1. _____

(passes food from the mouth to the stomach)

2. stomach

3. _____

(produces bile)

4. small intestine

5. gallbladder

6. large intestine

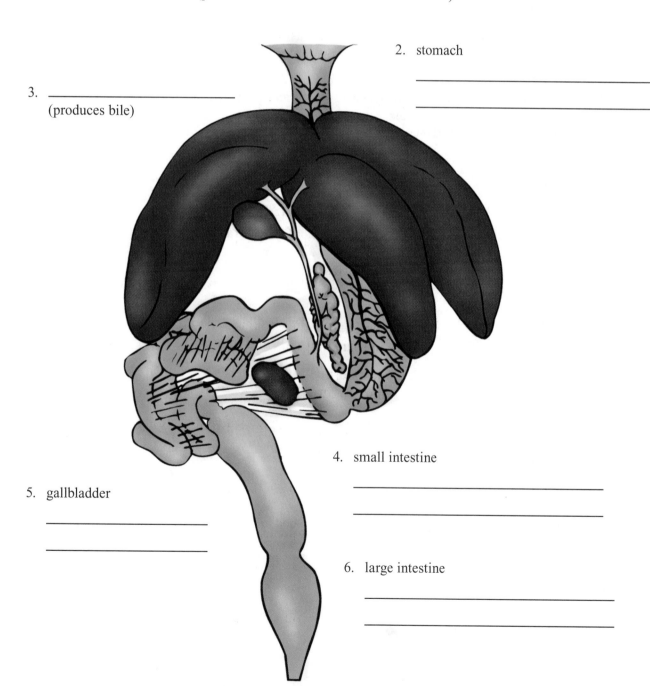

ideas

17B Body Systems in Vertebrate Animals

Directions

Choose the answer that best completes each of the following statements and record your choice in the blank by the number. Then use the letters of your answers (*A*, *B*, *C*, or *D*) and the key below to plot a trail on the map on page SA170. If all your answers are correct and you correctly plot the trail, your trail will end in the state that answers the question below the map.

If the answer to a statement is *A*, draw a line 5° northward from your last stopping point.

If the answer to a statement is *C*, draw a line 5° eastward from your last stopping point.

If the answer to a statement is *B*, draw a line 5° southward from your last stopping point.

If the answer to a statement is *D*, draw a line 5° westward from your last stopping point.

_____ 1. The air chambers inside an animal's body where blood can get oxygen and give off carbon dioxide are
    A. lungs.   C. nephridia.
    B. spiracles.   D. flame cells.

_____ 2. Blood vessels that take the blood to the heart are called
    A. capillaries.   C. veins.
    B. arteries.   D. aortic arches.

_____ 3. A dome-shaped muscle that separates the chest chamber from the abdomen in many animals and in humans is the
    A. mesoderm.   C. ventricle.
    B. diaphragm.   D. air sac.

_____ 4. A fluid that carries substances both in its cells and dissolved in its liquid is
    A. bile.   C. blood.
    B. enzymes.   D. urine.

_____ 5. Blood containing little oxygen is
    A. yellow.   C. red.
    B. blue.   D. clear.

_____ 6. The central nervous system includes the brain and
    A. skull.   C. sensory receptors.
    B. spinal cord.   D. sensory organs.

_____ 7. A structure between two heart chambers that allows blood to go only one way is a(n)
    A. artery.   C. vein.
    B. capillary.   D. valve.

_____ 8. Blood that carries an abundant amount of oxygen is
    A. deoxygenated.   C. unoxygenated.
    B. oxygenated.   D. thin.

name:

date: hour:

_____ 9. Spinal nerves branch off the
            A. vertebrae.   C. muscles.
            B. brain.   D. spinal cord.

_____ 10. The normal process of forcing air into and out of the lungs is called
            A. breathing.   C. coughing.
            B. sneezing.   D. swallowing.

_____ 11. Blood vessels that take the blood away from the heart are called
            A. atria.   C. capillaries.
            B. veins.   D. arteries.

_____ 12. The respiratory structures that have capillaries close to their surfaces to exchange oxygen and carbon
            dioxide in water are the
            A. lungs.   C. air sacs.
            B. tracheas.   D. gills.

_____ 13. Tiny blood vessels that allow substances to pass between the blood and body tissues are called
            A. capillaries.   C. arteries.
            B. veins.   D. aortic arches.

_____ 14. Bile aids in the digestion of
            A. minerals.   C. proteins.
            B. carbohydrates.   D. fats.

_____ 15. The kidneys connect to the urinary bladder through the
            A. ureters.   C. small intestines.
            B. urethra.   D. spleen.

_____ 16. Blood that has had most of its oxygen given to the body's cells is called
            A. diluted.   C. dissolved.
            B. oxygenated.   D. deoxygenated.

_____ 17. The number of chambers in a fish heart is
            A. one.   C. three.
            B. two.   D. four.

_____ 18. Undigested foods leave the digestive tract through the
            A. kidneys.   C. urinary bladder.
            B. small intestine.   D. anus.

_____ 19. Upon leaving the stomach, food normally moves to the
            A. esophagus.   C. gallbladder.
            B. small intestine.   D. liver.

_____ 20. The structures that filter wastes from the blood in vertebrates are the
A. flame cells.   C. kidneys.
B. urethras.   D. urinary bladders.

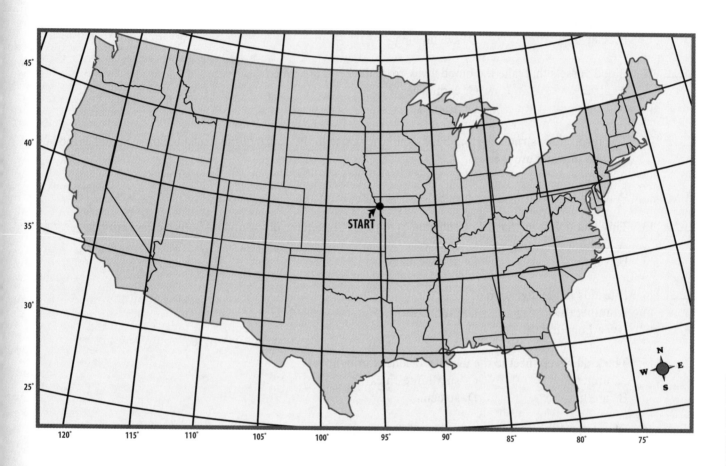

Which state has the largest number of poisonous reptile species? _____

ideas
17C Fish

name: _____

date: _____   hour: _____

Directions

Read the following statements. In the space provided, write *True* if the statement is true. If the statement is false, draw a line through the word or words that make the statement false. Then in the blank, write the word or words necessary to make the statement true.

_____ 1. Fish are invertebrates.

_____ 2. Fish are ectothermic.

_____ 3. A fish's scales are shed as the fish grows larger.

_____ 4. The lateral line is sensitive to vibrations in the water.

_____ 5. A fish has a three-chambered heart.

_____ 6. The lamprey is a jawless fish.

_____ 7. Sharks do not have swim bladders.

_____ 8. Sharks and rays are bony fish.

_____ 9. Fish have an open circulatory system.

_____ 10. In bony fish, respiration occurs as water moves in through the gills and out the mouth.

ideas
17D Amphibians

Directions

Choose the best word from the list below to complete each sentence. Write the word in the blank provided. Each word may be used once or not at all.

Appalachian	dry	maxillary	spiracles
Asian	estivation	metamorphosis	tailed
back	front	moist	tailless
coastal	hibernation	single	
double	incisors	skin	

1. The name *amphibian* literally means "_____ life."

2. The process that changes an amphibian from a gilled organism to a lunged organism is called

_____.

3. Amphibians must return to _____ places to lay their eggs.

4. _____ is a period of inactivity during hot, dry spells.

5. Frogs and toads are _____ amphibians.

6. A frog's tongue is attached to the _____ of its mouth.

7. Frogs have _____ and vomerine teeth.

8. Salamanders and newts are _____ amphibians.

9. Most amphibians can exchange gases through their _____.

10. The _____ region has the most salamander species.

ideas
17E Reptiles

Directions

Record your responses in the spaces provided.

1. Why do reptiles not have to return to water to lay their eggs? _____
    _____

2. What sensory organ do humans have that snakes do not? _____

3. Are most snakes poisonous or nonpoisonous? _____

4. Why are snakes capable of eating prey larger in diameter than themselves? _____
    _____

5. How can a large alligator approach its prey and yet be almost completely hidden? _____
    _____

6. How do sea turtles, tortoises, and terrapins differ? _____
    _____

7. Below is an illustration of an American alligator and one of an American crocodile. Label each correctly.

_____   _____

class investigation

17F **Fish Respiration Rates**

name: _____

date: _____   hour: _____

Setting Up

Place a live fish in a small aquarium. The water in the aquarium should be the same as the water to which the fish is accustomed. Do not use tap water unless it is well water or it has been dechlorinated. Place a thermometer in the aquarium.

Procedures and Observations

1. Locate and observe the operculum. The *operculum* is the flap that covers a fish's gills. The fish moves this flap back and forth to cause water to circulate over its gills. In the gills, gases are exchanged between the water and the blood.

2. Carefully count the number of times the operculum beats in fifteen seconds. Multiply this number by four to find out how many times it beats in one minute. Repeat the observation four times. Record your findings below.

   • Temperature: _____

   • Number of beats in one minute:

   First count: _____   Second count: _____

   Third count: _____   Fourth count: _____

   • Average number of beats per minute: _____

3. Place several cups of hot water in a plastic bag and close it tightly. Slowly, so as not to disturb the fish, lower the bag into the aquarium. Wait for the aquarium water to increase five degrees. Then slowly remove the bag of hot water.

4. Repeat your observations of the operculum's movements.

   • Temperature: _____

   • Number of beats in one minute:

   First count: _____   Second count: _____

   Third count: _____   Fourth count: _____

   • Average number of beats per minute: _____

5. Record any observations you make at this temperature that are different from those at the previous

   temperature. _____

6. Place several ice cubes in a plastic bag and close it tightly. Slowly, so as not to disturb the fish, lower the bag into the aquarium. Wait for the aquarium water to cool five degrees below the original temperature. You may need to replace the ice. Slowly remove the bag of ice.

Goals

- Observe the respiration of a fish.
- Determine the effects of temperature on the respiration rate of a fish.

Materials

- hot water
- ice cubes
- live fish
- plastic bags
- small aquarium
- thermometer

7. Repeat your observations of the operculum's beats.

   • Temperature: _____

   • Number of beats in one minute:

   First count: _____   Second count: _____

   Third count: _____   Fourth count: _____

   • Average number of beats per minute: _____

8. Record any other observations you make at this temperature that are different from those at the other temperatures.

   _____

   _____

   _____

   _____

9. Let the aquarium water return slowly to its normal temperature.

Summing Up

1. When was the fish's operculum the most active?

   ☐ high temperature   ☐ medium temperature
   ☐ low temperature

2. When was the fish's operculum the least active?

   ☐ high temperature   ☐ medium temperature   ☐ low temperature

3. How did the rate of operculum beats compare to the amount of activity of the fish? _____

   _____

   _____

4. Based on these observations, when was the fish's respiration rate the highest?

   ☐ high temperature   ☐ medium temperature   ☐ low temperature

5. Based on these observations, when was the fish's respiration rate the slowest?

   ☐ high temperature   ☐ medium temperature   ☐ low temperature

6. Is this fish an endothermic or ectothermic animal?

   ☐ endothermic   ☐ ectothermic

   Explain how the results of this investigation support your answer. _____

   _____

class investigation
17G **Frog Dissection**

name: _____

date: _____   hour: _____

Procedures and Observations

Examine the external structures of the frog.

1. Feel the frog's skin. Describe the texture. _____
_____

2. Remove a small section of skin from the frog's back. Look on the underside of the skin and notice the blood vessels located there. Why would the frog's skin need to have a rich supply of blood?
_____

3. Find the following structures: eyes, mouth, nostrils, and tympanic membrane.

4. Notice the difference in size between the frog's forelegs and its hind legs.

   How long are the forelegs? _____

   How long are the hind legs? _____

   Do you think this difference in size has anything to do with the different ways the frog uses its legs?   ☐ Yes   ☐ No

   What is the function of the forelegs? _____
_____

   What is the function of the hind legs? _____

5. Determine the sex of the frog. Examine the innermost toes ("thumbs") on the forelegs. The innermost toes are enlarged in males. Check the appropriate box.   ☐ male   ☐ female

Examine the frog's mouth.

1. Open the mouth of the frog and notice the grooves and ridges along the edge of the jaws. These grooves and ridges allow the mouth to close tightly. Why does the frog's mouth need to close tightly? _____
_____

   Does the frog have lips?   ☐ Yes   ☐ No

2. Move your finger along the edge of the upper jaw and feel the frog's tiny teeth.

   What are these teeth called? _____

   How does the frog use them? _____

3. Locate the frog's vomerine teeth at the front of the roof of the mouth.

4. Gently pull the tongue until it extends from the frog's mouth.

   Where does the tongue attach to the jaw? _____

   How is the free end of the tongue shaped? _____

   Normally when the frog is alive, a part of the tongue is sticky.

Goals
- Identify the organs of a frog.
- Prepare for a study of human organs by studying frog organs.

Materials
- dissection pan
- dissection pins
- forceps
- latex gloves (optional)
- preserved frog
- probe
- ruler
- scalpel
- scissors
- thin straw

Why is this characteristic important to the frog? _____

_____

Open the frog's body cavity.

1. Place the frog on its back in the dissection pan.

2. Beginning above the anus, place the scissors to the left of the whitish or reddish line that runs down the middle of the frog.

3. Break through the body wall with the point of the scissors and cut toward the mouth. Make sure to cut only the skin and muscles.

4. Continue cutting until you reach the frog's neck region. You will have to cut through the bone in the chest region.

5. Make additional perpendicular cuts across the top and bottom of the first cut. Pull back the cut sections and pin them to the dissection pan.

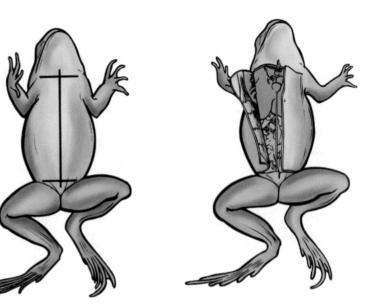

6. If you find obvious clusters of dark eggs, you have a female frog who was ready to reproduce. Carefully remove and discard these eggs without destroying any of the surrounding organs.

Examine the frog's heart.

1. Describe what the heart looks like. _____

2. Cut the heart in half, by slicing off the front half with the scalpel, so that there is a front half and a back half.

   How many chambers does the frog's heart have? _____

   What is the function of an upper chamber? _____

   How many lower chambers does the frog's heart have? _____

   What is the function of a lower chamber? _____

Examine the frog's lungs.

1. To help locate the lungs, open the frog's mouth and place a thin straw through the opening that leads to the trachea. Gently blow through the straw. As the lungs fill with air, they will become more noticeable to you.

2. Where are the lungs located in relation to the heart? _____

3. When the frog was alive, how did air enter its lungs? _____

_____

Examine the organs belonging to the digestive system.

1. Liver

   Where is the liver located in relation to the heart? _____

_____

   What color is it? _____

   What does the liver produce? _____

2. Gallbladder

   The gallbladder is a small greenish sac located between the lobes (sections) of the liver.

   What is the function of the gallbladder? _____

3. Esophagus

   To find the esophagus, open the frog's mouth and place a probe into the hole leading to the digestive system.

   Describe the esophagus. _____

4. Stomach

   Move the left lobe of the liver to find the stomach.

   What color is the stomach? _____

   Does it feel hard or soft? _____

   What is the function of the stomach? _____

5. Small intestine

   The small intestine is the small, tubular organ continuing from the stomach.

   Cut the tissues that hold the small intestine in place, but do not cut the small intestine.

   How long is the small intestine? _____

   What color is it? _____

   What does the small intestine do to the food that the frog eats? _____

   _____

6. Large intestine

   The large intestine is a large, tubular organ that continues from the small intestine.

   How long is the large intestine? _____

   Give two differences (other than length) between the large and small intestine. _____

   _____

   _____

7. Pancreas

   The pancreas is a yellowish organ that is thin and flat. It is located in the thin membrane that is attached to the stomach and the small intestine. (You may have difficulty locating this organ.)

   What does the pancreas produce? _____

Remove the digestive system.

1. Cut across the esophagus and the lower section of the large intestine. Carefully lift and remove the digestive system out of the body cavity. The remaining half of the heart will come with the digestive system.

2. Cut open the stomach and look inside.

   Is there any food in the stomach? ☐ Yes   ☐ No

   If so, can you recognize any of it? ☐ Yes   ☐ No

   If so, what did you find? _____

3. Rinse out the stomach and study the stomach's muscular walls.

How do these walls help digestion? _____

Examine the excretory and reproductive systems.

1. Kidneys

The kidneys are oval organs that are positioned against the frog's body wall.

How many kidneys does the frog have? _____

What color are they? _____

What do the kidneys do? _____

2. Urinary bladder

The urinary bladder looks like a small deflated balloon at the bottom of the body cavity.

What does the urinary bladder store? _____

3. Reproductive structures

If the frog is a male, locate the testes. These are two small organs attached near the kidneys.

If the frog is a female, locate the ovaries. If there were large masses of dark eggs filling the body cavity, you removed the ovaries when you removed the eggs. Ovaries with few or no eggs, however, are located near the kidneys.

When you complete this investigation, if your teacher informs you that you will be doing a study of the frog's nervous system, carefully wrap the preserved frog in moist paper towels and place it in a plastic bag. Otherwise, you can wrap it up in a paper towel and discard it in the trash.

18 VERTEBRATES II: BIRDS AND MAMMALS

ideas

18A Endothermic vs. Ectothermic

name:

date: hour:

Directions

Below are listed several words and statements that relate to being endothermic or ectothermic. In the space by each description, write *EN* if it relates to endotherms or *EC* if it relates to ectotherms.

_____ 1. Include amphibians

_____ 2. Include birds

_____ 3. Change body temperature based on surroundings

_____ 4. Can be active regardless of temperature

_____ 5. Cannot control body temperature by internal means

_____ 6. Include fish

_____ 7. Include insects

_____ 8. Include mammals

_____ 9. May have fur or feathers

_____ 10. May sweat

_____ 11. Do not change body temperature based on surroundings

_____ 12. Include reptiles

_____ 13. May pant for cooling

_____ 14. Include worms

_____ 15. Require more energy from food

ideas

18B **Birds**

Directions

Complete the crossword puzzle.

Across

2. Much energy and _____ must be available to flight muscles during flight.

4. Birds have wings and _____.

5. When a bird inhales and exhales, its _____ are filled with oxygen-rich air.

6. Usually birds build nests and _____ their eggs.

8. The _____ is a food-storage organ.

Down

1. Birds with _____ beaks probably eat meat.

3. Birds' lightweight bones are reinforced by a _____ structure.

7. Birds must _____ their eggs regularly so that normal development will not be disrupted.

ideas

18C Mammals

name:

date: hour:

Directions

Use the concept words from the list below to fill in the chart showing the relationships between the concepts. Words on the arrows show the relationships. Each concept word is used only once, and there is only one correct way to place all the concept words in this chart. Three words have already been placed in the chart to get you started.

~~eggs~~	marsupials	placental mammals
~~hair~~	milk	platypus
horse	monotremes	pouches
mammals	opossum	~~umbilical cord~~
mammary glands	placenta	

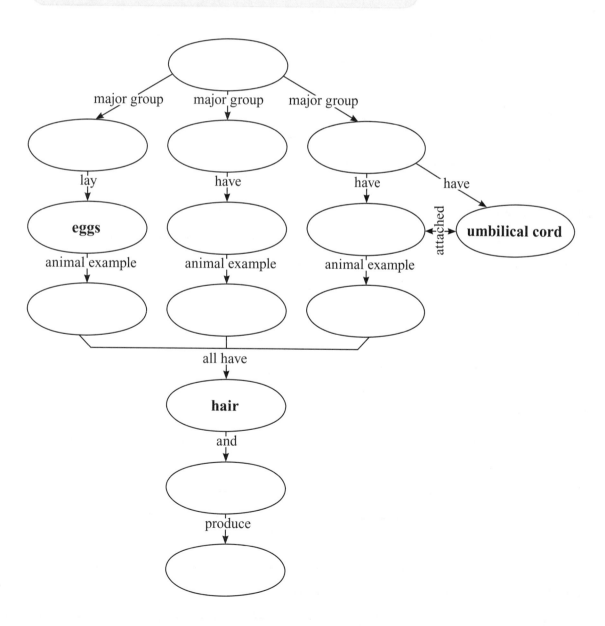

ideas
18D **Review**

Directions

Below each pair of terms, tell how the terms are similar; then tell how they are different.

1. endothermic / ectothermic

   similar: _____

   _____

   different: _____

   _____

2. sweating / panting

   similar: _____

   _____

   different: _____

   _____

3. yolk / egg white

   similar: _____

   different: _____

   _____

4. incisors / canines

   similar: _____

   different: _____

   _____

5. monotremes / marsupials

   similar: _____

   different: _____

   _____

6. placenta / umbilical cord

   similar: _____

   _____

   different: _____

   _____

7. hair / milk

   similar: _____

   different: _____

   _____

class investigation

18E Conserving Body Heat: Wool vs. Down

name: _____

date: _____   hour: _____

Procedures and Observations

1. Fill one container with wool and another with down. The containers should have equal amounts of the material to be tested. Label the containers. Label the empty container *Control*.

2. Put lids on all three containers and insert a thermometer through the hole in each lid. The thermometers should be positioned so that the thermometer bulb is about midway in the container. Do not allow the thermometer bulbs to touch the bottom or sides of the containers.

3. Before taking your first temperature reading, predict which container will cool the least in

   25 minutes: _____

4. On the table below, record the temperatures of all three containers; then put all three in the freezer. (Note: All three should be at approximately the same starting temperature.)

5. At five-minute intervals, record the temperatures of all three containers.

Goal

• Compare the effectiveness of fur (wool) and down (feathers) as insulators.

Materials

• down (feathers)
• freezer
• three containers (cups or glasses) with lids that have a hole
• three thermometers
• wool

Time	Control (°C)	Down (°C)	Wool (°C)
Start			
5 minutes			
10 minutes			
15 minutes			
20 minutes			
25 minutes			

Summing Up

1. Which container in this experiment had the greatest temperature change from start to finish? _____ _____

2. Which container in this experiment had the smallest temperature change from start to finish? _____ _____

3. Was your prediction correct? _____

4. Which container in this experiment had the greatest temperature change during a five-minute interval? ___

_____

5. What do you think would have happened if you had left the lid off the control container? _____

_____

6. If you had left the lid off the control container but on the two experimental containers, could you have

reached a reliable conclusion? _____

7. Are down and wool insulators? How do you know? _____

_____

8. Which of the materials tested in this experiment is the best insulator? _____

_____

9. What do down and wool do for endothermic animals? _____

_____

10. Explain how down and wool could be a disadvantage for endothermic animals. _____

_____

class investigation

18F **Observing Feathers and Hair**

name:

date: hour:

Procedures and Observations

1. Observe the contour feather. Bend it gently. Is it stiff? _____

   Examine the quill. Is it solid or hollow? _____

   Separate some barbs from the other barbs. Can you refasten them?
   _____

   Separate a barb and examine it with the hand lens or microscope.

   What can you see on the barb? _____

   _____

   Why do you think these are important? _____

   _____

   How long is your feather? _____ mm

   How long is the vane area of your feather? _____ mm

   How wide is the vane at its widest point? _____ mm

   Is the vane of equal width on either side of the central shaft?

   _____

   Does your feather have differences between the upper and lower

   surfaces? _____

2. In the space below draw a section of the contour feather as seen with your hand lens or microscope. Show the smallest details that you are able to see.

Goals

- Compare types of feathers.
- Observe the fine structure of feathers and hair.

Materials

- contour (wing or tail) feather
- down feather
- hand lens
- microscope
- prepared slide of animal hairs
- ruler with millimeter markings

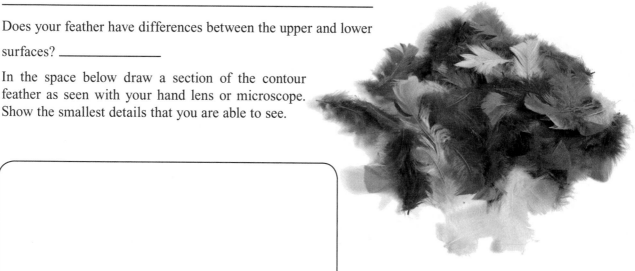

3. Observe the down feather with a hand lens. Is it stiff? _____ Can you fasten the barbs together? _____ In the space below draw the down feather as seen with your hand lens or microscope. Show the smallest details that you are able to see.

4. Examine the microscope slide of animal hairs. Describe what the hairs look like as seen through a microscope.

_____

5. In the space below draw the microscopic views of the hairs of three different animals. Your drawings should show how the animal hairs differ.

Summing Up

1. Which do you think are most important in flight, contour feathers or down feathers? _____

_____

2. How is the different function of a down feather related to its different structure when compared to a contour feather? _____

_____

3. Why do hairs not need to hold together like contour feathers do? _____

_____

4. What is the function of down feathers? _____

research investigation

18G **Compare and Contrast:**
Man vs. Beast

name: _____

date: _____   hour: _____

Procedures and Observations

1. Read each Scripture passage, looking for what it teaches us about humans and animals.

2. Fill in the table with what you learn from each passage.

Goal

• Discover what the Bible says about the similarities and differences between humans and animals.

Materials

• Bible

Scripture	Humans	Animals
Genesis 1:24–28; 2:19–22		
Genesis 9:2–6		
Psalm 8:4–9		
Proverbs 12:10		

Summing Up

1. What did you learn about how humans and animals are alike? _____

_____

2. What did you learn about how humans and animals are different? _____

_____

_____

19 ANIMAL BEHAVIOR

ideas

19A Innate and Learned Behaviors

name:

Part 1

date: _____ hour: _____

Directions

Answer the following questions in the space provided.

1. How are reflexes and instincts similar? _____

_____

_____

2. How are reflexes and instincts different? _____

_____

_____

3. What do you think would happen to an animal if its reflexes and instincts did not function properly? _____

_____

_____

4. Give an example of a learned behavior intentionally taught to an animal by man. _____

_____

_____

5. Give at least two examples of learned behaviors that animals might acquire in the wild, apart from man. ___

_____

_____

Part 2

Directions

Each of the Scripture passages listed in the table on the next page mentions or describes an animal doing something. Complete the table by naming each animal, describing what each does, and writing whether each action is innate or learned. Be prepared to state what God might be teaching you through each verse or passage.

Passage	Animal	Action	Innate or learned?
Genesis 24:11			
Exodus 23:28		attacking people	
Deuteronomy 22:10	ass (donkey)		
Deuteronomy 28:42			innate
Deuteronomy 32:11			
Esther 6:8		carrying a rider	
Matthew 15:27			
Luke 13:34			
John 10:4	sheep		
John 18:27			
2 Peter 2:22			
Revelation 9:5			innate
Revelation 19:17–21			

This painting graphically shows an Old Testament example of God's using an animal's innate behavior to accomplish His purposes. Use a concordance to figure out what book and chapter is depicted here.

_____

The Brazen Serpent, Benjamin West, P.R.A., from the Bob Jones University Collection

ideas
19B **Review 1**

name:

date: _____ hour: _____

Directions

Read the following examples and decide which of the various levels of behavior are being described. Then indicate your answers by writing the proper letters in the blanks provided. If the behavior is innate, you must tell whether the innate behavior is an instinct or a reflex. Some statements have more than one answer.

A. innate instinct
B. innate reflex
C. intelligent behavior
D. learned behavior

_____ 1. When given the proper materials, a bird kept isolated for its entire life builds a nest typical of its species.

_____ 2. During dinner a dog sits under the chair belonging to the family member who often gives the dog bites of food.

_____ 3. After watching the older lions in its pride, a young lion cub stalks its first prey.

_____ 4. A monkey uses a long stick to get to food that is beyond its reach.

_____ 5. When a bird becomes cold, its feathers stand up and it begins to shiver.

_____ 6. A guard dog attacks a prowler who comes into the yard but does not attack its owner when he similarly enters the yard.

_____ 7. A honeybee collects pollen from flowers to produce honey.

_____ 8. A honeybee stings your foot when you step on it while walking barefoot across a lawn.

_____ 9. When frightened, a de-scented pet skunk raises its tail and turns its back to the thing that frightened it.

_____ 10. At a security checkpoint, dogs sniff the packages of travelers. When a dog smells drugs, it barks and claws at the package.

_____ 11. After twenty tries, a rat can run the maze in less than one-third of its original time.

_____ 12. Screeching loudly, a mockingbird swoops down toward you as you walk by the tree where its nest is.

ideas

19C **Review 2**

Directions

Write clues relating to animal behavior for the crossword answers below.

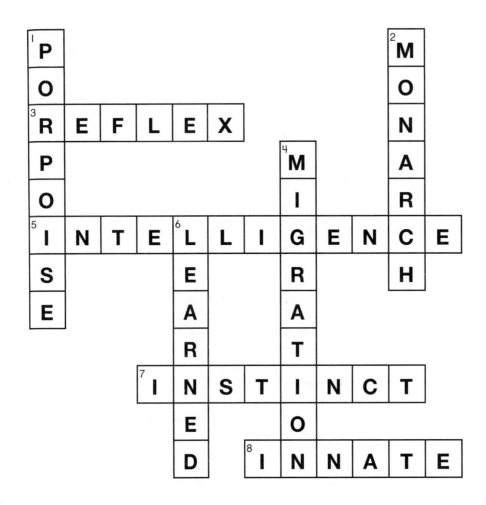

Across

3. _____

5. _____

7. _____

8. _____

Down

1. _____

_____

_____

class investigation

19D Myrmecology (The Study of Ants)

name:

date: hour:

Setting Up

A *microcosm* is a small area that simulates, as closely as possible, the situation in a larger area. Scientists often use microcosms to study organisms. Myrmecologists (scientists who study ants) use ant microcosms to study ant behavior. An ant microcosm chamber is a thin, clear container that people use to observe the actions of ants. If the container were thick, the ants would construct their tunnels in the middle of the sand or dirt and you would not be able to see them. Since ant microcosm chambers are thin, you can observe the tunnels that the ants build. You can build an ant microcosm or purchase a specially designed one.

1. Place sand or some other medium in the ant microcosm chamber and fill the chamber about halfway.

2. Add water so the sand is moist but not soggy.

3. Obtain your ants.

   • You can collect your own ants by placing a stick in front of a group of ants and permitting them to crawl up the stick and then placing them in your microcosm. You can also dig up an anthill and collect a mass of ants all at once, perhaps even a queen. If you collect your own ants, collect them from only one colony. If you put ants from different colonies in your ant farm, they will kill each other.

   • You can obtain ants from a science supply company. Carefully put your ants in the ant chamber. Be ready with sticks and various other devices to direct the ants into the chamber. Placing a paper funnel in the opening of the ant chamber often works well to direct the ants into the chamber. Do not injure the ants.

4. Place a piece of food in the chamber. A tiny portion of a corn flake is good to use.

Procedures and Observations

Care for your ant colony

1. Add several drops of water (more if your microcosm is large) every two or three days.

2. Add a small piece of food every three or four days. The major problem with keeping ant microcosms is overfeeding. If you put in too much food, it will begin to rot and will cause the ants to die. If food is not consumed before it begins to mold, remove the food. Removing the food can be difficult if the ants have taken their food deep into the colony. The best solution is to feed the ants very small amounts. If the ants ignore the food you introduce, do not feed them for several days.

Goals

• Become familiar with ants.

• Observe relationships within an ant colony.

Materials

• ant microcosm chamber

• ants

• eyedropper

• food (corn flakes, wheat or barley seeds, small potato slices)

• sand

3. Keep your ant farm in a well-lit area, but do not put it in direct sunlight or very strong light. The strong light will cause the temperature inside the ant farm to rise so high that the ants will die.

4. Keep your ant farm steady. If you must move it, do so carefully and slowly. Ants and their tunnels are sensitive to movement.

Myrmecology Notes

A normal ant colony has female workers and a queen. Each day, the queen lays hundreds of eggs that develop into the workers that build and protect the colony. Usually once a year the queen lays eggs that develop into males and other queens. The males and potential queens have wings, and they fly away from the colony. They mate in the air and then land. Once on the ground, they soon lose their wings and the males die. The new queens then establish new colonies.

The ants in your ant microcosm are most likely all workers. The queen usually remains deeply underground, and you would need to dig carefully to obtain her. If you purchased your ants, you will not have a queen since shipping queens is illegal. (It has been made illegal to prevent unwanted ants from being introduced to various parts of the country. Workers alone cannot produce a new colony.) Even without a queen, though, the ants in your colony will still carry on most of their normal functions. This is possible because their actions and reactions are not regulated by a queen. What are the ants' actions and reactions based on?

Ant workers, if properly cared for, can live for a year in an ant microcosm. For various reasons, however, they usually live for only a few months.

Observe your ant microcosm often

1. Record your observations. Although you may want to observe the ant farm several times a day, record your observations only once or twice a day. Use the questions below when making your observation record.

2. Make your recorded observations at the same time every day.

Observe the various activities occurring in your ant microcosm

1. What are the ants doing? Where are they tunneling? Where are they stacking sand? Where are their chambers built?

2. As they work on various projects, ants will work in large groups, in small groups, or sometimes alone. Indicate the size of the group that is working on each ant project you observe.

3. What do the ants do with the food?

4. What do the ants do when water is introduced?

5. Are all the ants working? Where are the ones that are not working? Is there any difference between those that are working and those that are not?

6. When an ant dies, what do the other ants do?

·uming Up

vou have observed the ant microcosm for several weeks, write a
mmary of what you saw the ants do. Include your observations
' reactions.

field investigation

19E An Animal's Response to Its Environment

name:

date: hour:

All animals constantly respond to their environment. We may not always be able to determine what stimulates the responses. Often, however, we can determine what the animal is responding to if we observe carefully and think about our observations.

Goal

• Observe and categorize an animal's reactions to stimuli in its environment.

Find some active animal in a large area. A squirrel in a yard or park, a dog in a yard, a bird near a bird feeder, a rabbit in a meadow, or a zoo animal in a large enclosure would be good to observe. If you cannot observe an animal in a large space, you can use an active animal in a smaller space: a fish in an aquarium or a bird, chameleon, guinea pig, or hamster in a cage. Observe the animal for three five-minute periods. These five-minute periods should each be separated by several minutes.

While you are watching the animal, observe the animal's reactions to stimuli. For each observation, record both the stimulus and the reaction. In order to do this, you may need to use a tape recorder, videocassette recorder, or a friend or two to record your observations. Animals will not wait for you to write down notes. You may even want to have a friend recording his own observations of the same animal at the same time you are. You could then compare notes and compile a more accurate list of the animal's reactions.

Compile your list of reactions on a separate sheet of paper. Then indicate whether each reaction was a reflex, an instinct, a learned reaction, or an intelligent behavior. Compute the percentage of the reactions in each group. Bring your list of observations, your decisions regarding what types of behaviors you observed, and your percentage figures to class. Present your findings to the class for discussion.

20 ANIMAL SEXUAL REPRODUCTION

ideas

20A Meiosis, Gametes, and Fertilization

name: _____

date: _____   hour: _____

Directions

In the space provided, describe the difference between the terms given.

1. ovaries / testes _____
   _____
   _____
   _____

2. eggs / sperm _____
   _____
   _____
   _____

3. eggs / zygotes _____
   _____
   _____
   _____

4. fertilization / zygote _____
   _____
   _____
   _____

5. haploid / gametes _____
   _____
   _____
   _____
   _____

ideas

20B External and Internal Fertilization

Directions

In each of the following statements, draw a circle around the correct choice in the parentheses. On the lines provided, explain why the incorrect choice is not acceptable.

1. (Male / Female) salmon produce milt. _____

_____

2. Salmon reproduce by (spawning / nesting). _____

_____

3. A baby animal develops within an egg during a period of time known as (incubation / gestation). _____

_____

4. When egg and sperm are united inside the female's body, (internal / external) fertilization takes place. _____

_____

5. (Yolk / Albumen) is the primary stored food that a developing chick will use to grow. _____

_____

6. An eggshell has tiny pores to allow (water / gases) to pass through. _____

_____

7. Crocodiles incubate their eggs by (heating them with rotting plants / sitting on them). _____

_____

8. The umbilical cord carries (amniotic fluid / blood). _____

_____

ideas

20C **Review**

name: _____

date: _____   hour: _____

Directions

All the scrambled words listed below deal with sexual reproduction in animals. Unscramble the words and write them in the blanks. For some of the words, a definition has been supplied. For those that lack a definition, you must write one in the space provided.

1. teelanxr   _____   the union of an ovum and a sperm outside an animal's body

   tetiiaifoznrl _____

2. tilm   _____   _____

3. butoiicnna   _____   the period of growth inside an egg

4. lenntira   _____   _____

   eilafzrtotiin _____

5. tetogansi   _____   the period of time an embryo spends inside the womb

6. yomber   _____   _____

7. balnume   _____   an egg white

8. geg   _____   _____

9. nnomia   _____   the fluid-filled sac around an embryo

10. liilcuamb   _____   _____

    rdoc   _____

11. getaprnn   _____   the condition of an animal with an unborn offspring

12. wpasginn   _____   _____

13. remsp   _____   the gametes produced by males

14. okly   _____   _____

15. yavor   _____   the organ that produces ova

16. rayammm   _____   the structures that produce milk for a newborn

    danlgs   _____

17. ritbh   _____   the normal end of pregnancy

18. caatelnp   _____   the structure that is attached to the wall of a uterus and provides nourishment and oxygen for an embryo

mother   father

1   2   3   4   5

class investigation

20D Sexual Reproduction: Means of Amazing Variation

name: _____

date: _____   hour: _____

Sexual reproduction offers one clear advantage that asexual reproduction (or cloning) does not offer—variation. Organisms produced by sexual reproduction are similar to, but not exactly like, their parents. In Chapters 7 and 8 of your text, you can read how this variation occurs. In this investigation you are going to verify that animals produced by sexual reproduction can have certain characteristics that are different from their parents.

Procedure and Observations

Observe the cat family on page SA200.
Describe the fur coat pattern of each animal.

mother _____

father _____

offspring #1 _____

offspring #2 _____

offspring #3 _____

offspring #4 _____

offspring #5 _____

1. How many of the offspring had fur coat patterns identical to the mother's or father's? _____

2. How many different kinds of fur coat patterns were found in the litter? _____

3. How many different kinds of fur coat patterns were demonstrated by the parents? _____

4. If the offspring were genetically identical to one parent, would the pattern of their fur coats be different from that parent? _____

Summing Up

1. Other than fur coat pattern, list five traits in which wild animals could vary from their parents.

_____

_____

_____

_____

_____

2. How could having different patterns of fur coats help an animal species survive for thousands of years?

_____

_____

_____

3. Why would not having variation be harmful to a species? _____

_____

_____

research investigation

20E Animal Reproduction Worksheet

name:

date: _____ hour: _____

Procedures and Observations

Data Research

Use encyclopedias and other reference books to find the information needed to complete the table. Some answers have been provided.

Goal
• Compare the various ways that animals reproduce.

Materials
• encyclopedia
• other reference books

Animal name	Length of incubation or gestation	Live bearer or egg layer?	Number of eggs or young at one time	Parental care provided? (yes/no)
guppy				no
bullfrog				
box turtle	over winter			
bald eagle		eggs		
common cuckoo				
cottontail rabbit		live		
Asian elephant			1	

Data Interpretation

Use the data in the table on page SA204 to answer these questions. Questions 4–7 may require additional outside research.

1. Which egg layer has the longest period of incubation? _____

2. Which organism produces the greatest potential number of offspring? _____

3. Which organism has the shortest gestation or incubation period? _____

4. What might account for the wide range in number of possible eggs laid by the largemouth bass? _____

_____

5. How does a scorpion mother care for her offspring? _____

6. What is unusual about the egg development of the Surinam toad? _____

_____

7. What might account for the thirty-day variation in hatching time for snapping turtle eggs? _____

_____

Animal name	Length of incubation or gestation	Live bearer or egg layer?	Number of eggs or young at one time	Parental care provided? (yes/no)
black widow	14–30 days	eggs	25–750	yes (eggs)
blue crab	14 days	eggs	1 million–3 million	yes (eggs)
lobster	11–12 months	eggs	5,000–10,000	yes (eggs)
emperor scorpion	7–9 months	live	15–40	yes
large mouth bass	3–7 days	eggs	2,000–43,000	yes
lined sea horse	21 days	eggs	250–600	yes (eggs)
Surinam toad	3–5 months	eggs	60–80	yes (eggs)
Gila monster	4–12 months	eggs	3–13	no
snapping turtle	3–4 months	eggs	25–80	no
brown pelican	30 days	eggs	1–4	yes
emperor penguin	63 days	eggs	1	yes
prairie dog	28–32 days	live	2–10	yes
orangutan	7–8 months	live	1	yes

Summing Up

1. What is the difference between incubation and gestation? _____

_____

_____

2. Which of the animals above do you think has the most unusual reproduction? Why? _____

_____

_____

3. What type of care might an animal provide for its young? _____

_____

21 THE ECOSYSTEM

ideas
21A Ecosystems and the Abiotic Environment

name:

Part 1

date: hour:

Directions

Listed below are three common relationships in ecosystems. Below the list are some examples of relationships in ecosystems. In the blank by each example, write the letter of the relationship that is being described. You will use each letter more than once.

Common Relationships in Ecosystems
A. Organisms affect other organisms.
B. Abiotic factors affect organisms.
C. Organisms affect abiotic factors.

_____ 1. To keep from becoming too hot, a lizard spends the hottest part of the afternoon in the shadow of a rock.

_____ 2. A groundhog digs tunnels in the soil.

_____ 3. A squirrel scampers up a tree, sits on a limb, and begins eating a pecan.

_____ 4. The roots of a tree have grown into the cracks of a rock. As the roots continue to grow, the rock slowly crumbles.

_____ 5. A leech attaches itself to a turtle's flipper and obtains a meal of blood.

_____ 6. Birds navigate their migrations by the stars.

_____ 7. A snake swallows a rat.

_____ 8. The warm soil and the abundant moisture trigger seeds to sprout.

_____ 9. When it rains, plants growing on a hillside prevent the water from running down the hill quickly and carrying soil with it.

_____ 10. A year of drought causes an oak tree to produce fewer acorns than normal.

Part 2

Directions

In the spaces provided, describe the difference between the terms in each pair.

1. ecology / ecosystem _____

_____

_____

_____

2. abiotic environment / biotic community _____

_____

_____

_____

3. intensity of light / duration of light _____

_____

_____

_____

4. humus / substrate _____

_____

_____

_____

5. evaporation / precipitation _____

_____

_____

_____

6. runoff water / groundwater _____

_____

_____

_____

ideas
21B **Succession on a Volcano**

name:

date: hour:

Directions

In each of the following statements, draw a circle around the correct choice in the parentheses. On the lines provided, explain why the incorrect choice is not acceptable.

1. The plants and animals that lived on Mount Saint Helens in Washington before its 1980 eruption included pine and fir trees, grouse, foxes, hares, deer, bobcats, bears, and mountain lions. Populations of these organisms made up the (natural biotic community / climax vegetation) of Mount Saint Helens. _____
    _____

2. When Mount Saint Helens erupted in 1980, almost all living things on the mountain were destroyed. This is an example of the (biotic community affecting the abiotic environment / abiotic environment affecting the biotic community). _____
    _____

3. In some areas, all life was destroyed. But within a few months of the eruption, some plants, such as pearly everlasting and fireweed, were found growing in these areas. These had sprouted from windblown seeds. Such plants are examples of (pioneer organisms / climax vegetation). _____
    _____

4. Pine and fir seedlings could not grow on the fresh volcanic surface of Mount Saint Helens because they require soil. Several generations of other plants are building the soil necessary for pines to grow. Soil building is an example of the (abiotic environment affecting the biotic community / biotic community affecting the abiotic environment). _____
    _____

5. As the soil is built, the first plants give way to other plants. If not hindered by more eruptions, pine and fir trees will once again grow on Mount Saint Helens. These predictable changes in the biotic community are called (succession / Krakatoa). _____
    _____

6. The appearance of pine and fir trees on Mount Saint Helens does not represent the final climax community, since other major species changes (will yet occur / will not occur). _____
    _____

7. The community surrounding Mount Saint Helens immediately before the 1980 eruption was not a climax community. It was still recovering from an 1857 eruption. A forest community of hemlocks and firs is the climax community for the mountains in that area. If no more eruptions occur, Mount Saint Helens will probably reach its climax community (before / after) the year 2103. _____

_____

_____

ideas
21C The Water Cycle

Directions

In the illustration below, draw arrows to show the water cycle. Draw label lines from the terms around the illustration to what they describe in the picture.

transpiration   precipitation   clouds

evaporation

stream

water entering   groundwater   water seeping   water table   runoff water
plant roots   through the
                                      ground

ideas

21D Rhythms in the Ecosystem

name: _____

date: _____   hour: _____

Directions

Unscramble the words and fill in the blanks. For some of the words, a definition has been supplied. For each that lacks a definition, you must write one in the blank provided.

1. hthymrs   _____ changes that take place on a regular basis

2. alnoesas   _____ _____

3. tunrlacno   _____ active at night

4. danicrica   _____ rhythms that happen every twenty-four hours

5. dlruian   _____ _____

6. rodycnam   _____ _____

7. odtrmna dbu   _____ _____

8. nilesepnra   _____ plants that grow year after year

9. nnaauls   _____ _____

10. nrebhiatoni   _____ _____

11. tinnerla ckclo   _____ the internal mechanism that controls rhythms in an organism

ideas
21E **Review**

Directions

Record your responses in the spaces provided.

1. List the major factors of the abiotic environment that are found in most ecosystems. _____

_____

_____

2. List several materials that are cyclic in an ecosystem. Why is it essential that these materials cycle in an eco-

   system? _____

_____

3. Choose an ecosystem. How does your choice qualify as an ecosystem? _____

_____

_____

4. List several factors of the abiotic environment that are significant in the ecosystem you chose in question 3.

_____

_____

5. List several populations that would be found in the ecosystem you chose in question 3. Indicate which of these

   populations are producers and which are consumers. _____

_____

_____

6. What are the differences between a winter resident bird, a summer resident bird, and a permanent resident

   bird? _____

_____

_____

research investigation

21F Our Environment (Part 1)

name:

date: hour:

Procedures and Observations

If you are like most people, you probably know very little about the area in which you live. You may be able to find your way around well, but you probably have never carefully observed the surroundings that characterize your environment. This investigation, along with certain investigations in the next two chapters, is designed to help you and your classmates discover what your environment was like before people started living in the area. You will also discover the various changes that humans have made in the area.

This project will require several weeks to complete and will consist of many assignments. Sometimes you will work alone; other times you will work in groups. Your entire class will keep a notebook so that you can find out what your classmates are learning about your environment and they can benefit from what you find out. This notebook will contain the reports and other materials prepared by your class. When completed, it will describe many aspects of your environment.

To keep your notebook neat and organized, follow the instructions and outline below when submitting a report for the notebook.

Goal
- Investigate your environment through published resources and develop a permanent reference of materials.

Materials
- encyclopedia
- other reference books

Note: This investigation continues in Research Investigations 22E and 23E. The three investigations are divided into sixteen different projects that each cover some part of the ecology of your area. Some projects will be done by your whole class; others by smaller groups. Your teacher may omit a few of the projects if they do not apply to your area or may add some projects pertaining to special situations in your area.

Outline for the *Our Environment* Notebook

I. The natural environment
   A. Location
   B. The abiotic environment
   C. The biotic community
      1. Producer organisms
         a. Algae
         b. Annuals
         c. Nonwoody perennials
         d. Woody perennials
      2. Consumer organisms
         a. Invertebrates
         b. Fish
         c. Reptiles
         d. Amphibians
         e. Birds
         f. Mammals
         g. Others (mushrooms and other fungi)
   D. Relationships between organisms
      1. Relationships within populations
      2. Relationships between populations
      3. Succession

II. Man's use of the environment
   A. Man and the abiotic environment
      1. Water sources and uses
      2. Energy sources and uses
      3. Pollution
      4. Sewage and trash
   B. Man and the biotic community
      1. Agriculture
      2. Extinct and endangered organisms
      3. Game, game management, and hunting

Preparing Reports for the Our Environment Notebook

Using paper or a word processor, write the report. At the end of the report, list the sources you used to find the information for your report. For books, magazines, and pamphlets, use the bibliography form that your teacher suggests. If you interviewed someone, list who was interviewed, his position, the interview date, and who did the interviewing. (Example: Mr. Harold Smith, Director of Farming Research at Wayne County Agricultural Station in Pumpkintown, Massachusetts; November 20, 2007; interviewed by Beth Harris and Scott Jones)

Below the list of sources, write, "This report was prepared by . . ." On the lines underneath, list in alphabetical order the names of the people who are responsible for the report.

Give the report to your teacher. Your teacher will read it and, if necessary, comment on it. If you include pictures (photographs or pictures cut from magazines or other sources) in your report, include them with the report when you first hand it to your teacher. You may also include original drawings.

If the report is not acceptable, your teacher will return it to you to revise. If the report is acceptable, your teacher will return it to you with blank paper attached to it. Using blue or black ink, neatly copy your report onto the paper that your teacher gives you. Use only the front side of the paper. If you used a word processor and any changes are necessary, revise and reprint your report.

Give the finished report and any drawings or pictures to the classmates who are responsible for keeping the notebook.

Project 1

Where Are We?

Before you can begin to describe an area, you have to know what area you are talking about. Determine which biome you live in. A biome is a large geographical area that contains a particular group of plants and animals and has a specific abiotic environment. The map on pages 514–15 of your text may give you some idea of the biome in which you live but is too small to give you specific information. You will need to consult other texts to determine your area's biome.

Biomes are divided into smaller areas that have particular characteristics. Determine the type and size of the area you live in. Some areas may include several states. Sometimes three or four different areas may be present in a single state. (This often happens in states that have mountains in one area or that border the ocean.) If several areas are nearby, determine which your class will use. If you choose a large area, you may want to limit yourself to a smaller section of the area.

A student who is good at drawing can prepare a series of maps. He should first draw your continent and shade in your biome. He should then outline the state in which you live. On another map he should enlarge the state, shade in the area of the biome you are using for your study, and outline the county in which you live. On this map he should include major bodies of water, such as rivers and large lakes.

If possible, obtain a topographical map of your county from a library or county government agency. Topographical maps include information about the land (hills, valleys, streams, lakes, etc.). Choose a student to draw a simplified county map for your notebook. In the drawing, he should include bodies of water and any other significant topographical features. He should also include major roads and cities. If the area you are studying does not fill the entire county, he should indicate this by drawing the county limits on your map.

Project 2

The Abiotic Environment

At various times your area probably receives wind, rain, sunshine, cold weather, and warm weather. How do these and various other factors combine to make up the abiotic environment of your area? Different students or groups of students can prepare reports on each of the following factors.

- *Temperatures.* In your area, what is the average daytime high temperature for each month? What is the average nighttime low temperature for each month? What is the average temperature for each month? Plot this information on a graph. Are there any significant or unusual aspects about the temperatures in your area?

- *Precipitation.* In your area, what is the average precipitation for each month? Plot this information on a graph. Is snow, ice, hail, sleet, or fog a common or significant factor in your area? Are there any significant or unusual aspects about the precipitation in your area?

- *Bodies of water.* What bodies of water are found in your area? If the bodies of water flow, how fast do they flow? How much seasonal difference is there in the amount of water they carry? How large are the standing bodies of water? How deep are they? What seasonal differences do they experience?

- *Sunlight.* How many daily hours of sunlight does your area average for each month? Plot this information on a graph. Are there any significant factors that affect the number of hours of sunlight that your area receives? Are cloudy days common in your area? If so, during what seasons?

- *Soil and substrate.* What kind of soil is found in your area? How deep is the topsoil? What is under the topsoil?

- *Winds.* In which direction are the prevailing winds in your area? Are they different during different seasons? What is the average speed (mph) of the winds for each month? Are storms common during a particular season? What are the winds like during storms? Does your area have hurricanes or tornadoes? If so, how often?

To find this information you will most likely need to do research in a library. You may need to ask a librarian for help in locating local statistics. Your chamber of commerce may have some climate data. Another source of information is the weather bureau for your area. Some of the information will also be available from county or state agencies. Various Internet websites also have long-term climate data.

Project 3

The Biotic Community

What organisms make up the natural biotic community of your area? Use field guides that deal with the organisms in your area. There are field guides to the trees, wildflowers, ferns, mushrooms, insects, fish, birds, reptiles, amphibians, mammals, and many other groups for virtually every region. A number of websites from organizations such as state extension or wildlife departments may also provide detailed information. Compile lists of significant organisms found in your area.

From these lists, you and your classmates should choose organisms that you would like to prepare reports about. Your teacher will determine the number of reports that each student should do. Each person should report on some large organisms and some small organisms. Do not report on an organism if it is found only in small numbers or if it is one of a large group of similar organisms in your area. For example, if there are ten different types of warblers in your area, you may want to deal with them all as a group or with only one, but do not write a different report for each warbler.

As much as possible, follow the outlines given below. Sometimes you may not be able to find all the information for the organisms you are researching. If you have not included enough information, your teacher will return the report to you with a note saying that you need to continue your research.

Animal

Name: (common and scientific)

Description: (size, color, physical characteristics, etc.)

Food: (what the animal prefers to eat, what it will eat if the preferred food is not available, and what it eats during different seasons)

Range: (the areas of the country in which the animal is found)

Habitat: (the area in which the animal lives, feeds, builds its nest, den, etc.)

Daily activity: (diurnal or nocturnal)

Seasonal activity: (migration, dormancy, or hibernation)

Picture: (photograph or drawing, if possible)

Plant

Name: (common and scientific)

Description: (size, type of stem, leaves, flowers, fruits, etc.)

Range: (the areas of the country in which the plant is found)

Habitat: (the area that provides the conditions necessary for the plant to grow)

Seasonal: (when it flowers, bears fruit, is dormant, sprouts, etc.)

Picture: (photograph or drawing, if possible)

Project 4

The Seasons

Establish several large groups within your class. Each group will be responsible for a different season. Depending on your area of the country, you may wish to divide spring into early spring and late spring and divide autumn into early autumn and late autumn. In some areas of the country, there will be only three, and in some cases only two, seasons.

Using the information that was gathered in Projects 2 and 3, describe your area during each of the various seasons. You may want to write your descriptions as those of a typical day during the season that you are dealing with. A sample you might like to follow is the description of the dawn on page 368 of your textbook. There are other methods you could use to describe your area during the various seasons. Be sure to include information about the abiotic environment and the biotic community.

class investigation

21G The Biotic Community of the Soil

name: _____

date: _____ hour: _____

Procedures and Observations

1. Collect about 1 L of topsoil. Especially include any organic debris on the surface. Thoroughly decomposed wood works especially well. Avoid areas that have been treated with insecticide, such as lawns, or recently cultivated areas, such as gardens. Forest soil is excellent for this investigation.

2. Assemble a Berlese funnel. This is a large funnel with a wire screen set inside it. Support the funnel with a ring stand and iron ring as shown. The wire screen should be cut or bent into a disc that fits the funnel about halfway down the fluted portion.

3. Place part or all of your soil sample on the wire screen in the Berlese funnel. Place the portion of the soil that has the most organic material (leaves, stems, twigs, etc.) on the screen first. It will help to keep the remainder of the soil from falling through the screen. The soil layer should be about 5 cm deep.

4. Position the funnel over a jar or beaker containing isopropyl alcohol to collect the organisms that fall through. You may substitute water for alcohol, but some organisms may then escape.

5. Suspend an incandescent light over the funnel about 4 in. above the soil. Leave the light on for about twenty-four hours. Organisms in the soil will burrow deeper to avoid the heat, light, and drying. As they do, they will fall through the screen and into the collection jar or beaker.

6. Many of the organisms are small, so you should use a hand lens (or stereomicroscope) to observe the collected organisms. Identify and count the organisms. Your teacher will help you identify them. Record your observations in the table on the next page.

7. (Optional) Put a small amount of soil on a nutrient agar plate or on a piece of bread moistened with water. Incubate this in a warm, dark area for 1–2 days. Observe the organisms that grow and include your observations in the table on the next page.

Goals

- Collect and identify the organisms in a soil sample.
- Demonstrate that a wide variety of organisms live in soil.

Materials

- hand lens
- incandescent light bulb (60–100 watts)
- isopropyl alcohol (optional)
- large funnel
- nutrient agar plate (optional)
- ring stand and iron ring
- sample of topsoil
- slice of bread (optional)
- small jar or 250 mL beaker
- wire screen (¼ in. mesh)

Type of organism	How many?	Notes and observations

Summing Up

1. How many different types of organisms did you find in your soil sample? _____
   _____

2. In your soil sample, what type of organism was most numerous? _____

3. If you did the optional soil incubation, what types of organisms did you find? _____
   Could there be more of these in the soil than of the larger organisms? _____

4. Do you think there may be organisms in your soil sample that you did not find? _____
   If so, what kinds of organisms? _____
   _____

Going Beyond

Repeat your observations using soil samples from different areas (a meadow, a swamp, a riverbank, deeper in the ground, etc). Record your findings and determine what differences in the biotic community of the soil exist between these areas.

field investigation
21H **Backyard Ecosystems**

name:

date:

hour:

An ecosystem is a limited area in which living and nonliving things interact. Thus a backyard, a school yard, or a park is an ecosystem. Each of these areas has a biotic community (made up of various populations of living organisms) and an abiotic environment (made up of nonliving factors). You observe these ecosystems every day. But what specific organisms and factors make up these ecosystems?

Choose a limited area and list various factors of its abiotic environment. Be sure to include factors that man controls. For example, mowing the lawn, watering, and adding fertilizer or pesticides are all abiotic environmental factors that are not natural to an area but are important parts of an ecosystem.

List the populations that make up the biotic community of the ecosystem you are studying, and be as specific as possible. In other words, do not just list "birds" but list the specific kinds of bird populations in the ecosystem. Include not only the plant populations but also the animal populations. Be sure to list both large organisms and small ones, such as earthworms and ants. Also keep in mind that some populations, such as grasshoppers and daffodils, may be "out of season." Do not forget that if pets use the area, they are also a part of the ecosystem, even though they be in it only part of the time. Bring your lists to school and be prepared to discuss your observations.

22 ORGANISM RELATIONSHIPS

ideas

22A Energy Exchange Between Organisms

name: _____

date: _____   hour: _____

Directions

For each of the food chain examples given below, fill in the ecological pyramid by writing in the organisms in the proper levels. Then answer the questions to the left of the pyramid. Sometimes you may need to write *none* in the blank. Empty blanks are considered to be wrong answers.

Food chain A (in alphabetical order): clover, hawk, rabbit

1. Name the producer(s) in this food chain. _____

2. Name the consumer(s) in this food chain. _____

3. Name the decomposer(s) in this food chain. _____

4. Name the herbivore(s) in this food chain. _____

5. Name the carnivore(s) in this food chain. _____

6. Which population in this food chain contains the most of the original energy? _____

7. Which population in this food chain contains the least of the original energy? _____

8. Give an example of a predator-prey relationship in this food chain. _____

_____

Food chain B (in alphabetical order): frog, grasshopper, snake, wheat

1. Name the producer(s) in this food chain. _____

2. Name the consumer(s) is this food chain. _____

3. Name the decomposer(s) in this food chain. _____

4. Name the herbivore(s) in this food chain. _____

5. Name the carnivore(s) in this food chain. _____

6. Which population in this food chain contains the most of the original energy?

_____

7. Which population in this food chain contains the least of the original energy?

_____

8. Give an example of a predator-prey relationship in this food chain.

_____

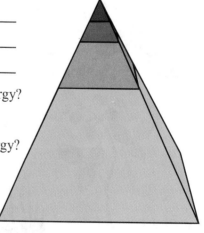

ideas
22B Food Chains and Food Webs

Directions

Draw arrows to represent the flow of energy between the various organisms in the food web illustrated below. Then on the blank by each organism, place one letter from Column 1, telling whether the organism is a producer or a consumer. If the organism is a consumer, place a letter from Column 2 beside the *C*, telling which kind of consumer the organism is. Any organisms that are involved in helping to decompose dead material are detritus feeders. These were covered in Chapter 11 on page 158.

Column 1
C - Consumer
P - Producer

Column 2
C - Carnivore
D - Decomposer
H - Herbivore
O - Omnivore
T - Detritus feeder

Food Web of a Meadow

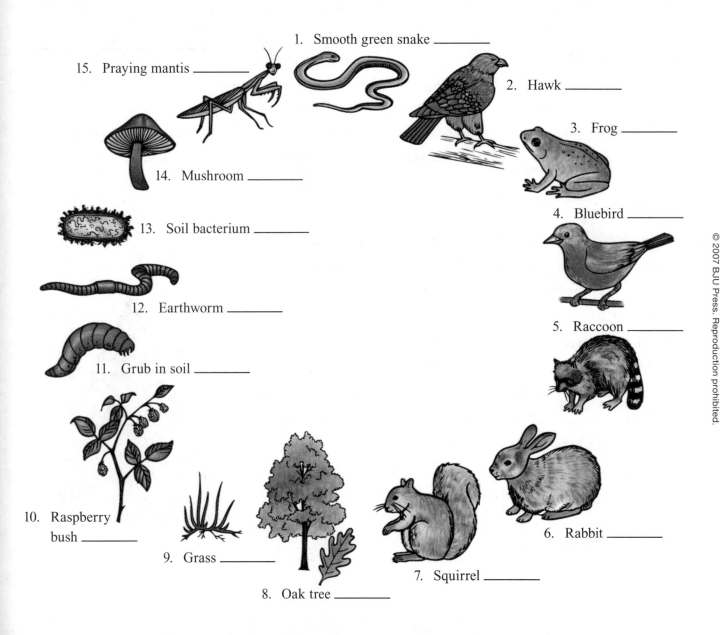

1. Smooth green snake _____
2. Hawk _____
3. Frog _____
4. Bluebird _____
5. Raccoon _____
6. Rabbit _____
7. Squirrel _____
8. Oak tree _____
9. Grass _____
10. Raspberry bush _____
11. Grub in soil _____
12. Earthworm _____
13. Soil bacterium _____
14. Mushroom _____
15. Praying mantis _____

ideas

22C Bible Creatures and Their Food-Chain Positions

name:

date: hour:

Directions

Below is a list of Scripture references. For each one, find the animal mentioned and write its common name in the *Name* column. In the next pair of columns, check whether the animal is a herbivore or carnivore. In the final three columns, check as many as apply. (Some animals will have more than one role.)

The Dead Abel, Peter Paul Rubens, from the Bob Jones University Collection

Reference	Name	Herbivore˙	Carnivore˙	Prey†	Predator†	Scavenger†
Exodus 8:2						
Exodus 10:4–5						
Leviticus 11:6						
Numbers 21:9						
Deuteronomy 8:15						
1 Samuel 17:15						
1 Kings 20:36						
1 Kings 21:23						
Job 39:27–30						
Proverbs 21:31						
Proverbs 30:28						
Isaiah 27:10						

˙Choose one   †Choose as many as apply

ideas
22D **Review**

Directions

Write the proper terms next to the following definitions and descriptions. Then find and circle the terms in the word puzzle on the next page. The terms may appear horizontally, vertically, or diagonally and may be forward or backward.

_____ 1. An animal that eats another animal

_____ 2. An animal that is eaten by another animal

_____ 3. The relationship between two organisms that are using the same factor in the environment

_____ 4. The relationship in which one organism is benefited and the other organism is not helped or hurt

_____ 5. The type of organism that does not live with others of its species

_____ 6. The type of organism that does live with others of its species

_____ 7. An organism that eats dead, decaying bodies

_____ 8. A word that means "used over and over again"

_____ 9. A plant that grows on another plant but does not receive nourishment from the plant it grows on

_____ 10. A group of birds

_____ 11. The relationship in which both organisms are benefited

_____ 12. A way to describe organisms that look like their surroundings

_____ 13. Bright colors or markings on an organism that advertise the organism's presence

_____ 14. A relationship in which an organism appears very similar to another organism

_____ 15. An organism that feeds off another living organism

_____ 16. A living organism that supplies materials to another organism

name:

date:

hour:

```
C  M  S  I  L  A  U  T  U  M  E  T  I  S  A  R  A  P
A  H  A  N  D  E  C  O  M  P  O  S  E  R  P  N  R  C
C  O  E  C  E  N  A  O  S  A  O  R  N  T  C  E  E  A
C  S  M  R  P  A  R  T  M  I  M  I  C  R  Y  I  E  M
O  T  I  M  B  R  N  C  N  M  I  L  C  Y  C  S  E  O
M  I  R  R  O  I  I  R  O  E  E  S  E  E  L  T  S  U
P  E  O  M  N  I  V  O  R  E  D  N  I  A  I  S  R  F
E  A  T  S  A  Y  O  O  N  N  S  N  S  O  C  I  A  L
T  E  A  N  E  E  R  T  R  E  A  Y  E  A  E  R  P  A
I  N  D  E  P  N  E  N  T  E  V  M  S  P  L  A  C  G
T  I  E  P  I  P  H  Y  T  E  C  E  A  S  E  I  N  E
I  S  R  A  I  F  L  O  C  K  T  E  D  N  E  D  S  D
O  P  P  O  C  Y  S  C  A  V  E  N  G  E  R  A  N  M
N  O  I  T  A  R  O  L  O  C  G  N  I  N  R  A  W  I
```

In the word puzzle are four additional words that describe different types of consumers. Find them and list them below.

17. _____

18. _____

19. _____

20. _____

research investigation
22E Our Environment (Part 2)

name:

date: hour:

See Research Investigation 21F for instructions for this investigation.

Project 5

Food Webs

Prepare diagrams of food webs that are present in your area. Use the organisms that your class wrote reports about in the notebook. Be sure that each food web applies to a particular season and a particular area. In other words, do not diagram squirrels eating both wild strawberries (a spring fruit) and apples (a fall fruit). You may need to prepare reports on more organisms in order to draw good food webs.

When you prepare the food web diagram, use names, not pictures, of the organisms. Place the diagram under "Relationships Between Populations" in the notebook.

Project 6

Relationships Within Populations

The relationships among organisms of the same kind in a particular environment can be interesting. Choose an animal that lives in a flock, herd, school, or some other social group in your area. In various books, research the social relationships within the animal's group. Write a brief report telling of the social structure involved in the group.

Project 7

Nonfood Relationships Between Populations

Some types of nonfood relationships are commensalism, mutualism, camouflage, warning coloration, and mimicry. What examples of these nonfood relationships can you find in your area?

Define a relationship and then list organisms (from your area) that are involved in that relationship. Briefly tell how each example you give illustrates the relationship. Use a separate sheet of paper for each of the relationships. Look for pictures that illustrate the examples you give and include the pictures in your report.

Project 8

Succession

Assume that a natural disaster destroys a twenty-acre section of the area your class is studying and all the plants and animals of the natural biotic community in that section are killed. What will happen now? The area will go through succession to reach its climax community again.

Go to a library or interview a knowledgeable person to find out what the stages of succession in your area are like. What are the pioneer organisms? What organisms will begin to live and grow in the area after the pioneer organisms? How many major stages are in the succession to the natural biotic community? How long will it take for the area to reach its climax community?

Write a report answering these questions. Include any other interesting or significant material you learn about succession in your area.

personal investigation

22F **Your Food Chain**

name:

date: hour:

Humans are consumer organisms. Every time you eat, you are a link in a food chain. But what food chains are you involved in?

Record the foods you eat during an entire day. You may need to divide some of the foods into their various parts. For example, you should consider a sandwich made of bread, cheese, and ham as bread, cheese, and ham—not simply a sandwich.

Determine which organisms your food came from and which link you are in the food chain. List the organisms that are involved in the food chain for each of the foods you ate. If you eat plants or plant products, you are the second link in the food chain. If you eat meat or animal products (such as milk or cheese), you are the final link (hopefully) in a three- or four-link food chain. By eating some foods, you may become the last link in a four- or five-link food chain. Put a *2* in the column if you were the second link in a particular food chain, a *3* if you were the third, and so on. A sample has been entered for you.

Food	I am link #	Other organisms in the food chain
roast beef	3	grass, steer

1. From your list of foods, what might a herbivore eat? _____

   _____

   _____

   _____

   _____

2. From your list of foods, what might a carnivore eat? _____

   _____

   _____

   _____

   _____

class investigation

22G Overcrowding

name:

date: _____   hour: _____

Procedures and Observations

1. Fill the pots with potting soil to about 2.5 cm (1 in.) below the rim. Do not add any fertilizer or plant food to the soil.

2. Plant three bean seeds in one pot and thirty in the other. Cover the seeds with about 1 cm (0.5 in.) of soil. Water each pot thoroughly and set them in a warm, well-lit area where they will have identical conditions (temperature, light).

3. Record the date you planted your seeds: _____

4. Regularly water the pot with three seeds with enough water to keep the soil moist but not soggy. The pot with thirty seeds should be watered with the same amount of water as the first pot, regardless of how much water it appears to need.

5. Once the seeds sprout, do not move the pots. If some seedlings in the crowded pot get more light than others, that is a consequence of overcrowding and should not be changed.

6. Observe the pots daily. Begin recording your observations on the chart below when the seeds sprout. In the columns that ask for observations about the sprouts, record data about the height, color, number of leaves, and general condition of the plants.

Goal

- Observe the effects of overcrowding on bean seedlings.

Materials

- potting soil
- thirty-three bean seeds (pre-soaked)
- two flower pots about 10 cm (4 in.) in diameter

Date	Pot with three seeds		Pot with thirty seeds	
	No. of sprouts	Observations	No. of sprouts	Observations

7. After you have completed your observations for a week or two, unpot the seedlings and carefully remove the soil from them. Do this by putting the seedlings in a large dish of water and gently moving them.

8. Record your observations of the differences between the root systems of the plants in the two pots. _____

_____

_____

9. As an alternative to steps 7 and 8 above, you could allow the seedlings to grow for four to six weeks before making your final observations. Depending on a number of factors, the seedling differences may be more obvious after an extended time period.

Summing Up

Write a paragraph comparing and contrasting the bean sprouts in the two pots. _____

_____

_____

_____

_____

_____

_____

_____

_____

_____

_____

_____

class investigation

22H **Lichens**

name:

date: hour:

Setting Up

1. Using field guides, find the types and locations of lichens that are common in your area.

2. Obtain samples of several different lichens. Be sure to obtain permission from the people who own the land where you collect your specimens. Be careful not to destroy other living things while you collect specimens.

3. Using a field guide, try to identify your specimens. If field guides are not available, at least classify them according to their form (crustose, foliose, or fruticose). (See the photos below.)

4. Bring your specimens to class.

Procedures and Observations

Observe the various lichen specimens

For each lichen, describe what you see. From the person who collected the specimens, find out where the lichen came from, and include that information in your description. After the name, write *C* for a crustose lichen, *F* for a foliose, or *T* for a fruticose.

1. lichen name: _____   description: _____
   _____

2. lichen name: _____   description: _____
   _____

3. lichen name: _____   description: _____
   _____

4. lichen name: _____   description: _____
   _____

5. lichen name: _____   description: _____
   _____

Goal

- Observe the mutualistic relationship of lichens.

Materials

- cover slips
- eyedropper
- glass slides
- lichen specimens
- microscopes
- prepared microscope slides of lichens

crustose

foliose

fruticose

Prepare a slide of a lichen and observe it through a microscope

1. Place a tiny piece of lichen in a drop of water on a glass slide.

2. Using two probes, tear the lichen into small shreds. This process is called teasing.

3. Place a cover slip on top of the teased lichen.

4. Observe this slide through a microscope.

5. Describe what you see. _____

_____

_____

_____

Observe a prepared slide of a cross section of a lichen

1. Focus the microscope on the prepared slide of a lichen.

2. Find the cells of the algae and fungi.

3. Describe what you see. _____

_____

_____

_____

Summing Up

1. What is a lichen? _____

_____

2. How does a lichen exhibit mutualism? _____

_____

_____

_____

3. Why can lichens grow in places where other organisms cannot grow? _____

_____

_____

_____

_____

field investigation

221 Observing Relationships

name:

date: hour:

Organisms are constantly interacting with each other. With even a casual observation of a natural setting, you can see dozens of interactions if you know what to look for.

The relationships discussed in Chapter 22 of your text are listed below. Beside each of these relationships is a point value. On a sheet of paper, make a separate column for each of these relationships. Then go to a beach, a field, a forest, a meadow, or some other natural area where you can observe both plants and animals.

At the top of your paper, record the place(s) in which you made your observations and the date(s) and time(s). List in the proper columns the names of the organisms involved in the relationships you observed. Try to earn fifty points. For each kind of relationship listed below, no more than five examples may be counted.

1. Predator and prey (2 points)

2. Parasite and host (5 points)

3. Scavenger and its food (4 points)

4. Decomposer and its food (1 point)

5. Independent organisms (1 point)

6. Couples that are mated for life (4 points)

7. Social organisms in a group (3 points)

8. Competition between animals of the same species (3 points)

9. Competition between plants of the same species (1 point)

10. Competition between populations (3 points)

11. Commensalism (5 points)

12. Mutualism (5 points)

13. Camouflage (4 points)

14. Warning coloration (5 points)

15. Mimicry (5 points)

Here are some examples of interactions you might see while visiting a pond with a marsh. The number after each example represents the relationship it could be used for.

• A dragonfly swoops after a mosquito. (1)

• A mosquito lands on your arm and begins to feed on your blood. (2)

• A crayfish nibbles on a dead fish in shallow water. (3)

• Mushrooms grow on a rotting stump along the bank. (4)

- A line of ants goes from their hill to the edge of the pond. (7)

- Water lilies cover the surface of one end of the pond, and their leaves overlap. (9)

- A green katydid is hidden in the plants along the water's edge. (13)

23 NATURAL RESOURCES

ideas

23A Renewable and Nonrenewable Resources

name:

date: _____ hour: _____

Directions

Below are listed several materials that are considered to be natural resources. By each material, write an *R* if it is a renewable resource or an *N* if it is a nonrenewable resource.

1. _____ aluminum

2. _____ coal

3. _____ cotton

4. _____ deer

5. _____ gold

6. _____ lumber

7. _____ natural gas

8. _____ petroleum (oil)

9. _____ trees

10. _____ trout

11. _____ water

12. _____ wool

These pine logs are going to a paper mill.

ideas

23B Agriculture and the Soil

Directions

Below are several groups of words. In each group, three of the four words (or phrases) are related to one another. Draw a line through the unrelated word and then write a sentence using the remaining words. Your sentence should show how the words are related. You may slightly change the form of the word in your sentence (for example, *legumes* to *legume* or *fertilizer* to *fertilizing*).

1. agriculture / livestock / crops / soil _____

_____

2. fertilizer / harvest / land grants / productivity _____

_____

3. humus / irrigation / depletion of minerals / soil productivity _____

_____

4. clover / humus / legumes / nitrogen _____

_____

5. depletion of minerals / fertilizer / legumes / irrigation _____

_____

6. crop rotation / field / crop / fertilizer _____

_____

ideas
23C Man's Role in the Ecosystem

Directions

Unscramble the words and write them in the blanks. For some of the words, a definition has been supplied. For those that lack a definition, you must write one in the space provided.

1. xpnoeenaitl   _____   A constant rate of increase

    ohwtgr   _____

2. trraethib   _____   _____

3. namhu   _____   The number of people on the earth at one time

    tiopnlaupo   _____

4. pupoailnot   _____   A condition that occurs when the birthrate of a population is greater

    inrcasee   _____   than the death rate

5. brtnaoio   _____   _____

6. dthea rtea   _____   The rate at which individuals leave the population

7. nopitlaoup   _____   _____

    crdeaese   _____   _____

8. ueiaaathns   _____   _____

9. yasdmdoo   _____   A supposed future time when man will destroy the earth by abusing it

10. srvacnontioe   _____   _____

ideas

23D Pollution

name: _____

date: _____   hour: _____

Directions

Complete the words missing in the following statements by filling in the necessary letters. The circled letters form words that complete the sentence on page SA238.

1. Today aluminum is cheaper to ___ ◯ ___ Y ◯ ___ ___ than to mine.

2. Gases and tiny particles form the major components of ___ ___ ___
   P ◯ ___ ◯ ___ ___ ___ ___ ___ .

3. Substances that the environment can recycle are called
   ___ ___ ◯ D ___ ◯ R ___ ___ ___ ___ ___ ___ substances.

4. The final stage of sewage treatment that removes chemicals from the water is called
   ___ ___ ___ T ◯ ___ ___ ___ treatment.

5. A solid, liquid, or gas may be a ___ ___ B ___ ___ ___ ___ ◯ ___ pollutant.

6. Chemicals and heat released into streams and lakes are common forms of
   ___ ◯ T ___ ___ ___ O ___ ◯ ___ ___ ___ ___ ___ .

7. One of the most abundant components of air pollution is the deadly gas
   ◯ ___ ___ B ◯ ___ ___ ___ ◯ ___ X ___ ___ ___ .

8. Solid unwanted or unusable materials are called ___ R ___ ◯ ___ .

9. ___ ◯ ___ ___ U ___ compounds are the second most abundant type of air pollutant.

10. An area where cities used to dispose trash was the city ___ ___ ◯ P .

11. The sewage treatment that reduces the amount of biodegradable materials is called
    ___ ◯ ___ ___ N ___ ___ ◯ ___ treatment.

12. Although too much pollution can be bad, not all pollution is ___ A ___ ◯ ___ U ___
    to an environment.

13. A dump that has layers of soil placed over it is called a ___ ◯ N ___ ___ ___ ___ ___
    ___ ___ ◯ ___ ___ ___ L ___ .

14. Unwanted products that are potentially harmful to man or the environment are called

___ ◯ _Z_ ___ ___ ___ ___ ___ ___   ___ _A_ ___ ___ ___ ___ .

15. The two major types of pollutants are substance pollutants and ___ ___ ___ _R_ ◯ ___

pollutants.

16. By law, many ___ ◯ _W_ ___ ___ ___ ___ _E_ ◯ ___ are made of recycled

paper.

In the environment man is both an ___ ___ ___ ___ ___ ___ ___ ___ ___ ___

___ ___ ___ ___ ___ ___ ___ ___ and a ___ ___ ___ ___ ___ ___ ___ .

research investigation

23E Our Environment (Part 3)

name:

date: hour:

See Research Investigation 21F for instructions for this investigation.

Project 9

Water Resources and Uses

Water is one of our three most important natural resources. In your area, where does the water that humans use come from? For this project you may wish to limit yourself to one city or to a section of your area. Find the answers to the following questions.

1. What are the primary sources of water for human use? How much water is used per day? How much of the water is used for industrial purposes? For agriculture?

2. Is the water treated before it is sent to the homes of the area? If so, what is done to it? Is the drinking water in your area hard or soft? If it is hard, what chemicals in the water make it hard?

3. Where is the water stored? Are there any reservoirs in your area? Are there water tanks?

4. Are there any private wells in the area? How many homes have private wells? How often are these wells inspected for water quality? In the past five years, how many wells contained water that was deemed unfit for human consumption? Why was it considered unfit? Is there a water shortage in the water table during certain seasons of the year?

5. Is there any danger that your area will not have enough water within the next few years? What water sources are being considered for meeting the needs of the future? Does your area supply water for other areas? If so, how much water does it supply? To which other areas does it supply water?

Your public library and city or county water department should be able to answer any questions you may have about your water resources.

Write a brief report answering these questions and telling any other interesting information you learned about your area's water supply.

Project 10

Energy Sources

What energy sources are available in your area? Does your area produce coal, oil, or natural gas? Are there hydroelectric dams in your area? Is solar power used much in your area? Does your area have an abundant amount of forests? If so, is any of the wood used privately or commercially as an energy source? Is wind energy or geothermal energy used significantly in your area? Does your area depend on other areas to supply you with energy?

If your area does produce its own energy, prepare a report telling the extent to which the various energy sources are used.

Project 11

Agriculture

What farm products are produced in your area? Farm products include not only fruits, vegetables, and typical farm animals but also products such as honey and animal fur. How much of each farm product is produced? In your report, do not include products that are grown in backyard gardens for the gardener's personal use. Instead, research the products that are grown for market. Make a list of these agricultural products (crops and animals) that your area produces and sells. If possible, indicate how much this amount of product is worth each year. What are some of the special problems that farmers growing these products face? Do unseasonably cold, hot, wet, or dry spells endanger crops? Are there certain insects or other pests that greatly threaten the farmers' crops in your area?

This information may be available in libraries or from county agents.

Project 12

Extinct and Endangered Organisms

Wolves, bald eagles, turkeys, bison, and other animals used to be common in many areas of the United States. But now development, hunting, and various other human activities have forced these animals out of many of the areas in which they once lived. Other animals, such as the passenger pigeon and the Carolina parakeet, were once common in areas of the United States but are now extinct.

Plants are also at risk of extinction from some human activities. Some of this threat comes from the over-harvesting of plants for their food, medicinal, decorative, or novelty value. In most cases, however, plant species are pushed into extinction by land-use changes. Wild areas may be cleared for crops, houses, or businesses.

What animals or plants were once common in your area but are now no longer found there? What caused them to leave or die out? In what areas are these animals or plants now found?

Are any of the animals or plants that were once in your area now extinct? If so, name them.

Are there any endangered species in your area? If so, what are they, how many of them are supposedly in your area, and where are they found? What is being done to protect these organisms?

You can find the answers to these questions in libraries or through state, regional, or national wildlife agencies. Sometimes this information is also available from game management agencies. Prepare a report answering these questions and telling any other interesting material you discovered about extinct and endangered organisms.

Project 13

Game and Game Management

name:

date: hour:

When people in your area go hunting or fishing, what do they bring home? How many of each game animal are believed to be in your area? Are any migratory? In your area, how many of each game animal are believed to be killed by hunters or fishermen each year?

When are the seasons for hunting the various game animals in your area? How many of each game animal may an individual kill? Are there any other restrictions that hunters must follow? What sizes or sexes of game animals may or may not be killed?

What do the game management authorities do to insure an abundance of game animals in your area? Do the game management authorities also manage nongame animals? If so, what animals do they control and how do they care for these animals?

Are there official bounties on any animals in your area? If so, what are they, and why are these animals considered harmful? How many of the bountied animals were killed last year?

You can find the answers to these questions in libraries or through the wildlife or game management authorities in your area. After you have found the information, prepare a report telling the answers to these questions and including any other interesting information you found out about game and game management in your area.

Project 14

Pollution

What problems does your area have with pollution? What are the major sources of air pollution in your area? Are there laws restricting the pollution? What types of pollution do these laws deal with? Is the air cleaner than, more polluted than, or about the same as it was five years ago? Is your area prone to thermal inversions, acid precipitation, smog, or other problems as a result of air pollution? If so, how often do these problems occur, and how severe are they?

What are the major sources of water pollution in your area? Are there laws restricting the pollution? What types of pollution do these laws deal with? Are there areas that are no longer suitable for swimming or fishing because of water pollution? Are the streams, rivers, and lakes in your area cleaner than, more polluted than, or about the same as they were five years ago? Has the water in any wells been deemed unfit for drinking because of pollution? What substance was found in the water? From where did this substance probably come?

Are there any other major forms of pollution that affect your area? If so, what are they, and what is being done about them? Are there any hazardous waste dumps that a government agency is cleaning up? Are any of these federal Superfund sites?

Project 15

Sewage and Trash

What type of treatment is given to sewage in the city or community where you live? What happens to the sewage after it is treated? What happens to the water that remains after the sewage is treated?

If your area uses septic tanks, use an encyclopedia and other books in a library to find out what a septic tank is and how it works. Write a brief report about septic tanks. Be sure to include problems that may result from the use of septic tanks.

What does your city do with the trash it collects? Are any of the materials in your trash recycled? Are any of them burned? Are any of them composted? If your city uses a sanitary landfill, where is it located? How long can your city continue to use the landfill before it is filled up? What will your city do then? Does your area dispose of trash for other areas?

Project 16

Conservation and Development

Are there sections of your area that serve as wildlife refuges, national or state parks or forests, or wilderness areas? If so, how large are these areas? Why have these areas been set aside? What are the purposes and uses of these areas? If possible, visit these areas and see what they are like. Find out from rangers or others responsible for the area what they do to maintain the area.

Are any areas being considered for conservation? If so, how large are they and why are they being considered?

What developments are planned for your area? Are major government projects being considered? Are dams, tourist attractions, major industrial complexes, nuclear energy plants, utilizations of natural resources (mines, oil wells, or the like), landfills, waste dumps, or other developments being considered for your area? Why are these developments needed? Are there objections to these developments? What are they? Were any studies done to determine what impact these developments would have on the environment? If so, what did they reveal?

personal investigation

23F Hunting with a Camera

name:

date: hour:

Hunting is not always easy. Knowing where to look, when to look, and what to look for can be a challenge. Even experienced hunters can spend long hours in the field and come back with nothing but tired feet.

Go on a hunting trip yourself. But rather than taking a gun, take a camera and photograph the game you find. You can then show your pictures to your classmates. Be sure that you are well aware of the proper safety procedures for hunting the game in your area. Make sure that you secure the proper permission to be in the area. Take pictures of the game you see, the area in which you looked for game, and any nongame animals you see. Prepare a report about your trip. Include the pictures you took while you were "hunting."

personal investigation

23G Estimates

The population of the world is a topic of great interest to politicians, scientists, and many others. In order to properly prepare for future needs, it is important to have accurate predictions on how many people might be on the earth in future years. There are many attempts to use these estimates to influence decision making. Sometimes these arguments use misleading statistics on how population increases might cause the loss of certain natural resources. In this exercise, you will plot population data on a graph and then estimate what the world population might be at several points in the future.

Goals

- Understand how estimates are made.
- Estimate future world population levels.
- Recognize the factors that affect the accuracy of estimates.

World Population: 1950–2035

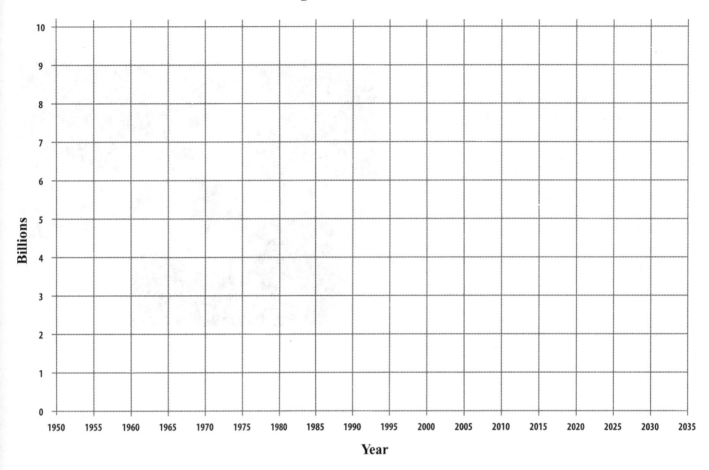

Year	Approximate world population in billions		Year	Approximate world population in billions
1950	2.6		1995	5.7
1955	2.8		2000	6.1
1960	3.0		2005	6.5
1965	3.4		2010	
1970	3.7		2015	
1975	4.1		2020	
1980	4.5		2025	
1985	4.9		2030	
1990	5.3		2035	

name: _____

date: _____   hour: _____

Procedures and Observations

1. Using the population figures for 1950 to 2005, plot each point on the graph that is provided. Since the graph provides horizontal lines only for every billion, you will need to estimate where to place each data point. For instance, if the figure for a certain year is 6.5 billion, you should mark it halfway between the 6 and the 7. A figure of 4.2 should be about two-tenths of the way between the 4 and the 5.

2. After you have plotted the values for 1950 to 2005, connect the points to form a continuous line.

3. Next extend your line as far as 2035, attempting to follow the direction the line is heading. If your original line seems to be a straight one, you might want to use a ruler or other straight edge to complete it. If your line seems to be curving, you should probably sketch it freehand.

4. Based on your graph, answer the following questions:

   To the nearest year, when did the world's population reach 4 billion? _____

   When did it reach 6 billion? _____

   What was the approximate population in 1987? _____

   What was the approximate population in 2004? _____

Going Beyond

1. Suppose you had to find out if the world population increased at the same rate from 2000 to 2005 that it did from 1960 to 1965? How would you find the answer to this question? _____

   _____

   _____

   _____

   _____

   _____

   _____

2. What factors will influence the rate at which the world population increases? _____

   _____

   _____

class investigation

23H **Recycling Paper**

name:

date: hour:

Procedures and Observations

1. Construct the screen frame as shown in the diagram. Your teacher may have already done this in advance. The screen frame should be smaller than the dishpan.

2. Cut or tear an amount of paper equal to a single two-page spread of a newspaper into pieces approximately 2 cm wide and long.

3. Place the torn paper into a blender with 1000 mL (nearly 1 qt) of water, and blend it until it becomes a cloudy liquid rather than wet, stringy bits of recognizable paper (15–30 seconds). This recycles the paper back into pulp.

4. Pour the pulp into the dishpan. Continue making pulp until the dishpan is filled to within 8 cm (about 3 in.) of the top.

5. Stir the pulp in the dishpan with your hands. You may need to add water if the pulp seems thick.

6. Hold the screen frame with both hands (screen side towards you). In one motion, lower it vertically into the pulp in the dishpan and then position it horizontally in the pulp. (See diagram.)

7. Holding the screen frame horizontally, lift it straight up out of the pulp. Wiggle the frame slightly while lifting to evenly distribute the pulp on the screen. A layer of pulp will be deposited on the screen. Steps 6 and 7 should take 10–30 seconds, depending on how much pulp is in the water and how thick you want your paper to be.

8. Allow the screen to drain over the dishpan for 15–30 seconds. You may tilt it slightly to help the water drain.

9. Flip the screen frame upside down on a piece of cloth. (The layer of pulp should be between the cloth and screen.)

10. Press down on the screen with the sponge to absorb water from the recycled piece of paper.

11. Carefully lift the screen frame from the recycled paper. The paper should adhere to the cloth instead of the screen. Then carefully peel the paper from the cloth.

Goal

- Demonstrate how paper is recycled.
- Make recycled paper.

Materials

- blender
- clothes iron (optional)
- heavy object such as a phone book (optional)
- large dishpan
- large sponge
- mesh screen (window screen)
- paper to be recycled (newspaper)
- piece of cloth (or blotting paper)
- staple gun with staples
- water
- wood frame

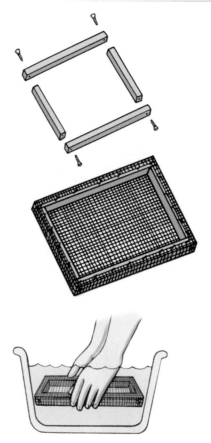

12. There are two general ways to dry your recycled paper.

   A. Sandwich your paper between two pieces of dry cloth. Put a heavy weight such as a phone book on top and let the paper dry for a day or two. Several such sandwiches can be stacked together and weighted by the same heavy weight.

   B. Iron your paper with a clothes iron on an ironing board. Be certain not to use the steam setting on the iron.

13. When cleaning up, do not pour leftover pulp down the drain. Pour it through the screen frame or a sieve to remove most of the pulp from the water. This pulp can be saved for later use or discarded.

Summing Up

1. How do you think the pulp you made differs from the pulp used to make brand-new paper? How are they similar? _____

   _____

   _____

2. How do the characteristics of the paper you made differ from the original paper you recycled? _____

   _____

   _____

3. How might the large-scale production of recycled paper cause pollution? _____

   _____

4. What recycled paper products have you seen in use? _____

   _____

   _____

Going Beyond

When making the pulp, include pieces of other materials in the mix. Onion skins, short threads, and crumbled leaves make good additions.

24 SUPPORT AND MOVEMENT

ideas
24A Human Skin

name: _____

date: _____ hour: _____

Directions

Complete the words missing in the following statements by filling in the necessary letters. The circled letters form a phrase that tells one of the most important functions of the skin.

1. The fluid secreted by the sweat glands is called

   ___ ___ ___ ___ (◯) ___ ___ A ___ ___ ___ ___.

2. The ___ ___ ___ D ___ (◯) ___ ___ ___ is the outer layer of skin, which continuously sheds dead cells.

3. The body adjusts the amount of ___ ___ (◯) O ___ in the skin to help control the body temperature.

4. Intense heat or prolonged friction can cause a ___ L ___ ___ (◯) ___ ___ to form.

5. The ___ (◯) ___ ___ I ___ is the inner, thicker layer of the skin.

6. A (◯) ___ ___ ___ ___ S is an area of thick, tough epidermis that protects the skin.

7. A yellowish pigment found in the skin is ___ ___ ___ ___ (◯) E ___ ___.

8. ___ ___ L ___ ___ (◯) ___ is the dark brown pigment that colors the skin.

9. A layer of loosely arranged fat cells and fibers below the skin is the

   ___ U ___ ___ ___ ___ ___ ___ E (◯) ___ ___ layer.

10. A ___ A (◯) is a darkening of the skin and is caused by a buildup of melanin.

11. Blood vessels in the skin contract and the pores of the sweat glands close when the body is

    ___ (◯) L ___.

12. Hair develops from cells in the hair (◯) ___ L ___ ___ ___ ___ ___ ___.

13. ___ ___ ___ T ___ ___ ___ ___ ___ ___ ___ (◯) is the study of fingerprints.

14. The hair and skin are kept soft, flexible, and water-resistant by the ◯ __I__ ____ produced by glands in the skin.

15. Overexposure to ultraviolet rays results in a ____ ◯ ____ __B__ ____ ____ ____.

A major function of skin is the

 ――― ――― ――― ――― ――― ――― ――― ――― ――― ―――   ――― ―――   ――― ――― ―――.
  1   2   3   4   5   6   7   8   9   10   11   12   13   14   15

ideas
24B The Skeletal System

name:

date: hour:

Directions

On the skeleton diagram below, label the following bones.

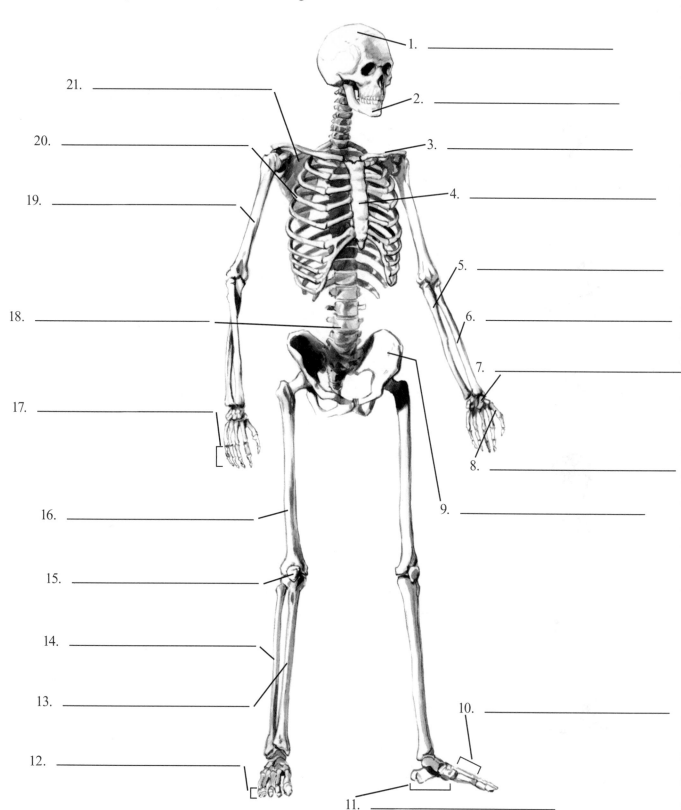

21. _____

20. _____

19. _____

18. _____

17. _____

16. _____

15. _____

14. _____

13. _____

12. _____

1. _____

2. _____

3. _____

4. _____

5. _____

6. _____

7. _____

8. _____

9. _____

10. _____

11. _____

ideas

24C Joints

Directions

Below is a series of diagrams of various movements. In the space provided, tell what type of joint is responsible for each action and which bones form the joint responsible for the movement.

Diagram	Type of joint	Bones forming the joint
	1. _____	_____
	2. _____	_____
	3. _____	_____
	4. _____	_____
	5. _____	_____
	6. _____	_____

ideas
24D The Muscular System

name: _____

Directions

date: _____ hour: _____

Below is a series of diagrams of actions and a list of muscles. Match the action with the muscles most responsible for the action by writing the muscle name in the space provided. In the diagram, color the area where the muscle is.

biceps	latissimus dorsi	sternocleidomastoid
deltoid	pectoralis	tibialis anterior
external oblique	rectus abdominis	trapezius
gastrocnemius	rectus femoris	triceps
gluteus	sartorius	

1. _____

2. _____

3. _____

4. _____

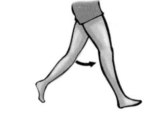

5. _____

6. _____

7. _____

8. _____

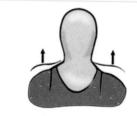

9. _____

10. _____

11. _____

12. _____

ideas

24E **Review 1**

Directions

Unscramble the terms and write them in the blanks. For some of the words, a definition has been supplied. For those that lack a definition, you must write one in the space provided.

1. metpreiuos   _____   The tissue that covers bones

2. lsitgnaem   _____   _____

  _____

3. tsondne   _____   _____

  _____

4. worarm   _____   The substance found in the cavities of bones

5. netsoso   _____   _____

  _____

6. ratcigale   _____   _____

  _____

7. eusdf   _____   _____

  _____

8. sypgno   _____   A type of bone that has many irregular spaces in it

9. vtbererea   _____   _____

  _____

10. tcarligea   _____   Structures that permit long bones to grow in length

    aestlp   _____

11. ssniotirat   _____   _____

  _____

name:

date: hour:

12. ouepstr   _____   _____

_____

13. revshi   _____   A muscle movement that creates heat for the body

14. nocratct   _____   _____

_____

15. aictlc daci   _____   A substance produced when muscles do not receive enough oxygen

16. ouayvlntr   _____   Muscle actions that you have control over

17. eeoslktn   _____   _____

_____

18. iouanvlntry   _____   _____

_____

19. osomht   _____   _____

_____

20. areht   _____   An organ that is made of involuntary striated muscle tissue

ideas

24F **Review 2**

Directions

In the spaces provided, describe the difference between the terms given. You may slightly change the form of the word (for example, *bone* to *bones*).

1. dermis / epidermis _____

_____

_____

2. endoskeleton / exoskeleton _____

_____

_____

3. ligament / tendon _____

_____

_____

4. cartilage / bone _____

_____

_____

5. voluntary muscle / involuntary muscle _____

_____

_____

6. striated muscle / nonstriated muscle _____

_____

_____

7. triceps / biceps _____

_____

_____

8. aerobic cellular respiration / anaerobic cellular respiration _____

_____

_____

class investigation

24G Structure of the Skin

name: _____

date: _____   hour: _____

Procedures and Observations

Obtain and set up your microscope. Focus your microscope on the slide of human skin. The epidermis should be toward the top, and the subcutaneous layer toward the bottom.

1. Find and observe the epidermis. Which layer is the epidermis?

   _____

2. Describe the epidermis. _____

   _____

   _____

3. Find and observe the dermis. Where is the dermis? _____

   _____

   _____

4. Look for the following structures in the dermis. If you can find them, describe their appearance. Leave blank the lines for those you cannot find.

   A. Hair _____

   _____

   B. Hair follicle _____

   _____

   C. Blood vessels _____

   _____

   D. Oil gland _____

   _____

   E. Sweat gland _____

   _____

   F. Nerve ending _____

   _____

   G. Muscle _____

   _____

5. Where are the oil glands located in relation to the hair follicles? What is the significance of this relationship?

   _____

   _____

   _____

Goal
- Observe and learn about the structures of the skin.

Materials
- microscope
- prepared slide of a cross section of human skin

6. Describe the shape of a hair inside the follicle. _____
_____

7. Pull a hair out of your scalp. Does the end of the hair from your scalp resemble the end of the hair you observed through the microscope? ☐ Yes ☐ No If not, how does it differ? _____
_____

8. Find and observe the subcutaneous layer. Where is the subcutaneous layer? _____
_____

9. Describe the subcutaneous layer in comparison to the dermis and epidermis. _____
_____

10. What structures can you find in the subcutaneous layer? _____
_____

class investigation

24H Observing a Beef Bone

name:

date: hour:

Observations

Carefully observe a beef bone. Locate all the structures described in the illustration on page 422 of your text. On the lines below, list the structures you can find on your section of bone. Describe them. Tell their colors, shapes, and textures; whether they are hard, soft, or firm; and anything else you can observe.

Goal

- Observe and learn the structures of a bone.

Materials

- fresh beef bone

class investigation

241 Heat from Muscles

name:

date: _____   hour: _____

Procedures and Observations

1. Choose a student to sit where everyone can see him. He should wear a short-sleeved shirt or roll up his sleeves.

2. Put one strip thermometer on each arm, over his biceps muscles. Allow about 15 seconds for the thermometers to indicate the correct temperature. Record these temperatures as the initial temperatures in the table on page SA262.

3. Choose one arm to be the exercised arm. With this arm the student should lift and lower the weight at a constant rate of about once every second. The other arm should remain motionless.

4. After 30 seconds, record the temperature of each arm. It is not necessary to stop the lifting and lowering to record the temperature.

5. Continue taking temperature readings every 30 seconds for several minutes or until the student's arm is too tired to continue.

Goal
- Demonstrate that muscle contractions produce heat.

Materials
- dumbbell or similar weight
- stopwatch or watch with a second hand
- two strip thermometers

Time (sec)	Temperature of exercised arm	Temperature of unexercised arm
Initial		
30		
60		
90		
120		
150		
180		
210		
240		

Summing Up

1. Did the temperature of the exercised arm increase? Why do you think this did or did not happen? _____

_____

_____

2. Did the temperature of the unexercised arm increase? Why do you think this did or did not happen? _____

_____

_____

class investigation

24J The Structure of Bones and Muscles

name:

date: _____ hour: _____

Procedures and Observations

1. Obtain and set up your microscope.

2. Focus your microscope on the prepared slide of human bone.

   • Before the bone was made into a slide, all the cell cytoplasm and blood vessels were removed. All that you will see are the hard, "bony" structures.

   • Examine the slide and compare it to the material on page 424 of your text. You may need to use high power in order to see some of the structures clearly.

   • Name and describe the various structures that you see.

   _____

   _____

   _____

   _____

   _____

Goal

• Observe the microscopic structures of muscles and bones.

Materials

• microscope

• prepared slide of a cross section of dry, ground human bone

• prepared slide of striated human muscle

3. Focus your microscope on a prepared slide of human muscle.

   • Examine the slide and compare it to material on page 426 of your text. You may need to use high power in order to see some of the structures clearly.

   • What type of muscle are you observing? Check the proper box in each pair.

   ☐ voluntary   ☐ involuntary

   ☐ striated   ☐ smooth

   • Name and describe the various structures that you see.

   _____

   _____

   _____

   _____

   _____

25 INTERNAL BALANCE

ideas

25A The Heart and Blood Vessels

name: _____

date: _____   hour: _____

Directions

Fill in the missing words in the following statements. The circled letters will form a word that describes the internal balance of the body.

1. Blood is pumped by the ◯ __ __ R __ .

2. The __ __ ◯ __ D carries substances through the body.

3. A heart M __ __ ◯ __ __ is an unusual heart sound.

4. An artificial __ __ __ ◯ __ __ __ E __ may be used to keep a damaged heart beating.

5. The blood entering the right atrium is __ E ◯ __ __ __ E __ __ __ __ __ .

6. The __ __ __ N __ __ ◯ filter wastes from the blood.

7. An __ __ __ __ __ ◯ __ M __ __ is an abnormal heart rhythm.

8. __ __ __ __ __ __ ◯ __ E __ blood enters the left atrium.

9. Arteries, veins, and capillaries are __ E __ ◯ __ __ __ .

10. The sac around the heart is the P __ __ __ __ __ __ __ ◯ __ __ .

11. Doctors use a __ __ __ T __ __ ◯ __ __ P __ to listen to the heart.

Maintaining the internal balance of the body is

__ __ __ __ __ __ __ __ __ __ __ .
  1   2   3   4   5   6   7   8   9   10   11

ideas
25B The Structure of the Heart

Directions

Label the following drawing by supplying the missing terms; then draw a line from each term to the proper structure in the drawing.

1. _____
   (carries deoxygenated blood to the lungs)

2. _____
   (carries oxygenated blood away from the heart to all parts of the body)

3. _____
   (collects blood from the lungs)

4. _____
   (returns oxygenated blood to the heart)

5. _____
   (prevents blood from passing back into the left atrium)

6. _____
   (allows blood to leave the left ventricle)

7. _____
   (pumps blood into the aorta)

8. _____
   (separates the right and left sides of the heart)

9. _____
   (pumps blood to the lungs)

10. _____
    (brings blood from the lower parts of the body to the heart)

11. _____
    (prevents blood from passing back into the right atrium)

12. _____
    (allows blood to leave the right ventricle)

13. _____
    (collects blood from the body)

14. _____
    (brings blood from the upper parts of the body to the heart)

Key: ☐ Oxygenated blood   ☐ Deoxygenated blood

ideas
25C The Path of Blood

Directions

On the diagram of the heart above, draw arrows indicating the flow of blood through the heart. Use one color for oxygenated blood and another color for deoxygenated blood. On the key, indicate which color you used for each type of blood.

ideas
25D The Blood

name:

date: hour:

Directions

Read the following statements. In the space provided, write *True* if the statement is true. If the statement is false, draw a line through the word or words that make the statement false. Then in the blank, write the word or words necessary to make the statement true.

_____ 1. Erythrocytes are shaped like discs that have been pressed in on both sides.

_____ 2. Leukocytes are smaller than erythrocytes.

_____ 3. If a coronary artery is blocked by a floating blood clot, a coronary thrombosis will result.

_____ 4. Blood plasma is a straw-colored fluid that contains dissolved foods, hormones, minerals, and other materials.

_____ 5. Another name for leukocytes is red blood cells.

_____ 6. If a person's blood cannot carry enough oxygen, the person has anemia.

_____ 7. Carbon dioxide easily combines with hemoglobin at the same place that oxygen combines with hemoglobin.

_____ 8. Infections in the body cause the number of erythrocytes to increase.

_____ 9. Hemoglobin carries oxygen.

_____ 10. Coronary atherosclerosis is the development of fatty tissues inside the walls of coronary arteries.

_____ 11. If a person's diet lacks lead, he may develop anemia.

_____ 12. Erythrocytes lack nuclei, but leukocytes have nuclei.

_____ 13. Some types of leukocytes engulf and digest foreign matter.

_____ 14. There are many more leukocytes in the blood than there are erythrocytes.

_____ 15. An arrhythmia in which the heart quivers but does not pump blood is called fibrillation.

_____ 16. Platelets are irregular cell fragments that are needed to form blood clots.

_____ 17. Blood pressure is the push that blood has against artery walls.

_____ 18. The septum separates the right side of the heart from the left.

_____ 19. If a person's heart is beating irregularly, that person has an arrhythmia.

_____ 20. The heart has two lower chambers called atria.

_____ 21. A person's blood pressure normally increases as he exercises vigorously.

_____ 22. Using a finger to push an artery against a bone will permit a person to count his blood pressure.

_____ 23. A major cause of high blood pressure is tension.

_____ 24. Blood moving away from the heart travels in the veins.

_____ 25. A human body normally contains about 8–10 L of blood.

_____ 26. Blood becomes oxygenated in the lungs and deoxygenated in other body tissues.

_____ 27. Hemoglobin is an iron-containing pigment that makes blood appear red.

_____ 28. Platelets are produced in bone marrow.

_____ 29. Blood plasma is about 50% water.

ideas
25E The Body's Defense System

name:

date: hour:

Directions

Read the following statements. In the space provided, write *True* if the statement is true. If the statement is false, draw a line through the word or words that make the statement false. Then in the blank, write the word or words necessary to make the statement true.

_____   1. A Christian worldview teaches that before the Fall there was no death but there were probably some diseases.

_____   2. The body's first line of defense is the erythrocytes.

_____   3. Inflammation is a local response to foreign invaders.

_____   4. A fever is a decrease in the body's normal temperature.

_____   5. The two major types of lymphocytes used in the immune system are T cells and B cells.

_____   6. The body forms antigens, which attack disease-causing agents.

_____   7. B cells attack and destroy foreign invaders.

_____   8. The immune system has a memory that can respond to specific antigens.

_____   9. An allergic response can be considered an abnormal response of the immune system.

_____   10. If someone has an autoimmune disease, his immune system is unable to tell the difference between foreign invaders and normal body cells.

ideas
25F The Excretory System

Directions

Write the proper terms next to the following definitions. Then eliminate the letters
used in your answers from the letter list. The remaining letters should be unscrambled
to form the answer to the bonus question.

_____ 1. Tubes that carry urine from the kidneys to the urinary bladder

_____ 2. A microscopic structure that filters the blood inside a kidney

_____ 3. A muscular sac that stores urine

_____ 4. One of the filtering organs of the excretory system

_____ 5. The tube that leads from the urinary bladder to the outside of the body

_____ 6. The substance that is filtered as it passes through the kidney

_____ 7. The substance that is excreted by the nephron after all the useful products
have been reabsorbed into the blood

_____ 8. A substance that is a waste product of protein digestion and is normally
found in urine

_____ 9. A condition indicated by too much sugar in the blood and urine

_____ 10. The proper name for an artificial kidney: _____ machine

_____ 11. What a physician does to urine in order to determine certain physical
conditions

_____ 12. The primary function of the urinary bladder

Bonus: The main function of the excretory system involves removing and eliminating _____.

Letter List

a	a	a	a	a	a	a	a	a	a
b	b	b	d	d	d	d	d	d	e
e	e	e	e	e	e	e	e	e	e
e	e	g	h	h	i	i	i	i	i
i	i	i	k	l	l	l	l	l	l
m	n	n	n	n	n	n	o	o	o
o	p	r	r	r	r	r	r	r	r
r	r	r	s	s	s	s	s	s	s
s	s	s	t	t	t	t	t	t	u
u	u	u	u	u	w	y	y	y	y

class investigation

25G Observing a Beef Heart

name:

date: hour:

Procedures and Observations

1. A beef heart is larger than, but similar to, a human heart. Examine the outside of the heart. Then remove the top section of the heart to see its chambers.

2. Use a blunt rod to probe into the blood vessels and see where they go. Find the heart structures and trace the path in which the blood flows through the heart.

3. Using the heart illustration on page 434 of your text as a guide, locate the structures on the beef heart.

4. Using a blue piece of yarn, trace the path of deoxygenated blood through the heart.

5. Using a red piece of yarn, trace the path of oxygenated blood through the heart.

6. Have your teacher inspect your work.

Goal

- Observe and identify the structures of the heart.

Materials

- dissected beef heart
- glass or wooden rods
- large forceps
- red and blue yarn

class investigation
25H **Using a Stethoscope**

name: _____

Setting Up

date: _____ hour: _____

Using alcohol and a tissue, clean the earplugs of the stethoscope. The earplugs should always be cleaned with alcohol and a tissue before they are put into the ears of another person. Whenever you put the earplugs of the stethoscope into your ears, be sure the diaphragm of the stethoscope does not tap against any hard object. The sound made by tapping a button or a tabletop can be very loud and can damage your ears.

Procedures and Observations

Place the earplugs of the stethoscope into your ears. Place the diaphragm of the stethoscope on a friend's cheek and ask the friend to chew. Describe what you hear.

_____

_____

_____

_____

Goals
- Learn how to correctly use a stethoscope.
- Listen to the sounds of your heart.
- Compare your pulse rate with your heart rate.

Materials
- alcohol
- stethoscope
- stopwatch or clock with a second hand
- tissues

Listen to the sounds of your heart

1. Place the diaphragm of the stethoscope on the center of your chest. Listen carefully.

2. Move the diaphragm of the stethoscope to the left of the center of your chest so that it is no longer over your sternum.

3. Move the diaphragm of the stethoscope slightly up and down to be sure that you do not have it directly over a rib.

4. Once you have found a good place where you can hear your heart, listen carefully. What does it sound like?

_____

_____

_____

_____

Determine how fast your heart beats while you are sitting quietly

1. Sit quietly for about five minutes before doing this exercise.

2. Count the number of times your heart beats in fifteen seconds. Recall that your heart makes two sounds for each beat. In other words, each "lubb-dubb" is a single beat.

3. Multiply by four the number of times your heart beats in fifteen seconds. This number will tell you how many times your heart beats per minute. Record this amount in the space on page SA274.

4. Repeat steps 2 and 3 three times and, for each count, record the number of beats per minute in the spaces provided. Average your results.

Heartbeat rate per minute

Count 1: _____   Count 2: _____   Count 3: _____   Count 4: _____

Average: _____

Determine how fast your pulse throbs while you are sitting quietly

1. You can feel your pulse by putting light pressure against a blood vessel that flows past a bone. Find the pulse in your neck or in your wrist by placing your fingers as illustrated in the photographs.

2. Count your pulse for fifteen seconds and then multiply the number by four. This number tells you your pulse rate for one minute. Record this number in the space below.

3. Repeat step 2 three times and, for each count, record the number of beats per minute in the spaces provided. Average your results.

Pulse rate per minute

Count 1: _____   Count 2: _____   Count 3: _____   Count 4: _____

Average: _____

Summing Up

1. What is the difference between your average heartbeat rate per minute and your average pulse rate per minute?

_____

_____

_____

2. Should there be a noticeable difference between your heartbeat rate and your pulse rate?   ☐ Yes   ☐ No

Why? _____

_____

_____

_____

class investigation
25I Heart Rate Increases

name: _____

date: _____   hour: _____

Setting Up

1. Be able to find your pulse quickly and to measure it accurately. (See Class Investigation 25H for instructions on measuring a pulse.)

2. Map out a route where you and your classmates can walk and run. It should be about 134 m (440 ft) and should start and end near your classroom.

3. Divide your class into teams of two people each. In each team, one person should do the activities and the other should measure the pulse rate and record the results. Both people should do the Summing Up section at the end.

4. Each time you measure a pulse rate for this exercise, do so for fifteen seconds and then multiply your answer by four to obtain the pulse rate for one minute.

Goals

- Determine whether heart rate is proportional to amount of exercise.
- Identify how much time the heart requires to return to its normal rate after exercise.

Materials

- stopwatch or clock with a second hand

Procedures and Observations

1. Lie quietly for three minutes. Record your pulse rate. _____ bpm (beats per minute)

2. Sit quietly for three minutes. Record your pulse rate. _____ bpm

3. While seated, move your arms back and forth above your head for three minutes. Record your pulse rate. _____ bpm

4. Sit quietly, checking the pulse rate periodically, until the pulse rate returns to normal. How long did you have to rest until the pulse rate became the same as the "sitting quietly" rate? _____ min _____ sec

5. Walk slowly around the mapped area. Record your pulse rate. _____ bpm

6. Rest until the pulse is the same as the "sitting quietly" rate. How long did you have to rest? _____ min _____ sec

7. Walk briskly around the mapped area. Record your pulse rate. _____ bpm

8. Rest until the pulse is the same as the "sitting quietly" rate. How long did you have to rest? _____ min _____ sec

9. Jog around the mapped area. Record your pulse rate. _____ bpm

10. Rest until the pulse is the same as the "sitting quietly" rate. How long did you have to rest? _____ min _____ sec

11. Run rapidly around the mapped area. Record your pulse rate. _____ bpm

12. Rest until the pulse is the same as the "sitting quietly" rate. How long did you have to rest? _____ min _____ sec

Summing Up

Fill out the charts by shading in the bars of the charts with the data you have obtained.

Chart A—Pulse Rate per Minute

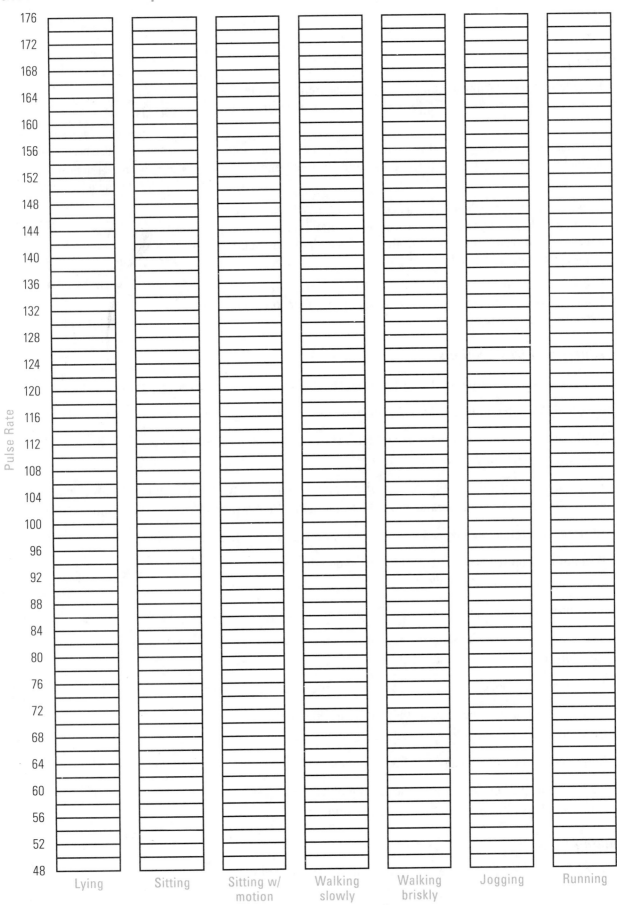

Pulse Rate

| 176 |
| 172 |
| 168 |
| 164 |
| 160 |
| 156 |
| 152 |
| 148 |
| 144 |
| 140 |
| 136 |
| 132 |
| 128 |
| 124 |
| 120 |
| 116 |
| 112 |
| 108 |
| 104 |
| 100 |
| 96 |
| 92 |
| 88 |
| 84 |
| 80 |
| 76 |
| 72 |
| 68 |
| 64 |
| 60 |
| 56 |
| 52 |
| 48 |

Lying Sitting Sitting w/ motion Walking slowly Walking briskly Jogging Running

Chart B—Time Required for the Pulse Rate to Return to Normal

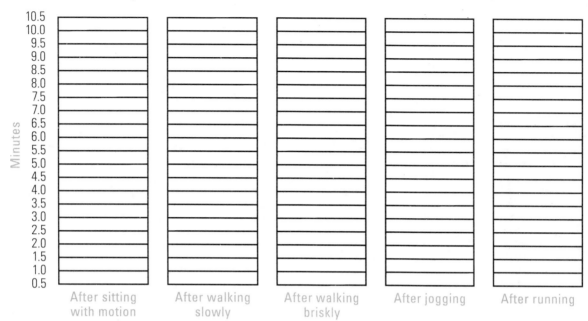

1. By comparing the charts, what are you able to determine about the relationship between pulse rate and the length of time needed for the pulse rate to return to normal? _____

    _____

2. Compare your chart to other students'. Are they about the same? ☐ Yes ☐ No

    Does any person in your class have an unusual chart? ☐ Yes ☐ No

    If so, what could explain the difference? _____

    _____

    _____

    _____

    _____

class investigation

25J **Blood**

name: _____

date: _____   hour: _____

Procedures and Observations

Obtain and set up your microscope. Focus your microscope on a prepared slide of normal human blood. You will need to use high power in order to observe the blood cells clearly.

1. Locate and observe the erythrocytes. Describe their appearance.

    _____

    _____

    _____

    _____

2. Are there different types of erythrocytes?   ☐ Yes   ☐ No

    If so, tell the differences between the types you see.

    _____

    _____

    _____

    _____

3. What is the primary function of erythrocytes? _____

    _____

    _____

4. Locate and observe several leukocytes. Describe their appearance and compare them with the erythrocytes.

    _____

    _____

    _____

5. Compare the number of leukocytes to the number of erythrocytes. _____

    _____

    _____

6. Are there different kinds of leukocytes?   ☐ Yes   ☐ No

    If so, describe the differences between the kinds you see. _____

    _____

    _____

    _____

7. What is the primary function of leukocytes? _____

    _____

    _____

Goals

- Observe blood cells.
- See some of the effects that certain diseases have on blood.

Materials

- microscope
- prepared slide of normal human blood
- prepared slides of diseased human blood

8. Observe several slides of the blood of humans who had blood disorders. Record the names of the blood diseases you observed and describe the differences between normal blood and each diseased blood.

_____

_____

_____

_____

_____

_____

9. In the space below draw and label an erythrocyte or a leukocyte that is representative of one of the blood disorders you observed.

26 ENERGY

ideas

26A Metabolism

name:

date: hour:

Directions

Below is a list of terms and a series of examples. Decide which term is being described in the example and write its letter in the space.

A. Basal metabolic rate
B. Digestive system
C. Metabolic rate
D. Metabolism
E. Respiratory system

_____ 1. All the processes your body carries on to keep you alive

_____ 2. How quickly your body uses energy

_____ 3. The structures responsible for supplying oxygen to the body

_____ 4. The rate at which your body uses energy when you are sleeping quietly

_____ 5. The structures responsible for supplying food for the body to use

_____ 6. Decreases as a person ages

_____ 7. The structures that exchange carbon dioxide and oxygen

_____ 8. Increases as you engage in strenuous physical activity

_____ 9. The measurement of body activity at rest

_____ 10. The structures that supply the glucose for aerobic cellular respiration

ideas
26B **Structures of the Respiratory System**

Directions

For each pair of terms, describe the difference between the terms.

1. bronchi / bronchioles _____

_____

2. pharynx / larynx _____

_____

3. glottis / epiglottis _____

_____

4. bronchi / alveoli _____

_____

5. thorax / diaphragm _____

_____

6. trachea / esophagus _____

_____

ideas
26C The Digestive System

name:

date: hour:

Directions

Below are drawings of the human digestive system. Label the drawings by supplying the missing terms. Then draw a line from each term to the proper structure in the drawing. Some of the label lines have been drawn for you.

2. _____
(the eight front teeth used for biting)

3. _____
(the twelve rear teeth used for grinding)

1. _____
(the four pointed teeth)

4. _____
(the structure that moves food around in the mouth)

5. _____
(the eight teeth with broad tops for crushing food)

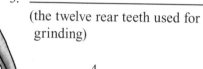

16. _____
(the structure that receives food and begins both mechanical and chemical digestion)

6. _____
(the glands that produce saliva to lubricate food and begin chemical digestion)

15. _____
(the muscular tube that leads to the stomach)

7. _____
(the structure that extends from the back of the mouth to the esophagus and the larynx)

14. _____
(the organ that stores bile until it is needed for digestion)

8. _____
(the pouch in which food is mixed with digestive juices)

13. _____
(the organ in which chemical digestion and absorption occur)

9. _____
(the organ that produces bile)

10. _____
(the accessory organ that produces enzymes for digestion)

12. _____
(the small tubular organ attached to the large intestine)

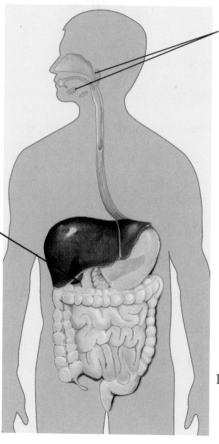

11. _____
(a long tube that absorbs water and minerals)

ideas
26D **Digestion**

Directions

Below is a list of scrambled words. Unscramble the words and write them on the lines to the right of the words. Then match them to the definitions given below by putting the proper letters in the blanks by the definitions.

A. stucd   _____

B. iavlas   _____

C. anbosiotrp   _____

D. laptro nvie   _____

E. sinmvtai   _____

F. lalgrbeladd   _____

G. lorcaie   _____

H. cerlu   _____

I. loacloh   _____

J. pndxpaei   _____

_____ 1. A process that takes place primarily in the small intestine

_____ 2. The structure that carries blood from the digestive organs to the liver

_____ 3. Tiny tubes that carry the secretions of glands to the areas where they are used

_____ 4. The organ that stores bile

_____ 5. A unit of measure for food energy

_____ 6. Essential substances required by some living things

_____ 7. A substance that the liver tries to filter out of the blood

_____ 8. An open sore that discharges a fluid and does not heal normally

_____ 9. A small tubular organ attached to the large intestine

_____ 10. The enzyme-containing fluid secreted in the mouth

ideas

26E Review

name: _____

date: _____ hour: _____

Directions

Record your responses in the spaces provided.

1. Suppose that a person's BMR (basal metabolic rate) causes him to use 1500 calories per day, and his additional metabolism causes him to use an additional 1800 calories per day. If the person consumes 4000 calories per day, what will probably happen? _____

   _____

   If the same person consumes only 3000 calories per day, what will probably happen? _____

   _____

2. Why is mucus important in both the respiratory system and the digestive system? _____

   _____

   _____

3. List as many functions of the liver as you can. _____

   _____

   _____

   _____

4. Why is it important that blood from the digestive system pass through the liver before entering the rest of the body? _____

   _____

   _____

   _____

5. Describe the immune system of the body. In your description be sure to use and define the following words: *immune*, *antibodies*, and *vaccines*. For extra credit also use the word *leukocyte*. (See Chapter 25.) _____

   _____

   _____

   _____

   _____

   _____

   _____

   _____

   _____

class investigation
26F **Digestive Enzymes**

name:

date: hour:

Procedures

Use a marking pencil to label five test tubes *A* through *E*.

Test A

- In test tube A place a crushed piece of cracker. Add enough water to moisten the cracker.
- Add 5 mL (1 tsp) of Benedict's solution and heat the contents to a boil. Place in test tube rack to cool.

Test B

- Rinse out your mouth with water. Then collect in test tube B about 5 mL of your saliva.
- Add 5 mL of Benedict's solution and heat the contents to a boil. Place in test tube rack to cool.

Test C

- Place a cracker on your tongue. Do not chew it. Hold it there for five seconds.
- Break the cracker into small pieces and place it into test tube C.
- Add 5 mL of Benedict's solution and heat the contents to a boil. Place in test tube rack to cool.

Test D

- Chew a cracker only five chews. Place the chewed cracker into test tube D.
- Add 5 mL of Benedict's solution and heat the contents to a boil. Place in test tube rack to cool.

Test E

- Chew a cracker thoroughly. It should be a soft mass. Place the chewed cracker into test tube E.
- Add 5 mL of Benedict's solution and heat the contents to a boil. Place in test tube rack to cool.

Goal

- Observe starch being broken down into sugar by digestive enzymes.

Materials

- Benedict's solution
- Bunsen burner or butane lab burner
- graduated cylinder
- marking pencil
- plain saltine crackers
- test tube rack
- test tube tongs
- test tubes

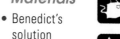

Observations

When heated, Benedict's solution will change color if sugar is present.

- If no sugar is present, it will remain blue.
- If a small amount of sugar is present, it will turn yellow.
- If a medium amount of sugar is present, it will turn orange.
- If a large amount of sugar is present, it will turn brick red.

Compare the color of the five test tubes. Record your responses below.

Test tube	Color	Amount of sugar present
A		
B		
C		
D		
E		

Summing Up

1. Which test tube or tubes have the most sugar? _____

2. Which test tube or tubes have the least sugar? _____

3. Crackers are predominantly starches (carbohydrates). When starches are digested, what are they broken down into? _____

4. From your data, does the amount of sugar increase as the cracker is chewed more? ☐ Yes   ☐ No
   If so, explain why. _____
   _____
   _____
   _____

27 CONTROL

ideas

27A Neurons, Nerve Impulses, and Reflexes

name: _____

date: _____   hour: _____

Directions

Match each term with its definition.

axons	coordination	hormones	nervous	sense organs
brain	dendrites	impulse	neurons	sensory neuron
cell body	endocrine	interneuron	peripheral	spinal cord
central	eye	motor neuron	reflex	synapse

_____ 1. The organization of the systems and processes of the body

_____ 2. The system that produces hormones to control and coordinate the body

_____ 3. The part of the neuron that contains the nucleus

_____ 4. Cells of the nervous system that are capable of transmitting impulses

_____ 5. The part of the central nervous system that is found in the skull

_____ 6. The system of the body that includes the brain, eyes, ears, and nerves

_____ 7. Extensions of a neuron that carry impulses away from the cell body

_____ 8. The sense organ responsible for sensing light

_____ 9. Chemicals produced by the glands of the endocrine system

_____ 10. The membrane changes that travel along a neuron

_____ 11. Structures, such as the eye and ear, that receive various kinds of stimuli

_____ 12. The division of the nervous system that is composed of the brain and the spinal cord

_____ 13. A neuron that is in a reflex arc and serves as a go-between for the other cells in the reflex arc

_____ 14. The space that impulses jump across by means of a transmitting chemical

_____ 15. The division of the nervous system that is composed of the nerves and the sense organs

_____ 16. An immediate, inborn reaction to a stimulus

_____ 17. The part of the central nervous system not found in the skull

_____ 18. In a reflex arc, the neuron that receives the stimulus

_____ 19. Extensions of a neuron that carry impulses toward the cell body

_____ 20. In a reflex arc, the neuron that carries an impulse to a muscle

ideas
27B Bob Uses His Brain

Directions

Below is a list of the divisions of the brain, followed by a list of statements describing Bob's actions. For each statement, choose the brain division that is most involved with Bob's action. Write the proper letter choice in the space by the number.

A. Brain stem
B. Cerebellum
C. Cerebrum, frontal lobe
D. Cerebrum, occipital lobe
E. Cerebrum, parietal lobe
F. Cerebrum, temporal lobe

_____ 1. Bob decided to play catch with Bill.

_____ 2. Bob starts to walk to Bill's house.

_____ 3. On the way, Bob smells something.

_____ 4. Bob recognizes the smell as being that of hot tar.

_____ 5. Bob sees something.

_____ 6. Bob realizes that it is a sign that says "Road Construction."

_____ 7. Bob understands why he smelled tar.

_____ 8. Bob hears something behind him.

_____ 9. The noise frightens Bob, and he jumps.

_____ 10. Bob takes a deep breath.

_____ 11. Bob recognizes that someone had yelled, "Watch out!"

_____ 12. Bob decides to turn around and see who spoke to him.

name:

date: hour:

_____ 13. Bob turns around.

_____ 14. Bob recognizes a traffic control officer.

_____ 15. Bob realizes a truck is coming at him.

_____ 16. Bob's heart begins to beat faster, and his blood pressure goes up.

_____ 17. Bob decides he should move.

_____ 18. Bob turns and walks onto the lawn.

_____ 19. Bob feels heat as the truck passes.

_____ 20. Bob hears something.

_____ 21. Bob recognizes Bill's voice.

_____ 22. Bob realizes Bill has called his name.

_____ 23. Bob realizes that Bill is coming toward him.

_____ 24. Bob smiles and decides to go toward Bill.

_____ 25. Bob goes toward Bill.

ideas

27C The Eye

Directions

Write the definitions for each of the terms; then label the diagram. The sclera has
been labeled for you.

1. sclera _____

2. choroid _____

3. retina _____

4. optic nerve _____

5. vitreous humor _____

6. lens _____

7. aqueous humor _____

8. pupil _____

9. cornea _____

10. iris _____

1.

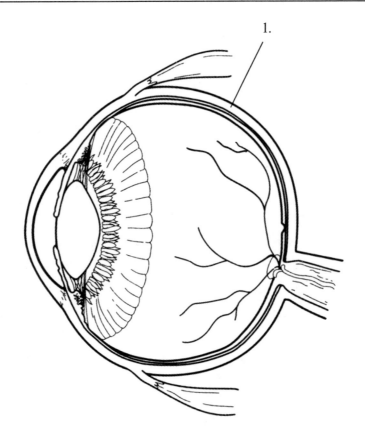

ideas

27D The Ear

name: _____

date: _____   hour: _____

Directions

Write the proper term by the definition; then label the diagram. Number 1 has been labeled for you.

1. _____ (the structure that collects sound waves)

2. _____ (the ear bone that connects the eardrum and the anvil)

3. _____ (the air-filled chamber that contains the ear bones)

4. _____ (the section of the ear that is made up of the cochlea and the semicircular canals)

5. _____ (the structures that sense body balance)

6. _____ (the coiled tubular structure in the inner ear that contains fluid)

7. _____ (the tube that connects the pharynx and the middle ear and relieves pressure in the middle ear when necessary)

8. _____ (the ear bone that connects the anvil and the cochlea)

9. _____ (the ear bone that connects the stirrup and the hammer)

10. _____ (the thin membrane between the outer ear and the middle ear)

11. _____ (the tube that permits sound waves to reach the eardrum)

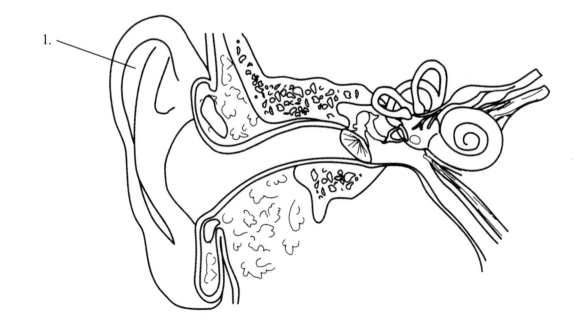

1.

ideas
27E The Endocrine System

Directions
Fill in the chart by selecting the correct descriptions from the lists below the chart.
All the blanks on the chart will have at least one entry; some will have two.

Locations (Use only five.)

Behind the stomach	In the neck
Below the brain	On top of the kidney
In the chest	Under the sternum
In the lower abdomen	Under the stomach

Hormones (Use all.)

Epinephrine	Reproductive hormones
Growth hormone	Thyroxine
Insulin	

Notes (Use all.)

Are called the glands of emergency	Produce gametes (ova or sperm)
Can cause a goiter	Produce hormones that cause puberty
Can cause diabetes mellitus	Produces digestive enzymes
Controls the body's metabolic rate	Produces more hormones than any other gland in the body
Is called the master gland of the body	Supply the blood with more oxygen and food when necessary

Gland	Location	Hormones produced	Notes
Adrenal glands			
Ovaries or testes			
Pancreas			
Pituitary gland			
Thyroid gland			

ideas

name:

date: _____   hour: _____

Directions

Below are several groups of words. In each group, three of the four words (or phrases) are related to one another. Draw a line through the unrelated word and write a sentence using the remaining words, showing how they are related. You may slightly change the form of the word in your sentence (for example, *neuron* to *neurons* or *smell* to *smelled*).

1. internal coordination / synapse / nervous system / endocrine system

   _____

   _____

2. dendrite / axon / cell body / cerebellum

   _____

   _____

3. peripheral nervous system / nerve impulse / transmitting chemical / synapse

   _____

   _____

4. interneuron / motor neuron / neuron / sensory neuron

   _____

   _____

5. hemispheres / lobes / cerebrum / brain stem

   _____

   _____

6. spinal cord / cerebrum / brain stem / cerebellum

   _____

   _____

7. sclera / synapse / choroid / retina

   _____

   _____

8. choroid / retina / iris / pupil

   _____

   _____

9. aqueous humor / vitreous humor / lens / iris

   _____

   _____

10. lens / rods / cones / retina

_____

_____

11. outer ear / ear bones / eardrum / ear canal

_____

_____

12. eustachian tube / cochlea / pharynx / middle ear

_____

_____

13. smell / pain / cold / touch

_____

_____

14. stirrup / cochlea / inner ear / semicircular canals

_____

_____

15. eardrum / ear bones / cochlea / semicircular canals

_____

_____

16. pancreas / insulin / pituitary gland / thyroid

_____

_____

17. endocrine / sugar / hormones / ductless

_____

_____

18. diabetes / thyroid / goiter / thyroxine

_____

_____

19. dwarfs / insulin / pancreas / sugar

_____

_____

20. growth hormone / pituitary gland / dwarf / ductless

_____

_____

ideas
27G **Review 2**

name: _____

date: _____   hour: _____

Directions

Record your responses in the spaces provided.

1. Why is internal coordination of the body essential? _____
_____
_____

2. Name three significant differences between the type of control the nervous system has over the body and the type of control the endocrine system has over the body. _____
_____
_____
_____

3. What is a hormone? What do hormones do? List several hormones and tell their functions. _____
_____
_____
_____

4. In what two systems does the pancreas function? What are its functions in each system? _____
_____
_____
_____
_____

5. The ovaries and testes do not begin producing their hormones until the early teenage years. What happens to a person of your sex when these hormones begin to be produced? What name is given for the time period when these changes occur? _____
_____
_____

6. What is a reflex arc? Explain why reflexes are important. _____
_____
_____
_____
_____

class investigation

27H The Skin's Sensation of Temperature

name:

date: _____ hour: _____

Setting Up

1. Put some tap water into a glass. Place two fingers into the water. Add hot or cold water to make the water feel lukewarm (neither cool nor warm).

2. When the water is lukewarm, use a thermometer to measure its temperature.

3. You will prepare seven glasses, each containing water of a different temperature. One glass should contain water at the lukewarm temperature, as determined in step 1.

4. Three glasses should have hotter water: 5°F hotter than the lukewarm water, 10°F hotter, and 15°F hotter. Similarly, prepare three glasses of colder water: 5°F colder than the lukewarm water, 10°F colder, and 15°F colder.

5. Label the glasses appropriately: *hot, very warm, warm, lukewarm, cool, very cool,* and *cold.*

6. Prepare twenty-one small pieces of paper. On three of them write *hot*, on three write *very warm*, on three write *warm*, and so on. Fold these pieces of paper and place them in a dish.

Goals

- Demonstrate the skin's ability to detect differences in temperature.
- Observe the fallibility of the senses.

Materials

- cold water
- hot water
- large glasses or cups
- thermometer

Procedures and Observations

You should frequently test the temperatures of the various glasses of water and, if necessary, add hot or cold water so that they maintain their original temperatures throughout the experiment.

1. Choose a person to test the water. Make sure the person looks away (or is blindfolded) so he cannot see the glasses. He will use the same index finger in each glass, briefly drying his finger before testing the next glass.

2. Determine which glass you dip his fingers into by drawing a piece of paper out of the dish. For each test, move the glass to the person testing the water. If you move his hand to the glass, he may be able to tell which glass it is by its location.

3. Dip his finger into the glass for 5 seconds and then remove it. Have him tell you which glass he thinks it was.

4. Fill in the chart by putting a check for the correct water temperature and an *X* for the temperature that the person said it was. If the person's response was correct, darken the entire square. Repeat steps 2–4 until the chart is filled in.

Responses

	Hot	Very warm	Warm	Luke-warm	Cool	Very cool	Cold
1.							
2.							
3.							
4.							
5.							
6.							
7.							
8.							
9.							
10.							
11.							
12.							
13.							
14.							
15.							
16.							
17.							
18.							
19.							
20.							
21.							

Summing Up

1. How often was the person incorrect? _____ How often was he correct? _____

2. How often was the person only one temperature off? _____

3. How often was the person only two temperatures off? _____

4. How often was the person correct about a temperature being higher or lower than the previous temperature tested? _____ How often was he incorrect? _____

5. Compare your group's results with those of other groups. Are they about the same? ☐ Yes ☐ No

   If not, what do you think accounts for the difference? _____

   _____

   _____

6. What are your conclusions about the skin's ability to determine temperatures? _____

   _____

   _____

   _____

class investigation

27| The Pupil Reflex

name: _____

date: _____   hour: _____

Setting Up

The iris (colored portion) of the eye controls the size of the pupil (black portion). The pupil is actually an opening into the eye. When the pupil is large, a great amount of light enters the eye. When the pupil is small, very little light enters the eye. The size of the pupil is controlled by a reflex. This reflex is stimulated by the amount (intensity) of light available to the eye.

Goals
- Demonstrate a reflex.
- Understand the purposes of reflexes.

Procedures and Observations

You will need to perform the following procedures with a partner.

Materials
- darkened room
- penlight (small flashlight)

1. Sit in a darkened area for several minutes. This should cause your pupils to become large. If they do not, go to a darker area.

2. Shine a penlight into the right eye of your partner, being careful not to shine it into his left eye.

   - What happens to the pupil of the right eye? _____

   - What happens to the pupil of the left eye? _____

   - How fast does the reflex take place? _____

3. Turn off the penlight and allow the eyes to readjust to the dim light.

4. Repeat the above experiment but shine the penlight into the left eye. Does the same thing happen?
   ☐ Yes   ☐ No   If not, what does happen? _____

Summing Up

1. Why is the pupil reflex necessary? _____

   _____

   _____

2. Why must the reflex happen quickly? _____

   _____

   _____

class investigation

27J **Afterimages**

$\mathcal{S}$*etting Up*

1. Cut circles, triangles, squares, and other simple shapes from colored construction paper. You should have at least four different colors of each shape. Each figure should be about 5 cm (2 in.) square.

2. Glue or tape each of these shapes in the center of a sheet of white paper (one shape per sheet of paper). If you use tape, use tiny rolls of tape behind the shape so that none of the tape is visible.

3. Using a pencil, place a tiny dot in the center of each shape.

Procedures and Observations

1. Place a sheet of white paper with a colored shape on it in a brightly lit area about 50 cm (18–20 in.) away from your face.

2. Stare at the dot in the center of the shape for 20 seconds. Keep your eyes on the dot for the entire time.

3. Look at some light-colored area in the distance (the ceiling is good) and then close your eyes. What you see immediately after you close your eyes is called an afterimage. Describe the afterimage you saw. (Be sure to describe its color and its shape in relation to the color and shape you stared at.)

_____

_____

_____

_____

4. After you have performed this experiment and have seen an afterimage, you should wait until you no longer can see that afterimage before you do the experiment again.

5. Try obtaining other afterimages using different colors and shapes. Record your findings on the chart. In the "Notes" column, record anything unusual you observe about the afterimage.

6. If time permits, you may want to form some afterimages by using colored shapes on pieces of colored paper. What are the results?

Goals

- Demonstrate afterimages.
- Evaluate the functioning of the cones of the eye.

Materials

- colored construction paper (both dark and bright colors)
- brightly lit area
- glue or tape
- scissors
- white paper

Shape	Shape color	Afterimage color	Notes

Summing Up

The cones in your eyes have different chemicals that break down when exposed to different colors. Thus when you look at something blue, a certain chemical breaks down. When you look at something red, a different chemical breaks down, and so on. Different shades of color are seen when different amounts and combinations of these chemicals break down.

Afterimages result when you break down a large amount of a particular color's chemical and then look away. The temporary lack of that particular chemical causes the afterimages.

1. About how long did the afterimages last? _____

2. What observations can you make about different colors of afterimages? _____

   _____

   _____

3. List normal, everyday situations in which afterimages occur. _____

   _____

   _____

   _____

   _____